Fundamentals of process safety

The Authors

Vic Marshall studied part-time for Associate Membership of the IChemE while working as a plant chemist for British Celanese. He went on to work for Theodore St. Just and Simon Carves before joining Bradford University, where he played a major part in building up the new Chemical Engineering Department. After appearing as expert witness for the trades unions at the Flixborough Inquiry, he devoted the rest of his career to safety, both as Director of Safety Services for the University and as a researcher and consultant.

Vic was a pioneer in the study and practice of process safety, publishing many papers and a seminal book, *Major Chemical Hazards*. He served on the Major Hazards Committee of the Health and Safety Commission and on many other advisory bodies. For this and related work he was awarded the Council, Franklin and Hanson Medals of the IChemE. He died in 1996.

Steve Ruhemann studied chemical engineering at Imperial College. He worked for Bataafsche Petroleum Maatschappij, the British Paper & Board Industry Research Association and AEI-Birlec Ltd before joining Bradford University's Chemical Engineering Department, where he taught a variety of subjects. Since 1989 he has specialized in teaching Process Safety. Steve has served for many years on the local and national Executive Committees of the Association of University Teachers, and as its national President.

Fundamentals of process safety

Vic Marshall and Steve Ruhemann

Published by
Institution of Chemical Engineers (IChemE),
Davis Building,
165–189 Railway Terrace,
Rugby, Warwickshire CV21 3HQ, UK
IChemE is a Registered Charity

© 2001 Steve Ruhemann
Reprinted 2002
Reprinted 2008
ISBN 978 0 85295 431 7

Typeset by Techset Composition Limited, Salisbury, UK
Printed and bound by CPI Antony Rowe, Eastbourne

ii

Foreword

The chemical and process industries have brought benefits to humanity which are so widespread that it is only possible for us to give a few examples of them. Virtually everything we use today is a product, at least partly, of these industries. Houses, clothes, furniture, books, computers, health products, medicines and leisure equipment are all, to a greater or lesser degree, products of these industries. Even the automotive industry, where raw materials are mainly metallic, requires rubber and plastics for indispensable items such as tyres, paint and seats. The finished product then requires fuel, produced by petroleum refining, to make it go.

When things go wrong, however, these benefits can be costly, in terms of human injury and death, and damage to property and the environment. Explosions, fires and toxic releases, exemplified by such disasters as Flixborough, Seveso, Bhopal and Mexico City, are examples of what can happen if those who design or operate process plants get things badly wrong. Moreover, for every major event which makes the headlines, there are perhaps hundreds of lesser events, each with its toll of injury and damage.

This book is concerned with hazards — the situations which have the potential to give rise to such disasters — and the nature of the harm which may be inflicted on people, property or the environment when their potentials are realized.

Our aim

It is the duty of all in the process industries to contribute in any way they can to reduce this toll of harm. To this end, those who graduate from universities in the relevant disciplines, aspiring to gain responsible posts in these industries, must understand the basic principles which underlie process safety. Our aim in writing this book, therefore, is to help them to do so.

The study of this book alone will not adequately prepare graduates for immediate responsibility in industry. For this they still need to refer to more specialist literature and will require specific practical training, both initial and recurrent. In our view, however, it is not the responsibility of universities to provide such training, nor is it practical for them to attempt to do so. It is rather the role of enterprises to train their employees to apply these principles to the particular circumstances of their industry.

The study of process safety

The process industries — or at least their more enlightened practitioners — have always had a concern for safety. *Safety Rules for Use in Chemical Works*[1] — the third edition of a work originally published in 1928 — gives some general guidance and many detailed instructions for the safe conduct of chemical processing operations. Its approach, however, is largely of the kind described as 'tactical' (see Chapter 6), reflecting the relatively small scale of operations typical at the time.

The intervening years have seen an immense growth in the scale of chemical manufacturing, with a corresponding increase in the severity of the harm caused when accidents occur. At the same time, public awareness of such events has been greatly enhanced by the growth of the communications media, so that they have — quite properly — become matters of general concern on which governments have been obliged to institute public enquiries and enact legislation.

Manufacturing organizations, government agencies and professional institutions have therefore found it necessary to devote substantial resources to the study of the causes and consequences of such disasters and the means of preventing them and minimizing their effects. Early studies examined the disasters from the standpoint of the particular installation and process, but it has become increasingly apparent that, in terms of science, engineering and management, all accidents have common features, even those arising in different plants using different processes to make different products.

The distinct identity of the subject of process safety (many people initially called it loss prevention, and some still do so) originated in the recognition of these common features, and it is now explicitly acknowledged, for example, by the Institution of Chemical Engineers (IChemE)[2]. It is still at an early stage of development as an academic subject, and there is continuing debate as to how it should best be taught. It is hoped that this text will make a useful contribution to this debate and development.

We acknowledge that process safety is actually a part of a wider area of concern dubbed by Marshall[3] as 'social acceptability', which also includes the subject now becoming established as 'environmental protection'. We believe that these subjects are closely related and should be associated in academic study.

Existing publications on process safety

There are many books in print on the subject of process safety. The Center for Chemical Process Safety (CCPS) of the American Institute of Chemical Engineers (AIChE) and IChemE list, between them, some 40 books which have been published on various aspects of the subject. There are also a number of independently authored works in the area.

There is a wide range of guidance publications by governmental regulatory agencies, including those by the Health and Safety Executive (HSE) in the UK and the National Institute for Occupational Safety and Health (NIOSH) in the USA. There is also a range of publications by the trade associations and individual firms in the process industries.

Of particular note is the seventh edition of Perry's *Chemical Engineers' Handbook*[4], an extremely important reference work first published in 1934. 'Perry' has always been divided into sections covering distinct parts of the knowledge base of the profession, but the present edition is the first to include one entitled 'process safety', an event which may perhaps be considered to reflect the coming-of-age of the subject.

The need for a different approach for students

It may seem, therefore, that the subject area is already more than adequately covered. However, without wishing to minimize the importance of these publications, we believe that, with very few exceptions, they have not been written for students, but rather for practising engineers and technologists who have a considerable amount of knowledge and 'hands-on' experience. Some of them have also been written by specialists, for specialists.

This book presents the fundamentals of process safety in a way that can be assimilated by students, who typically lack prior practical knowledge and experience. We have endeavoured to present this material within a coherent, integrated, academic framework, which is grounded in fundamental science, with the aim of making the subject more amenable to systematic study and more clearly related to the other subjects in their curriculum.

The book is largely based upon a conceptual model which we have devised and which is expounded progressively in the course of the text. The model is founded on a set of defined and inter-related concepts.

Students have limited time to study a subject which is only a fairly small part of an undergraduate course. This makes it all the more important that the book should concentrate on fundamentals. Even so, it can only provide the elements of the subject and, therefore, such important topics as, for example, quantitative risk assessment and gas dispersion, are treated only in an introductory manner.

Readership

Early drafts of the book have been used successfully in the teaching of a process safety module to undergraduate students of chemical engineering at the University of Bradford. We hope that it will prove suitable for students taking first degrees in such subjects as chemical engineering, chemical technology, energy technology, petroleum engineering, and safety engineering. We hope, also, that it may be useful as an introductory text for graduates in these disciplines who have not received any formal education in process safety and who now wish to study it.

Finally, it is our impression that lecturers attempting to teach the subject are significantly handicapped by the lack of a single text embodying it at an elementary level, especially if it is not their primary area of specialization. We therefore hope that they will find support in this book.

References

1. ABCM, 1951, *Safety Rules for Use in Chemical Works: Part I Model Rules,* 3rd edn (Association of British Chemical Manufacturers, UK).
2. IChemE, 1998, *Accreditation of University Chemical Engineering Degree Courses: a Guide for Assessors and University Departments* (IChemE, UK).
3. Marshall, V.C., 1990, The social acceptability of the chemical and process industries — a proposal for an integrated approach, *Trans IChemE, Part B, Proc Safe Env Prot*, 68(B2): 83-93.
4. Perry, R.H., Green, D.W. and Maloney, J.O. (eds), 1997, *Perry's Chemical Engineers' Handbook,* 7th edn (McGraw-Hill, UK).

Acknowledgements

In writing this text we have inevitably drawn on a very wide range of sources. We have tried conscientiously to acknowledge all of these by appropriate citations and I hope that we shall be forgiven for any accidental omissions. It is perhaps appropriate here to pay a general tribute to the hundreds of authors who have contributed to what has become, in recent years, a rich literature indeed.

I owe a particular debt to Dr I.M. Clark, who read a draft of the book and, though kindly giving it his general approval, made a large number of suggestions for improvement, most of which I have been glad to incorporate.

I am extremely grateful for the willing assistance we have received from the Subject Librarians of the University of Bradford, specifically Anne Costigan, Martin Wilkinson, Pamela Tidswell and Ken Tidswell. I have also had considerable help in the tracking down of sources from John Williams, the University's Safety Advisor. My perseverance in completing the book owes much to the constant encouragement of my colleagues in the University's Department of Chemical Engineering, whom I have to thank for many helpful discussions. Thanks are due also to the many students who have, by their responses and occasional criticisms, contributed significantly to its refinement (special mention should be made here of Mark Talford, who kindly undertook to read the whole text). I have to thank Peter Dowhyj for drawing Figure 4.2 and Wendy Bailey and Jane Gibb for their clerical assistance. Audra Morgan of IChemE has been extremely helpful in the final stages of preparation of the book for publication. Notwithstanding all this help, such remaining errors as will surely come to light are of course the sole responsibility of the authors.

It falls to me, as the surviving author, to express my gratitude for the immense contribution of my late colleague and friend Vic Marshall. Not only did he originally conceive the idea of the book and write the first drafts of the greater part, but the entire text has been informed by his pioneering studies in the field of process safety, including his *magnum opus Major Chemical Hazards*. It is a privilege to have been associated with him in its preparation, and a great responsibility to have had to complete it alone after his sad demise in 1996.

Finally, I must acknowledge my debt to Joan Marshall for her unfailing support and encouragement.

Steve Ruhemann
March 2001

Contents

Introduction

Scope

This book is concerned with safety in the process industries. Since it is directed mainly at technology students it is largely devoted to the description and discussion of the scientific and technological aspects of the subject. However, the control and minimization of process hazards, though very dependent on such knowledge, is ultimately a human activity, and this aspect of the subject has also been introduced.

The arrangement of the book

The book is structured in a coherent way, with the various aspects of the subject logically arranged.

Chapter 1 outlines the fundamental concepts on which the book is based, especially those of *hazard* and the *hazard system* and *risk*, and defines a number of the most important terms. The basics of quantitative characterization and assessment of hazards are then considered.

Chapter 2 outlines the many possible kinds of event where a hazard source may be realized. The various physical and chemical processes through which such *realizations* are manifested are described in some detail.

Chapter 3 discusses the role of *transmission paths*, which are the media by which the harms from hazard *sources* may be transmitted to hazard *receptors* — that is, people, property and the environment — and also the concept of *attenuation* (the processes by which the intensities of harmful emissions are reduced *en route* to the receptors).

Chapter 4 classifies the most important *harms* that may be caused to people, property and the environment by various kinds of emission brought about by hazard realizations. The various concepts of *dose*, representing the amount of a harmful emission striking a receptor are discussed in general terms and the difficult problems of quantifying harm and correlating it with dose are introduced. The specific harms to people, equipment, buildings and the environment that may result from the various types of emission are described.

Chapter 5 presents, with some analytical comment, a number of case histories of serious accidents that have occurred in the process industries, selected to illustrate the phenomena discussed in the preceding chapters.

Chapter 6 is concerned with all aspects of the control of hazards. The roles of *tactics* and *strategy* in hazard control are discussed and a brief introduction is given to the methodology of hazard assessment. Then, using as a template the model of *acute* process hazards which has been evolved in the course of the book, a *strategic* approach to minimize first the magnitudes of these hazards and then the risks of their realization is presented, in the context of the evolution of a manufacturing project. After an introductory discussion of the difficult issue of determining the level of risk that may be tolerated, the book is concluded with a brief account of the role and organization of management to achieve these ends and of the part played by legislation and enforcement in ensuring that the responsibilities of management are fulfilled.

Nomenclature

The literature of the subject contains many inconsistencies in terminology which may present difficulties to students. These reflect the normal, rather imprecise usage of everyday speech and also the relative novelty, in academic terms, of the subject of process safety.

When discussing phenomena that may well be critical in terms of danger to life and property, accuracy of expression is vital. The book therefore aims to give precise definitions to the terms that are used and endeavours to maintain a consistent terminology and usage throughout, based upon these definitions.

Terms are defined in the text where they are first used in a substantive way. As far as possible, definitions are taken from readily available works of reference. For general scientific terms, *The Penguin Dictionary of Science*, which is referred to in the text as PDS has been used[1]. For more specialized terms, *The Penguin Dictionary of Physics*, referred to as PDP[2], the *Oxford Concise Dictionary of Chemistry*, referred to as OCDC[3], and *The Penguin Dictionary of Mathematics*, referred to as PDM[4] have been used.

For the specialized terms used in hazard and risk analysis the principal source was *Nomenclature for Hazard and Risk Assessment in the Process Industries*[5]. We consider this book to be indispensable and recommend that all students possess it. It has occasionally been necessary to introduce terms which are not yet generally accepted to represent certain concepts which are still undergoing development.

The sources of all definitions that are taken from the literature have been identified. Where no suitable definition could be found in the literature, a definition has been formulated.

References

References are provided to sources which give more extended treatments of the subject areas of the text. These should also be useful as background material for those who teach the subject and may provide source material for projects and tutorial exercises.

Background literature

As the literature of the subject is so rich, it was decided to let the many references supplied on particular topics speak for themselves and to make only a few specific recommendations.

Firstly, the subject as presented is largely grounded in the science and technology of the process industries. It is suggested that anyone intending to teach it needs to have access to the main reference sources of that field and of its 'parent' profession, chemical engineering. For the former, refer especially to Shreve's *Chemical Process Industries*[6] and the *Kirk-Othmer Encyclopedia of Chemical Technology*[7]. For the latter, the most important is undoubtedly Perry's celebrated *Chemical Engineers' Handbook*[8].

Secondly, for the subject of process safety, all English-language practitioners would endorse the recommendation of the *magnum opus* of the late-lamented Professor Frank Lees, *Loss Prevention in the Process Industries*[9], as the most comprehensive source book in the field.

Finally, there is a wide range of publications on various aspects of process safety published by the UK Institution of Chemical Engineers (IChemE) and the American Institute of Chemical Engineers (AIChE) (especially the latter's recent offshoot, the Centre for Chemical Process Safety or CCPS). The many publications of the UK Health and Safety Executive (HSE) and the USA National Institute for Occupational Safety and Health (NIOSH) include

3

incident reports, data, guidance notes and codes of practice: they should be available for reference (much of this material is now accessible on the Internet).

Dimensional analysis

To assist clarity of analysis, wherever appropriate, the dimensions of the physical quantities used in terms of the fundamental magnitudes length (L), time (T), mass (M) and temperature (θ) have been given. For the sake of clarity, the derived magnitude energy ($E \equiv MLT^{-2}$) has also been used.

Units

SI units are used throughout. Where appropriate, the customary decimal multiples of these units are used such as the tonne ($1\,t \equiv 10^3\,kg$) for mass, the micron ($1\,\mu m \equiv 10^{-6}\,m$) and the kilometre ($1\,km \equiv 10^3\,m$) for length, and the bar ($\equiv 10^5\,Pa$) for pressure.

Chemical names

Regarding the names of chemical compounds, we have adhered as far as possible to those recommended in the various publications of the International Union of Pure and Applied Chemistry (IUPA) (though we may not have been able to maintain total consistency). These are the names which are used in OCDC[3]. Where it seems desirable, earlier names may be given in parentheses.

References

1. Uvarov, E.B. and Isaacs, A, 1986, *The Penguin Dictionary of Science*, 6th edn (Penguin, London).
2. Illingworth, V. (ed), 1991, *The Penguin Dictionary of Physics*, 2nd edn (Penguin, London).
3. Daintith, J. (ed), 1990, *A Concise Dictionary of Chemistry*, 2nd edn (Oxford University Press, Penguin, London).
4. Daintith, J. and Nelson, R.D, 1989, *The Penguin Dictionary of Mathematics*, (Penguin, London).
5. Jones, D. (ed), 1992, *Nomenclature for Hazard and Risk Assessment in the Process Industries*, 2nd edn (IChemE, UK).
6. Shreve, R.N., Norris, R. and Basta, N., 1993, *Shreve's Chemical Process Industries Handbook*, 6th edn (revised by N. Basta) (McGraw-Hill, USA).

7. Kirk, R.E., Othmer, D.F., Kroschwitz, J.I. and Howe-Grant, M., 1993, *Kirk-Othmer Encyclopedia of Chemical Technology*, 4th edn (Wiley, USA).

8. Perry, R.H., Green, D.W. and Maloney, J.O. (eds), 1997, *Perry's Chemical Engineers' Handbook*, 7th edn (McGraw-Hill, USA).

9. Lees, F.P., 1996, *Loss Prevention in the Process Industries: Hazard Identification, Assessment and Control*, 2nd edn, 3 vols (Butterworth-Heinemann, UK).

Basic concepts

1

1.1 Process safety

1.1.1 Definition of process industries

The 'process safety' of this title means 'safety in the process industries'. There is no universal agreement as to what constitutes 'process industries'. Thus, by any formal definition, one would probably have to include the iron- and steel-making industry, and the smelting of non-ferrous ores. However, these have never been regarded as process industries by those operating in them.

For the purposes of this book, therefore, 'process industries' is defined as:

Process industries — those industries which form the subject matter of Shreve's *Chemical Process Industries*[1] or the Kirk-Othmer *Encyclopedia of Chemical Technology* series [2].

The process industries thus defined include those which manufacture or transform inorganic and organic chemicals, petroleum, natural gas, pharmaceuticals, soap, oils, fats, rubber, paper, plastics, synthetic fibres, industrial gases, and those which purify water and sewage.

Since the chemical industries are a sub-set of the process industries, the term is treated as including them.

1.1.2 Features of the process industries

Equipment used
Virtually all the process industries handle gases and liquids. Many handle solids, but usually in particulate form. Such solid materials often lend themselves to treatment as quasi-fluids — that is, as free-flowing powders,

6

slurries or suspensions in gases, but these have distinctive properties, as will be shown.

The equipment consists in the main of closed vessels connected by piping through which the process fluids are pumped or blown, their flow being regulated by valves, and their associated storage facilities.

The equipment, and its inter-connections, may be displayed in diagrammatic form by means of flow diagrams.

The authoritative work which describes and illustrates the equipment used in the industries is *Perry's Chemical Engineers' Handbook*, to which we shall refer to as 'Perry'[3].

Properties of the materials handled

The materials handled by the industries range from harmless to flammable, explosive, highly reactive, toxic, asphyxiating, or corrosive. They may be handled under vacuum or at high pressures, and over a wide range of temperatures from near absolute zero to more than 2000°C.

The principal, though not the only, concern of controlling harm caused by the process industries lies in preventing or limiting unwanted releases of energy or matter. Put another way, it is largely a problem of preventing loss of containment or minimizing its consequences.

Scale-up

A feature of the process industries lies in what is termed 'scale-up' for which there is often strong economic justification.

In continuous processes, with few exceptions, it is technologically feasible to increase the capacity of a single process stream without limit. This is done, in effect, by increasing the cross-sectional area of the stream. In this way, to give an example, sulphuric acid plants have had their capacity increased, over the last 50 years, from 10s of tonnes per day to 1000s of tonnes per day, a factor of a 100 times.

Batch processes have also been scaled up, though not so dramatically, by increasing the sizes of reaction vessels.

These increases in scale, however, brought with them associated increases in the inventories of hazardous materials contained within process streams, and this has been a major factor in increasing hazards. In certain circumstances, moreover scaling up may exacerbate some specific safety problems (*vide*, especially, Chapter 2, Section 8).

7

1.1.3 Definition of process safety

Concentration upon essentials

It is our intention to concentrate upon those hazards which are characteristic of, and peculiar to, the process industries. Thus detailed attention is not given to those hazards which the process industries share with manufacturing industry in general, such as those arising from falls of persons or of material on to persons, electric shock, machine tools and hand-tools, traffic movements, etc. Though these account for the majority of the accidents in terms of numbers, they do not account for the most serious ones. This class of accident has been dealt with very adequately elsewhere and detailed accounts of such accidents, and the measures for their prevention, are given in National Safety Council[4] and Ridley[5].

The special problems of laboratories are not considered, though it is acknowledged that there is some overlap of subject matter. This is especially true of chemical engineering laboratories and pilot plants. Problems of safety in chemical laboratories are treated in Furr[6] and in RSC[7]. The problems of chemical engineering laboratories and pilot plants are treated in Marshall and Townsend[8]. There are two highly specialized areas which are not discussed: ionizing radiation from nuclear reprocessing and the release of micro-organisms from biochemical processes.

A further line of demarcation is that between accident and disease. This difference is viewed as being primarily one between short exposure and long exposure. Accidents may take only fractions of seconds, whereas occupational disease involves long exposure, perhaps for weeks or for years. The subject matter of this book, partly for reasons of space, is confined to accidents — that is, *acute* events — and *chronic* events such as industrial disease will not be discussed. (The terms *acute* and *chronic* are defined in Section 1.2.2, page 11).

Definition

'Process safety' is defined for the purposes of this book as follows:

> **Process safety** — the branch of safety which is concerned with the control of those accidents which are special and characteristic features of the process industries.

Process safety is centrally concerned with preventing acute releases of energy or of substances in harmful quantities, and with limiting the magnitude and consequences of such releases should they occur. It is especially preoccupied with those major releases which may injure, not only employees but also members of the public, or which may damage property, both on-site and off-site, or produce acute harm to the environment. There is considerable overlap between the concerns of process safety and those of environmental protection, and this is reflected in industry and in professional and public organizations by a tendency to associate the two subjects in their structures.

How process safety is achieved

Process safety is achieved by the reduction of hazards and/or their associated risks to a level which is deemed acceptable by the organization and/or by society at large. The meanings of *hazard* and *risk* are discussed in this chapter, and the issue of *social acceptability* is considered in Chapter 6.

1.2 The concept of a hazard system

1.2.1 Definitions of hazard

'Hazard' in ordinary speech

'Hazard' seems to be of Arabic origin and is associated with games such as, for example, golf and billiards. Today it is usually associated with harm or loss. In ordinary speech it is sometimes, confusingly, used as a synonym for 'risk', and its usage by professional writers has sometimes been contradictory. It is necessary therefore to define it strictly and to use it solely in accordance with this definition.

The IChemE definition

Jones[9] defines 'hazard' as follows:

Hazard — a physical situation with a potential for human injury, damage to property, damage to the environment or some combination of these.

Though it is our general policy to utilize, wherever possible, the definitions given by Jones[9], the definition of 'hazard' given above was not entirely adequate for these purposes. The definition of '*hazard system*', given below, constitutes an extension of the IChemE definition of 'hazard' and does not contradict it.

Definition of a hazard system

This book is based upon the following model of a hazard system:

9

Hazard System[#*] — a system having, in the general case, three basic kinds of components, a source[#] and one or more receptors[#], together with one or more transmission paths[#]. The source has the potential for injury to people or damage to property or the environment. A receptor has the potential for sustaining injury or damage should the potential for harm in a source be realized. A transmission path[#] is a medium by which, or through which, harm is transmitted from the source to the receptors and simultaneously attenuated[#]. Some hazard systems may also include interposed barriers[#] which are intended to attenuate the harm.

A hazard system is illustrated schematically in Figure 1.1. Chapters 2, 3 and 4 of the book deal respectively with hazard sources, transmission paths and receptors, and the strategies for the control of hazards discussed in Chapter 6 are classified similarly.

Realization
Jones[9] does not define *realization*. It is defined here as follows:

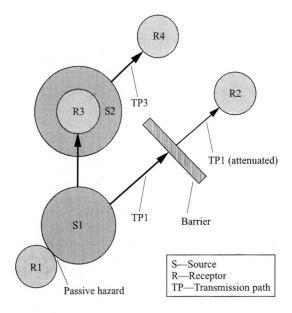

Figure 1.1 The hazard system

---

* In this book, it has been necessary to endow several terms which are used in ordinary speech with special meanings. These are distinguished by the superscript[#] where they are defined.

Realization[#] — an event or events by which the potential in a hazard system becomes actual. Realizations are discussed in detail in Chapter 2.

Shorthand

When 'hazard' is simply referred to, it implies a *hazard system* as defined above. References to 'sources' or 'receptors', will be to these as elements in a hazard system as defined above.

1.2.2 The analysis of hazards

Secondary sources[#]

In a hazard system, secondary sources may arise in two ways:

(a) a receptor may constitute a secondary hazard source if it possesses potential for harm to people, property or the environment, so that the realization of the primary source may realize in turn the potential of the secondary source (for example, a pressure vessel may be damaged by blast from an explosion) — this is illustrated at R3/S2 in Figure 1.1;

(b) alternatively, the realization of the primary source may create a new hazard source such as, for example, a flammable cloud formed by a vapour escaping from a vessel.

Overlapping of systems

A receptor may be a receptor for more than one source. For example, people on a site may be exposed simultaneously to the potential for harm from two or more sources.

Differing laws

Though the potential of a source may be expressed completely in terms of the physical dimensions of length, mass and time and of chemical composition, the harm suffered by a living receptor is also governed by the laws of biology and medical science.

Differing levels of realization

Typically a source has the capacity to be realized at many different levels of severity which in some cases fall upon a continuum. For example, a process vessel may suffer loss of containment at any level between a pinhole leak and catastrophic failure.

11

Chronic sources and acute sources

A hazard source may be *chronic* or *acute*. These terms are defined by IChemE[9] as:

- **chronic** — persistent, prolonged and repeated;
- **acute** — immediate, short term.

The subject matter of this book is confined to acute sources. These have realizations whose durations may range from fractions of a second in the case of explosions, to hours in the cases of fires and toxic emissions.

The realization of acute hazards may be assumed to occur at random and (except in a statistical sense) unpredictable intervals. Their occurrence is governed by the laws of chance: thus, they may be regarded as constituting 'accidents'.

Passive or active

A *passive*[#] hazard is one the harm from which can only be realized by actual contact with, or penetration by, a receptor. It may be regarded as having zero or negative range. Examples are hot surfaces, which have to be touched, or confined spaces, which have to be entered, to bring about a realization. Such hazards do not require transmission paths to transmit harm.

An *active*[#] hazard is characterized by realizations which comprise emissions of harmful matter or energy. Some active hazards have a harmful range of many kilometres. The range of such harms is heavily dependent upon the severity of the realization.

Mobile or static sources

Most hazard sources in the process industries arise from fixed equipment and are thus *static*. Hazards may also arise, however, from vehicles such as tankers, which are obviously *mobile*.

1.2.3 The exclusion of certain hazards

For the reasons of editorial policy set out in Section 1.1.3 (page 8), certain types of hazards have been excluded from consideration, in particular those hazards which the process industries have in common with manufacturing industry in general, the hazards of laboratories and the special hazards of nuclear reprocessing and biochemical engineering.

1.2.4 The nature of receptors

Basic types

There are two basic types of receptor. There are *animate* receptors — that is, people and flora and fauna — and *inanimate* receptors, which include buildings and process equipment.

As noted above, different laws apply to the two kinds of receptor. Whereas damage to inanimate receptors may be described, in principle at any rate, in terms of the laws of physics and chemistry, injury to animate receptors also requires the application of appropriate biological laws for its description.

Mobile and static receptors

Animate receptors may be regarded as mobile in the sense that they do not have a definite, permanent, location. Inanimate receptors, with the exception of transport vehicles, are static.

On-site or off-site

Injury or damage may occur both on-site and off-site. Hazards which have the potential to cause off-site injury or damage are often referred to as 'major hazards' or 'major-accident hazards'. Clearly, only active hazards can have such potential.

Attenuation[#]

The harm inflicted on a receptor by the realization of a source may be *attenuated* (Latin: 'made thin') by effects relating to distance and/or to barriers. These effects are discussed in Chapter 3.

Chronic and acute harms to receptors

As noted earlier, the harms of chronic origin are not discussed. Acute injury to people and acute damage to property are discussed in detail in Chapter 4.

1.3 The characterization of hazards

1.3.1 The binary nature of hazard

When a major accident — say an airplane disaster — occurs, resulting in multiple fatalities, it provokes large headlines in the news media and widespread demands for investigation and action. Actually, many more people are killed every year in numerous small accidents, such as car crashes, involving only one or two fatalities, but these attract far less attention.

Although the ethical implications of this contrast are not of concern here, two implicit facts concerning the nature of hazard are:

- its characterization involves two essential attributes: its *magnitude* and the *likelihood* of its realization; and
- experience shows smaller realizations to be more likely to occur and larger ones less so.

These characteristics present philosophical problems when it is required to compare one hazard with another, or to evaluate the effectiveness of policies designed to enhance safety. They will inform much of the discussion in succeeding chapters.

1.3.2 The magnitudes of hazards and their realizations

The magnitude of an airplane disaster was specified in terms of a number of fatalities. Expressing this in terms appropriate to the present study, the *hazard* is represented by the *potential* deaths of all on board and perhaps of some people on the ground. Tragic experience forces us to assume that such an accident will always have this result (sometimes called the 'worst-case scenario'), although in principle a wide range of outcomes is possible depending on various circumstances (the least severe being, perhaps, a safe forced landing with no injuries).

The same is true of process industry hazards. In general, the magnitude of a realization will lie on a spectrum, but the *hazard*, representing *potential*, must be quantified in terms of the worst possible outcome. It should of course be noted that fatalities are often not involved, and that the consequences are sometimes expressed in terms of financial loss.

As will be seen later, the assessment of hazard magnitude involves a complex process of calculation, starting with the amount of energy and/or harmful material contained in the hazard source and taking account of all the circumstances that may condition its realization.

1.3.3 The concept of risk

The likelihood of the realization of hazards

There has been much discussion on the most acceptable way to express this idea, but there is now widespread — though not universal — agreement on the use of the term **risk**. In dictionaries, this word is usually treated as a synonym for *hazard* as defined above. Insurers use it variously to mean the potential cost of settling a claim or the person for whom or the event against which insurance is effected. In common speech, the word *risk* (origin: French *risque*) is used in a variety of senses, though perhaps most commonly as we shall define it below, in that of the *likelihood* of some undesirable event.

In common speech, it does not matter if *hazard* and *risk* are used interchangeably, but from the point of view of a scientific analysis of safety it is essential that a clear distinction is drawn between the two terms.

Definition of risk

The definition of risk given by Jones[9] is accepted here:

> **Risk** — the likelihood of a specified undesired event occurring within a specified period or in specified circumstances. It may be either a *frequency* (the number of specified events occurring in unit time) or a *probability* (the probability of a specified event following a prior event), depending on the circumstances.

It is implicit in our concept of a hazard system that the risk of realization of an identified hazard is greater than zero.

Definition of frequency

'Frequency' has been given a number of meanings. For the purposes of this book, it is defined as follows:

> **Frequency** — the mean number of specified events occurring in unit time. It thus has the dimensions T^{-1}.

Definition of probability

Confusion can arise, however, because there is an alternative meaning given to *frequency* in probability theory. Here one encounters expressions such as 'the *frequency* with which the throw of two dice yields a double six'. These expressions have nothing to do with time measured by a clock and would be equally true if the dice were thrown at one millisecond intervals or at 1000-year intervals. The reference here is actually to a *ratio* of numbers of events. Following Jones[9], this concept is defined as *probability* as follows:

> **Probability** — a number on a scale from 0 to 1 which expresses the likelihood that one event will succeed another.

It is thus a *number* between zero (impossible) and one (certain) and hence is dimensionless. This is the only sense in which *probability* is used in the book.

15

Probability in risk analysis appears as *sequential* probability which is concerned with questions such as the likelihood that an emission of flammable gas will be succeeded by its ignition. Such problems cannot be addressed *a priori* as problems in throwing dice may be, and are addressed on the basis of the historical record or the results of experiments.

Probabilities may be manipulated in accordance with well established laws. The most important of these is the sequential law. The law states that in a sequence of events $A \rightarrow B \rightarrow C \rightarrow D \rightarrow$, ... if the probability of $A \rightarrow B = P_{AB}$ and the probability of $B \rightarrow C = P_{BC}$ and the probability of $C \rightarrow D = P_{CD}$ ... then the probability of $A \rightarrow D = P_{AB} \times P_{BC} \times P_{CD}$.

It follows that if event A occurs with a frequency f_A, then the frequency of event D will be $f_A \times P_{AB} \times P_{BC} \times P_{CD}$, with dimensions T^{-1}.

In risk assessment sequences of this character arise where an initial event, which is characterized by a frequency, is followed by a series of sequential events conditioned by (dimensionless) probabilities. The final product thus has also the dimensions of a frequency.

1.3.4 The concept of reliability

Definition of reliability

Reliability is defined by Jones[9] as follows (a similar definition is given in CCPS[11]):

> **Reliability** — the probability that an item is able to perform a required function under stated conditions for a stated period of time or for a stated demand.

Green and Bourne[12], which is cited in Section 1.4, gives a definition in similar terms. However, for consistency these definitions should refer to 'likelihood' rather than 'probability'.

The relationship between risk and reliability

Risk and reliability may be regarded as 'mirror images'. Where risk is expressed as a frequency and has the dimensions of T^{-1}, and reliability has the dimensions of T and has the meaning of a life-time, the two parameters are mutually *reciprocal* for a given application (that is, risk × reliability = 1). Where risk is expressed as sequential probability it is a dimensionless ratio, and so is reliability. Risk is the probability of failure and reliability is the probability of survival so, for a given application, the two parameters are *complementary* (that is, risk + reliability = 1).

16

1.4 The assessment of hazards

1.4.1 Introduction

Simply stated, the global purpose of *process safety* is to minimize the hazards associated with process operations. In order to control hazards, they must be quantified. In view of the binary nature of hazard outlined in Section 1.3.1 (page 13), this requires measures of hazard which take account of both of its attributes, magnitude and risk. This is not easy, and it has not been possible to devise a single index which is suitable for all purposes. However, a number of measures exist which have different applications, and two of the most important are introduced here.

1.4.2 Measures of hazard

Nomenclature

The binary nature of hazard presents a problem with nomenclature. This has been resolved by specifying measures of the sort to be defined below as 'derivatives of risk', though it must be emphasized that their fundamental nature is distinct from that of 'risk' itself. These concepts will be illustrated by referring to fictitious records of a particular kind of natural hazard such as rock falls from a mountain, drawing (with some corrections) on the text of Marshall[13].

Individual risk

This is defined by Jones[9] as follows:

> **Individual risk** — the frequency at which an individual may be expected to sustain a given level of harm from the realization of specified *hazards*.

A range of realizations which produce a range of levels of harm is envisaged below.

For illustration, imagine a village with a population of 300, lying at the foot of a mountain which is subject to occasional rock falls. Over a period of 50 years, 10 people have been killed by such falls. It can be concluded that the average historical individual risk of death from this cause for someone who is always present in the village is $10/(300 \times 50)$, or 6.67×10^{-4} per annum.

It may be that some inhabitants are exposed to the hazard only for part of the time because of absences from the village. This can be accounted for by introducing an 'occupancy factor' representing the fraction of the total time for which either a particular individual or the average person is present. Thus, if Mr

A is present for 128 hours per week during 46 weeks of the year, the above result should be multiplied by $(128/168)(46/52) = 0.67$, giving an individual risk value of 4.5×10^{-4} per annum.

Given the relevant data, similar calculations could be carried out for the risk of non-fatal injury at some specified level. These calculations assume that all locations in the village are equally exposed, but it would be possible to divide the total area into zones of equal risk to make a more accurate calculation.

Societal risk

The statistic *individual risk* is used to predict the number of persons in a group (defined usually by reference to geographical location) who may be expected to suffer a given level of harm from a particular hazard within a specified period. It says nothing directly about the total number of persons who may be affected by an individual incident.

The process industries are, however, prone to hazard realizations that cause death or injury to numbers of people. A statistic is needed to tell us about the likelihoods of events of different magnitudes. Such a statistic is defined by Jones[9] as follows:

Societal risk — the relationship between frequency and the number of people suffering a given level of harm in a given population from the realization of specified hazards.

It may be estimated as a summation of the individual risks of exposed receptors.

This concept may be illustrated, too, by reference to the fictitious mountain village. Marshall (loc. cit.) hypothesizes that the fatalities referred to above were distributed between five separate incidents as shown in Table 1.1.

If these data are analysed in terms of societal risk, Table 1.2 can be drawn up.

The data in the first and third columns may be represented by a frequency-versus-magnitude or f/N histogram as in Figure 1.2.

It is apparent that the exact death toll in a particular incident is a matter of chance and that, on the record, some specific numbers of fatalities do not occur, so that their frequency appears as zero. If falls occur which kill one, two and four people, however, it would be absurd to predict that none will occur which

Table 1.1 Statistics of fatalities in rock falls

Date of fall	1/8/34	3/10/41	4/12/52	3/1/63	1/2/71
No. of deaths (N)	2	1	1	4	2

Table 1.2 Calculation of societal risk

N	f_{50}	f	F_{50}	F
1	2	0.04	5	0.10
2	2	0.04	3	0.06
3	0	Nil	1	0.02
4	1	0.02	1	0.02
5	0	Nil	Nil	Nil

N — number of fatalities in an incident
f_{50} — number of incidents with N fatalities in 50 years
f — frequency of incidents with N fatalities (per annum)
F_{50} — number of incidents with $\geqslant N$ fatalities in 50 years (*cumulative*)
F — frequency of incidents with $\geqslant N$ fatalities (*cumulative*) (per annum)

Figure 1.2 f/N histogram for rock falls

kills three, or which causes no fatalities at all. In order to facilitate more realistic predictions than are possible with the point values, it is common practice to use cumulative frequencies, as is shown in the fourth and fifth columns of the table. The corresponding histogram is shown in Figure 1.3.

Such data are commonly represented by an F/N diagram (alternatively, F/c or 'frequency-consequence diagram'), as shown in Figure 1.4. When the data cover a wide range of values it is convenient to plot them on logarithmic co-ordinates, and the graph may then be smoothed to a curve. These concepts are discussed more fully in Chapter 6.

The spectrum of realizations

The magnitude of a hazard realization will generally lie on a spectrum, with the smaller realizations occurring more frequently and the larger ones less so. Such data may also be displayed in tabular form or, graphically, in histograms.

Figure 1.3 F/N histogram for rock falls

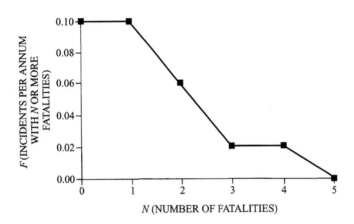

Figure 1.4 F/N diagram for rock falls

As with societal risk, such a classification includes the problem where, the more precisely the magnitude of a release is specified, the lower is the level of risk that must be assigned to it. As the range within which the realization approaches zero, so does the risk. Similarly, the more precisely the limits of harm are set, the smaller is the risk that the specified degree of harm may be sustained. Again, this dilemma may be avoided by specifying the risk associated with a realization equal to or greater than a given magnitude, thus generating a F/N or *cumulative* frequency-versus-magnitude (as opposed to f/N) diagram.

Example

Consider a pressurized system. The number of scenarios for the failure of this system is unlimited, ranging from a pin-hole leak to catastrophic disintegration.

Experience suggests that the risk of the former class of failure is much greater than that of the latter. In fact the designers will have taken great care when designing such a system, by choice of suitable materials and adherence to appropriate codes, to avoid catastrophic failure. Given a sufficient number of years of operation of this and similar systems, it may be possible to tabulate breakdown severity in terms of the cost of repairs as shown in Table 1.3.

From this table it is possible to draw either a f/N diagram showing frequency of repair costs equal to N against N or a F/N diagram showing cumulative frequency of repair costs equal to or exceeding N against N. These two types of diagram are shown in Figures 1.5 and 1.6. The f or F values in these diagrams are expressions of risk.

1.4.3 Quantitative risk assessment

Quantifying hazards is a complex matter requiring a great deal of scientific knowledge and refined methodology and the mass of procedures which have been developed for this purpose is called collectively quantitative risk assessment (usually abbreviated by the acronym QRA). This nomenclature is not entirely satisfactory, since we are concerned with evaluating, not merely *risk* as defined earlier but the so-called 'derivatives' of risk such as *individual risk* and *societal risk*. However, it is the established usage.

Table 1.3 Notional repair costs of a pressurized system

Range of cost of repair (N) (units of currency)	Frequency of occurrence (f) (per annum)	Severity
10 to 100	50	minor
100 to 1000	5	moderate
1000 to 10,000	1	serious
10,000 to 100,000	2×10^{-2}	severe

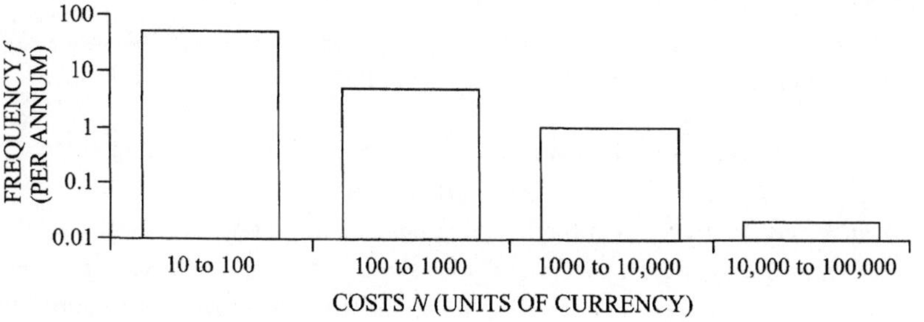

Figure 1.5 Histogram of repair costs

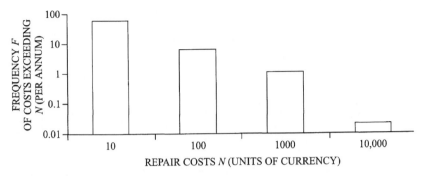

Figure 1.6 Cumulative histogram for repair costs

Definition

Jones[9] does not define QRA. Rather, it assumes that 'risk assessment' *implies* quantification and defines it as follows:

> **Risk assessment** — the quantified evaluation of the likelihood of undesired events and the likelihood of harm or damage being caused together with the value judgements made concerning the significance of the results.

Up to now, the more limited quantitative assessment of the *risk of source realizations* has been discussed. Carrying the analysis through to the receptor requires the consideration of additional material which will be discussed in later chapters.

The methodology of QRA

QRA makes the fullest use of 'historical' information — that is, data derived from practice and laboratory experiments. It combines this with theoretical considerations to provide an approach which is partly analytical and partly synthetic. This is inescapable because any novel process must contain elements on which practical experience does not exist.

It uses such techniques as the construction of logic diagrams, fault tree analysis and event tree analysis. These are defined by Jones[9] as follows:

> **Logic diagram** — a representation of the logical combination or sequence of events leading to or from a specified state.
> **Fault tree analysis** — a method for representing the logical combinations of various system states which may lead to a particular outcome (top event).
> **Event tree analysis** — a method for illustrating the intermediate and final outcomes which may arise after the occurrence of a selected initial event.

The application of these techniques is further described by IChemE[9].

Sources of information

The estimation of source risk requires a great deal of data, some of which are not readily accessible to students. Such data, which have great commercial value, have been gathered over decades, especially by those who make such items as, for example, aircraft or nuclear reactors. It will normally be indexed in libraries under 'Reliability Studies'.

The data may be derived from laboratory tests or from records of service failures which major companies often record in detail. The subject is further discussed in Section 2.2.9 (page 31).

Concluding comments

These methodologies are discussed in outline in Chapter 6. It is stressed, however, that QRA is a complex undertaking demanding a high level of specialized skill and knowledge, and is therefore a sphere of activity of safety professionals rather than of general management, although it is essential for the latter to be aware of its uses and limitations.

References in Chapter 1

1. Shreve, R.N., Norris, R. and Basta, N., 1993, *Shreve's Chemical Process Industries Handbook*, 6th edn (revised by N. Basta) (McGraw-Hill, NY).
2. Kirk, R.E., Othmer, D.F., Kroschwitz, J.I. and Howe-Grant, M., 1993, *Kirk-Othmer Encyclopedia of Chemical Technology*, 4th edn. (Wiley, NY).
3. Perry, R.H., Green, D.W. and Maloney, J.O., (eds), 1997, *Perry's Chemical Engineers' Handbook*, 7th edn (McGraw-Hill, NY).
4. National Safety Council, 1988, *Accident Prevention Manual for Industrial Operations*, 2 vols (NSC, USA).
5. Ridley, J.R., 1990, *Safety at Work* (Butterworth-Heinemann, UK).
6. Furr, A.K. (ed), 1990, *CRC Handbook of Laboratory Safety*, 3rd edn (Wolfe, Cleveland, USA).
7. Royal Society of Chemistry, 1992, *Hazards in the Chemical Laboratory*, (RSC, UK).
8. Marshall, V.C. and Townsend, A. (eds), 1991, *Safety in Chemical Engineering Research and Development* (IChemE, UK).
9. Jones, D.A. (ed), 1992, *Nomenclature for Hazard and Risk Assessment in the Process Industries*, 2nd edn (IChemE, UK).
10. Marshall, V.C. and Ruhemann, S., 1997, An anatomy of hazard systems and its application to acute process hazards, *Trans IChemE, Part B, Proc Safe Env Prot*, 75(B2): 65–72.

11. CCPS, 1989, *Guidelines for Chemical Process Quantitative Risk Analysis* (AIChE, USA).
12. Green A.E. and Bourne A.J., 1972, *Reliability Technology* (Wiley Interscience, USA).
13. Marshall, V.C., 1987, *Major Chemical Hazards* (Ellis Horwood, Chichester, UK).

Hazard sources and their realizations

2

2.1 Introduction

Chapter 2 begins with an account of the realizations of those sources which seem to have the greatest significance in the process industries. The phenomena associated with these realizations are then described.

Although we consider that, in principle, it is possible to assign levels of risk to such realizations, we have not attempted to do this here because the level of risk would be highly specific to any particular site.

In the last chapter, hazards were classified into passive and active categories. Typically, passive hazards are relatively small and do not release significant emissions of energy or matter to their surroundings — these are discussed in Section 2.3. Active hazards have sources whose realizations entail the emission of significant quantities of energy or matter or both to their surroundings. Sections are devoted to releases of mechanical energy, thermal energy and chemical energy.

The central place occupied by releases of chemical energy, and their complexity, have justified seven sections being devoted to them. Six principal categories are identified and a section devoted to each. The mechanisms by which harm is transmitted to receptors are described in Chapter 3, which is devoted to transmission paths. The nature of harms to receptors is the subject of Chapter 4.

2.1.1 Energy and power

Definitions

The terms 'energy' and 'power' are used in this chapter in strict accordance with their scientific meanings. The dimensions are ML^2T^{-2} and ML^2T^{-3}, respectively. The convention of thermodynamics in which energy emitted by a system is accorded a negative sign is followed. The power emitted correspondingly has a negative sign. Though specific energy may be expressed with respect to mole or mass, the latter is used. Similarly, specific power is expressed in terms of mass units. It is argued that the severity of hazards is much more dependent upon specific power emitted than on specific energy emitted.

Transformation of energy

From an academic standpoint, the realizations of process hazards may be regarded as transformations of energy from one form into another. In this they resemble the processes themselves, except that the transformations are unplanned and undesired.

Given the definition of a hazard system presented in Chapter 1, in which all possible receptors of energy emitted from a source are included in the hazard system*, the First Law of Thermodynamics requires that the *sum total* of energy in such a system is unchanged by the realization of the hazard: it is the *forms* of the energy that are changed. Such transformation of energy results, however, in an increase in the entropy of the system. Thus one way of looking at process safety is to see it as a set of measures to prevent or minimize any unwarranted increase in the entropy of a hazard system.

Geometry

The term 'geometry' is used in this, and later, chapters. For the purposes of this book, it is defined as the description of the spatial inter-relationships between sources, receptors and barriers in a hazard system.

Geometry describes size, shape, configuration and orientation and may be represented by scaled drawings.

2.2 Causation and realizations

2.2.1 The philosophers and causation

Philosophers have debated this subject since the time of Aristotle, if not before, and it remains one of the central themes of philosophy. Though this book is not the place for philosophical discourse on the subject, it is clear from the discussion that the problem of what constitutes causation is by no means simple.

By way of example, is it true to claim, as some history books have done in the past, that the First World War was caused by an assassin's bullet in Sarajevo?

---

* The system is in thermodynamic terms, an *isolated* one.

Whilst no one would doubt that the assassination of the Archduke Ferdinand played a role in starting the war, historians point to many other factors such as growing imperial rivalries and the intensive arms race which preceded the war. But some historians have gone further back in time to discover what they regard as the root causes of the conflict and there is now some consensus that the assassination was the initiating but not the root cause of the war**.

The study of process accidents shows that they too have both initiating causes and root causes. The general question is discussed in Chapter 6 and case histories in Chapter 5, where attention is drawn to both root causes and initiating causes.

This chapter concentrates on initiating causes.

2.2.2 Definition of initiating cause

For the purposes of this book, 'initiating cause' is defined as follows:

Initiating cause — An event or series of events in sequence which results in the realization of a hazard.

An initiating cause is sometimes termed a 'proximate' cause.

2.2.3 Literature

There is a wide range of literature which discusses initiating causes. Some of this literature is concerned with anecdotal accounts of accidents or case histories. A number of representative case histories are featured in Chapter 5, where these are considered to be archetypal in character.

Other sections of the literature deal with generic causes in which case histories are analysed for a common cause.

2.2.4 Some examples of initiating causes

The number of possible initiating causes is virtually infinite, so only an indicative list is presented. Those conducting Quantitative Risk Analysis must examine hazard systems exhaustively to determine possible causes which may apply to the system under examination, and also have to estimate their likely frequency of occurrence.

Initiating causes may be tiny in relation to the realizations they produce. Thus, a spark of 2×10^{-4} joules may ignite a vapour cloud and release 2×10^9 joules — a ratio of 10^{13}.

** The familiar metaphor of the spark igniting a flammable mixture which is already present is remarkably apt to the present purpose.

2.2.5 Categories of initiating causes

The causes of failures in the process industries may be classified into two general categories — internal and external.

- Internal causes — These may be further classified into two categories: physical/mechanical and chemical. Examples of these are listed in Tables 2.1 and 2.2.
- External causes — These may similarly be classified into the categories of physical/mechanical and chemical. Examples of these are listed in Tables 2.3 and 2.4.

2.2.6 The nature of realizations of hazard sources

A realization from an active source is generally a composite event: typically, it entails a failure of containment followed by an emission of matter or energy or both.

Some examples of failure modes are given below. The nature of emissions is discussed in later sections of this chapter, and the hazards these realizations present to receptors are discussed in Chapter 4.

There are many possible failure modes so only examples can be given.

Table 2.1 Typical internal physical/mechanical causes

(1)	Incorrect assembly	(12)	Cavitation
(2)	Inappropriate materials of construction	(13)	Wear and tear of moving parts
(3)	Cracking	(14)	Unbalanced loads in moving machinery
(4)	Fabrication defects such as welding		
(5)	Unbalanced forces, especially in pipework	(15)	Friction leading to overheating
		(16)	Electrostatic build-up
(6)	Local stress concentrations	(17)	Low temperature embrittlement
(7)	Excessive speed of rotation	(18)	Overpressure
(8)	Thermal expansion or contraction	(19)	Underpressure
(9)	Fatigue	(20)	Failure of agitation
(10)	Creep	(21)	Mechanical blockages
(11)	Erosion		

Table 2.2 Typical internal chemical causes

(1) Corrosion by chemical attack
(2) Corrosion by bacteriological attack
(3) Ageing of plastic materials of construction
(4) Internal explosions
(5) Unplanned chemical reactions
(6) Blockage with process materials

Table 2.3 Typical external physical/mechanical causes

(1)	Tempest	(14)	Impingement of cryogenic fluids
(2)	Lightning	(15)	Failure of cooling medium
(3)	Flood of natural origin	(16)	Entry of excessively hot heating medium
(4)	Blizzard		
(5)	Extreme atmospheric temperatures	(17)	Maintenance operation
(6)	Earth tremors	(18)	Modifications
(7)	Mining subsidence	(19)	Collision of vehicle with static source
(8)	Collapse of structures supporting the equipment		
(9)	Collapse of structures onto the equipment	(20)	Collision of mobile source with static object
(10)	Flood from release of process fluids	(21)	Damage to containers being handled
(11)	Blast from explosions	(22)	Damage to connections during loading and unloading
(12)	Missiles from explosions		
(13)	Radiant or convective heat impingement	(23)	Disintegration of neighbouring machinery

Table 2.4 Typical external chemical causes

(1) Maloperation of sampling points or drains
(2) External corrosion
(3) Introduction of foreign materials
(4) External fire or explosion

Notes on the tables
(1) Causes may act in sequence. Thus electrostatic sparking may lead to internal explosion and heat generated by friction may lead to unplanned chemical reaction.
(2) The duration of initiating events may range from fractions of a second, such as a spark, to years, as with metal fatigue or corrosion.

2.2.7 A note on the term 'explosion'

It is already clear that many hazard realizations involve a class of phenomenon commonly called 'explosion'. It is difficult to find a satisfactory general definition of this term, and a great deal of confusion is caused by its imprecise use. Dictionary definitions are very varied, each tending to focus on one particular aspect of the phenomenon, and there appears to be no general agreement as to what constitute its essential features.

In the most general sense the term may be used to describe any very rapid or violent process, whether material or, by analogy, social, economic, political or cultural. In a material context, it normally refers to events involving the sudden release of a large amount of energy, the nature and effects of which may or may not be specified.

One difficulty with the term lies in the fact that it is often used, not in an *absolute*, but in a *relative* sense, that is, of the undesired *acceleration* of an already-occurring process relative to its normal speed, which may be quite slow or very fast. Usually, it carries the implication of a phenomenon increasing in an *uncontrolled* way (though one may speak, counter-intuitively, of a 'controlled explosion'). It is in this sense that the term 'thermal explosion' is used with reference to *runaway* chemical reactions (see Section 2.8, page 80).

Because of these problems, the term will be employed sparingly, using as far as possible the more precise terms which are defined in the relevant sections. However, since it is impossible to avoid it altogether, an appropriate definition is offered.

The explanation that seems to be most relevant to the purposes of this book is given by the Health and Safety Commission[1]. This is as follows:

'**Explosion** — a rapid release of energy which causes a pressure discontinuity or shock wave, which then moves away from the source at a rate determined partly by the differential pressure and partly by the properties of the medium through which the shock wave is propagated. This pressure discontinuity and the subsequent shock wave are termed the blast wave.'

This definition excludes the *runaway* chemical reactions referred to above. Since, also, we have decided to exclude consideration of nuclear processes, we shall restrict the use of the term further to include only those events which involve the sudden evolution of a large volume of *gas* from a much smaller volume of material which may be initially solid, liquid or gaseous. This encompasses both purely *physical* phenomena such as the sudden release of a compressed gas or vapour (see Section 2.5, page 40) and a variety of phenomena involving chemical reactions, which are defined more precisely and discussed in Sections 2.9 onwards.

2.2.8 Categories of failure

It is convenient to think of the items which make up process plant as falling into the four categories below. The boundaries between the categories are not rigid and the classification of any item is a matter of judgement. The higher categories will include items from the lower categories.

(1) **Components** — these are the smallest items. They are generally mass produced and have a wide application throughout industry in general. Examples are nuts, bolts and flanges, pipes and fittings, thermocouples, pressure gauges, sampling points and drains.

(2) **Equipment** — includes more complex items such as valves, pumps, blowers, agitators, piping systems, heat exchangers, filters, electric motors and other prime movers, electrical switch-gear, instrumentation systems, computers.
(3) **Machinery** — includes conveyors, elevators, crushers and grinders, centrifuges and lifting gear.
(4) **Vessels** — includes items which are specific to the process industries such as reactors, distillation columns, scrubbers, waste-heat boilers and storage tanks.

Of the categories given above, failures of components are the most numerous, followed by those of equipment items. It is reasonable to accept that they account for the majority of failures. The severity of the consequences of failure is generally least with components and greatest with vessels.

2.2.9 Data on failures
As previously pointed out, risk and reliability are complementary studies and data on failure rates may be found in the literature under either heading. As components are so widely used and are manufactured in such large quantities, it is easier to determine their failure rates with a high level of statistical reliability than is the case with, say, process vessels.

The US Centre for Process Safety has published *Guidelines for Process Equipment Reliability Data*[4] which refers to databases concerned with the categories listed above together with generic data on equipment, machinery and vessels. Some specimen failure rates from this and other publications are set out in Table 2.5 overleaf. They are mean figures and are expressed as the risk of catastrophic failure per million hours of service (approximately 100 years).

2.2.10 Some examples of realizations

Management and failure
It is a prime task of management to anticipate realizations such as those which we have mentioned in this chapter. The tables given above, whilst not exhaustive, list more than 50 initiating events. It is only possible to give a few examples of the many realizations to which they may give rise.

Failures of piping systems

Failures of joints
Joints are generally sealed with gaskets. These may fail for a variety of reasons, for example, mechanical — such as when a joint is unevenly bolted up and

31

Table 2.5 Indicative failure rates

Reference source	CCPS[4]	Green[5]	Davenport[6]
Components			
Nuts and bolts		0.02	
Gaskets		0.5	
Ball bearings		10–20	
Expansion bellows		5	
Pressure gauges		15	
Hoses	0.57	4–40	
Straight steel pipes	0.027		
Equipment			
Motors, induction	3.2	5	
Motors D C	22.5		
Valves (manual)		15	
Pneumatic transmitters	109		
Flame detectors	432		
Tubular heat exchangers	31		
Fans	9.09		
Pumps (centrifugal)	104		
Screw conveyors	942		
Vessels			
Metallic (atmospheric pressure)	0.986	3	
Metallic (pressurized)		0.3	0.004

Notes on the table
(1) These values should not be used without consulting the original references. They are heavily influenced by service conditions and by how failure is defined.
(2) The number of significant figures is that given in the reference and may be fortuitous. It should not be taken as an index of accuracy.

thus subjected to local stresses — or chemical — such as when process fluids attack the gasket material.

Failures of pipes
Pipes in process plant may vary greatly in diameter, from, say, six millimetres to two metres or more, and the size greatly influences the severity of a realization. They may be rigid and be fabricated in, for example, metal or plastic or glass. Alternatively they may be flexible and made of metal or an elastomer or some combination of these. Flexible pipes are most used for connections such as between static and mobile containers and vice versa.

Fractures may range from cracks or tears to complete severance, which is sometimes called a 'guillotine' fracture. In the latter case there may be full-bore leakage from both ends. Such fractures may arise from an external blast, or from the collapse of a structure onto the pipe, or from a collision with a vehicle.

Failure of hoses may arise from vehicles moving off from a filling point without the hose being disconnected, causing the equivalent of a guillotine fracture.

Failures of bellows
Bellows may be fitted to accommodate thermal expansion or contraction in piping systems. They are necessarily thin-walled and, if incorrectly installed, may 'squirm' because of unbalanced forces and may burst, producing the equivalent of a guillotine fracture (see Chapter 5, Flixborough, page 227).

Failures of pumps
Pumps may fail either on the body or on the shaft seal. Body failure may occur as a result of corrosion, erosion or cavitation — the latter being peculiar to pumps and arising from the formation and collapse of vapour bubbles. Shaft seal failures may occur through corrosion, lack of lubrication, misalignment, excessive tightening of the gland, or vibration. The probability of failure of dynamic seals, such as shaft seals, is typically age-dependent and defects are self-worsening.

Failure of machinery

Rotating machinery
Rotating machinery, if it operates at a high peripheral speed, may become an active hazard through disintegration. Examples are machines for fine grinding such as pin mills or classification devices such as centrifuges or hydro-extractors. Disintegration may occur through metal failure due to unbalanced loads which cause uneven local stresses, corrosion or wear and tear of the bearings.

Conveying machinery
Failure may give rise to fire. Dust explosions may be initiated by friction leading to hot-spots or sparks.

Failure of vessels

General
The discussion is confined to 'unfired' vessels, as steam boiler failure lies outside the remit of this book. The severity of any realization from vessel failure depends on such factors as the chemical properties and physical state of the contents, their temperature and pressure and the mass of the material which may escape. The position of any breach in the walls may determine whether it

leaks a gas or a liquid — the mass flow rate is higher with a liquid than it is with a gas.

Punctures

These are likely to arise from external physical causes such as the collapse of a structure or a collision in an accident involving moving vehicles. The severity of the realization depends upon the size of the opening which, in turn, depends upon the energy expended in the impact.

Cracks

These may arise under normal circumstances initially from corrosion or local over-stressing. With a tough material, crack propagation is likely to be slow, allowing time for remedial action.

Catastrophic failure

Vessel failure may range from a pin-hole leak to total disintegration. The latter, though rare, constitutes a severe realization. The risk of catastrophic failure is least with tough materials, which do not easily propagate cracks, and greatest with brittle materials, which do so readily. Structural steel at ordinary temperatures is tough, whereas cast iron, glass and ceramics are brittle. All metals increase in strength with declining temperature but structural steel, though its strength increases, becomes more brittle. The brittleness of steel may also be increased by contact with substances such as liquid ammonia.

Special steels are needed to withstand the temperatures encountered in handling liquefied gases (see Chapter 5, Cleveland, Ohio, page 222) and in severe Arctic conditions. There have been a number of catastrophic failures of tankers transporting liquefied gases. Further information on toughness, brittleness, and the propagation of cracks may be obtained from Gordon[7].

Flame engulfment of store tanks containing liquefied gases has led to a number of catastrophic failures. This phenomenon is loosely called a *BLEVE* (boiling liquid-expanding vapour explosion) — this will be discussed later (see Section 2.5.4, page 51). Examples of BLEVEs are given in Chapter 5 (see Feyzin and Mexico City, pages 225 and 232).

Catastrophic failure of vessels may occur through the vessels being overfilled and thus having inadequate room for the thermal expansion of the liquid contents. An example is given in Chapter 5 (see Spanish campsite, page 237).

Catastrophic failures of reactors and storage vessels have occurred as the result of runaway reactions. These are discussed in detail in Section 2.8, page 80.

Storage tanks and process vessels designed to operate at atmospheric pressure are seldom able to withstand partial vacuum. If pumped out without venting, they are liable to collapse inwards (implode).

2.3 Passive hazards

2.3.1 Introduction

As characterized in Chapter 1, passive hazards are those hazards whose range of harm is either zero or negative. Zero-range passive hazards require the receptor to come into actual contact with the surface of the source; negative-range passive hazards require the receptor actually to penetrate the boundaries of the source. Such hazards are usually without off-site implications.

They are divided here into two categories — physical passive hazards and chemical passive hazards.

2.3.2 Physical passive hazards

Hazards from machinery

Mechanical machinery with moving parts is employed in the chemical and process industries for transporting materials, size reduction (comminution), mixing and separation, and also for extruding plastic materials. Detailed descriptions of such machines can be found in Perry's Handbook and in specialized works.

It may be said generally that the hazards of such machinery are primarily the concern of mechanical engineers and of safety professionals who specialize in the safety of machinery. For this reason, such matters are only discussed briefly.

Such machinery must be enclosed with guards, and accidents are relatively rare. Interlocking systems which prohibit the machinery from being switched on when the guards are not in place may help prevent accidents. However, sometimes guards and casings are removed and the interlocking system where such exists is put out of action in order to observe the machinery in operation. This has led to accidents.

More commonly, accidents have occurred through persons entering the machinery whilst it was shut down for inspection or repairs and the machinery then being inadvertently switched on again. The risks of such incidents are characteristic of those associated with human operational behaviour. Rigorous working systems and a strong safety culture are required to prevent them. This topic is discussed in Chapter 6, especially in the context of 'Permits to Work'.

Hot and cold surfaces

The hazard arising from a hot surface does not need elaboration. However, serious injury may also arise from contact with cold surfaces, the severity depending upon the temperature and the duration of the exposure.

2.3.3 Chemical passive hazards

Enclosed spaces

There have been many accidents through entry into enclosed spaces, arising through the presence of toxic agents or through lack of oxygen (asphyxia). Toxic agents are discussed in Chapter 4, and include hydrogen sulphide and carbon monoxide.

Asphyxia is probably the more common cause and can arise in a number of ways. The air may have become depleted in oxygen by reaction with a reducing agent, for example, through reaction with steelwork to produce rusting or by slow reaction with organic substances to produce carbon dioxide. Alternatively, the air may have been displaced deliberately by the introduction of an inert gas such as nitrogen. Inhalation of pure nitrogen produces instant asphyxia.

The protection of workers entering enclosed spaces for purposes of maintenance and so on is an important responsibility of management, effected by such measures as 'permit-to-work' procedures, interlocks and safe working practices. These matters are discussed in Chapter 6.

2.4 Mechanical energy releases

2.4.1 Subject matter of section

There are a number of hazards whose realization may give rise to forms of mechanical energy release and which can consequently cause harm in process plants. However, in accordance with our policy of concentrating on those hazards which are both characteristic of, and peculiar to, the process industries, only a relatively brief account of them is given.

It is beyond question that the control of these hazards is a very important sector of safety management in the process industries. However, the expertise appropriate to their management does not form part of the normal expertise of process engineers and technologists.

2.4.2 Impact of vehicles

Impact on-site

Moving vehicles (which constitute mobile hazards) may collide with structures, plant, equipment or piping and give rise to the release of chemicals or of energy even though the vehicle itself may be empty or carrying non-hazardous goods. Serious hazards may arise from specialized vehicles for earth-moving (bulldozers and trench diggers) or for lifting (mobile cranes) or for moving and stacking (forklift trucks).

In a collision, the kinetic energy of the vehicle (equal to one half the product of its mass and the square of its velocity) is transformed into energy of deformation. Both the vehicle and the object with which it collides usually suffer deformation. Speed restrictions on process sites are obviously important in limiting collision damage, but so is driver training.

A particular issue in this context are contractor operations. They may not be familiar with the specific hazards of the site, so their work must be carefully controlled.

Impact off-site

There have been many serious transport accidents resulting in the release of energy and the spillage of chemicals. These are often collisions involving road vehicles and railroad vehicles. In some cases these collisions have been with other vehicles and sometimes they have involved fixed structures.

Velocities may be much higher off-site than on-site, and in the case of head-on collisions the kinetic energy available for transformation may be doubled. It would go beyond the scope of this book to examine this area in detail. Readers who wish to study it further, are referred to ACDS[8] which analyses the problems in depth. Case histories of two railroad accidents under 'Crescent City' and 'Mississauga' are provided in Chapter 5 (pages 223 and 233).

2.4.3 Structural collapse

Temporary structures

These include scaffolding, which may be for new buildings or for maintenance, and the shoring up of trenches. Many injuries, some of them fatal, occur in these areas. Their supervision requires special expertise and process engineers and technologists should not take responsibility for such supervision without this specialized training.

Fixed structures

These include buildings, supporting structures for plant, bridges and retaining walls. These are the provinces of mechanical, structural and civil engineers. However process engineers must ensure that supporting structures are adequate at all times. For example, although a structure may adequately support a vessel which may be almost empty during its normal operation, it may not be adequate if the vessel is filled with water for a pressure test.

2.4.4 Machinery

Types of machinery

The process industries employ a large number of types of machinery. These are described in Perry's Handbook and in specialist monographs. They are designed by mechanical engineers and electrical engineers, though they are usually operated by process engineers and technologists.

Today, with the exception of steam-driven electric generators, virtually all the electrically driven machinery used may be divided into two classes. The first is directly driven by electric motors. These have characteristic speeds which are approximately equal to the mains frequency (50 Hz in the United Kingdom, 60 Hz in North America) or some sub-multiple of this speed — that is, 1/2, 1/3 or 1/4. These speeds involve the cheapest drives, and are used wherever possible. Such machinery is thus very common, and most pumps, fans and machinery for fine grinding utilize such drives.

Other electrically driven machines are driven by electric motors through gearing. Though most examples of such machines are geared down to provide a slow drive, there are examples of machines being geared up to produce a high-speed drive. Examples of geared-down machines are those used for conveying solids, for crushing rocks and for slow agitation. Geared-up machinery is used for ultra-fine grinding and for ultra-centrifuges.

Rotative hazards

A common hazard of rotating machinery lies in its potential for disintegration and the consequent projection of missiles. Generally speaking, the higher the speed, for a given rotor diameter, the greater is the hazard. If a rotating machine disintegrates it will tend to project parts of the rotor as missiles which will be projected tangentially with a velocity roughly equal to the peripheral speed of the rotor.

Thus the peripheral speed of the rotor is one major determinant of the hazard. The other is the mass of the missile projected.

Calculation of peripheral speed

We are calculating a *speed* not a *velocity*. The velocity, which is a vector, is continually changing, whereas the speed, which is scalar, remains constant.

Some typical rotor diameters and peripheral speeds are shown in Table 2.6. These relate to UK practice. The speeds shown are approximate, as the motors are not synchronous.

$$S_p = D_R \times \pi \times \Omega/60 \; [\text{m s}^{-1}] \tag{2.1}$$

where,

S_p — peripheral speed (m s^{-1})

D_R — diameter of rotor (m)

Ω — rotational speed (revs per minute)

(For comparison, the speed of sound in air is ca $300 \, \text{m s}^{-1}$).

Peripheral speeds do not differ from one machine to another as widely as one might expect. Where D_R is large the rotational speed is usually designed to be low, and vice versa. Machines in which D_R is high tend to be of the more massive kind and to have the potential to project large missiles. Thus, the larger the machine, the greater the hazard for the same peripheral speed.

Miscellaneous hazards

An additional hazard is that of vibration, which may lead to equipment failure through fatigue or to the collapse of supporting structures. There are other mechanical hazards such as, for example, the generation of sparks.

Centrifuges

Lindley[9] is a monograph on the safe operation of centrifuges. It provides definitions and descriptions of the various types of centrifuge from laboratory scale to full-scale machinery.

Table 2.6 Speeds of various types of rotating equipment

Equipment	Diameter (m)	Rotational speed (rpm)	Speed (peripheral) (m s^{-1})
Steam driven generator	2.0	3,000	320
Centrifugal pump	0.5	1,500	40
High speed grinders	0.25	9,000	120
Basket centrifuges	1.5	1,500	120
Gas centrifuges	0.05	50,000	130

2.5 Pressure energy releases

2.5.1 Introduction

The hazards discussed in this section are those which arise from the accidental release of pressure energy where this is purely physical in nature. Pressure releases which arise from chemical reaction are discussed in later sections on chemical energy releases. The releases discussed are from systems in which the pressure is either an integral feature of the operation or has been imposed to test the integrity of the system.

The hazards of such pressure releases are discussed under six topic headings:

(1) releases of free-flowing powders;
(2) releases of liquids;
(3) releases of liquefied vapours;
(4) implosions [collapses of partially evacuated vessels];
(5) releases of compressed gases;
(6) releases of liquefied gases.

Accurate calculation in this area is often impossible to achieve but, nevertheless, approximate calculations which indicate the order of magnitude of the hazard may still be very useful. This is because, other factors apart, the behaviour on failure of a pressurized system is highly dependent upon its geometry. The geometry after failure is usually conjectural. Thus even when there are reliable flow equations, unless the size and shape of the aperture is known it is difficult to apply them with any degree of accuracy. Data in this area, when they are quoted in the literature with many significant figures, should therefore be treated with caution.

2.5.2 Releases of free-flowing powders

The study of how powders behave is known in the UK as 'powder technology', but this special title is not used in the US. The flow of powders is a far more complex study than that of liquids or gases and is a highly specialized subject area. Perry's Handbook devotes its Chapter 7 to 'Solids Transport and Storage', but this contains very little quantitative information on the flow properties of powders. This is not surprising because these properties depend upon many factors including particle density, bulk density, particle size, particle size distribution, particle shape and moisture content, as well as the geometry of the system.

Relationship between depth and pressure.

It might seem, at first sight, that the pressure at any point on the walls of a vessel containing a powder would vary uniformly with the depth of the powder above it, and that it could be calculated from the bulk density of the powder and its depth. This is not so. If a pressure transducer is installed at the bottom of a powder storage vessel and the vessel is then progressively filled with a free-flowing powder, it will soon be seen that the relationship between depth and pressure is not linear.

Though pressure increases with depth initially, the dependence decreases and eventually the pressure remains constant regardless of depth. This is generally attributed to 'arching', with pressure being distributed laterally to the vessel walls. This effect cannot be quantified beyond pointing out that the depth at which a constant pressure is achieved is a function of the aspect ratio H/D and that it may occur at $H/D = $ ca. 3.

Spillages of powders, whether through structural failure (which could occur, for example, through charging a vessel with a powder of density higher than that for which it was designed) or through maloperation, are likely to lead to a short-range realization. Spilled powders tend to accumulate close to the point of discharge. A heap, more or less conical in shape, according to the geometry of the surroundings, will be formed and this may lead to human injury or property damage.

2.5.3 Releases of liquids

Classification of liquids

Most liquids encountered in the process industries are Newtonian — that is, having a viscosity which is independent of the rate of shear. They include water and most liquids of low molar mass. However, non-Newtonian liquids are not uncommon and these are discussed briefly later.

The behaviour of spilled Newtonian liquids

When Newtonian liquids are spilled, their behaviour is highly dependent upon the geometry of the surface on which they fall. If the surface is flat and horizontal, they will spread out under gravity at a rate which is an inverse function of their viscosity. Low-viscosity liquids will flow with a low surface gradient and tend to form surface waves. They will have a high kinetic energy and this is their principal hazard. If the spillage is through the medium of jets, kinetic energy will play an even greater role.

Calculation of rates of release

There are many standard texts on fluid mechanics which set out the theoretical principles of the flow of fluids. The subject is treated, for example, in Chapter 6 of Perry's Handbook[10].

Practical problems include the prediction of the flow rate of Newtonian liquids through apertures of known geometry. Flow rates depend upon factors such as viscosity and density and the pressure driving force. Crowl and Louver[11] reviews the basic fluid mechanics and gives worked examples of such problems.

Non-Newtonian liquids

Some liquids encountered in the process industries are non-Newtonian — that is, their viscosity is not independent of the rate of shear. They tend to be liquids of high molar mass such as polymers or they may be aqueous solutions of such substances.

Their properties may differ widely from Newtonian liquids. Some, such as Bingham plastics, may behave like solids for much of the time (thus when spilled they have a strong tendency to 'pile up'). Manufacturers who handle non-Newtonian liquids must be aware of how they will behave in the event of spillage and of the hazards they present. These hazards include those which arise from such properties as being slippery or sticky. Comparatively accessible texts on this subject are Wilkinson[12] and Barnes[13].

Hydraulic rupture

Vessels containing a liquid may rupture through excessive pressure being applied, and a special case is where they are being hydraulically tested. Hydraulic testing is almost universally practised today; only in special cases are vessels pneumatically tested. This is because, though the energy released during the failure of a vessel under hydraulic test is far from negligible, it is only a fraction of that which would be released during failure under pneumatic testing at the same pressure.

Failure during hydraulic testing is characterised as a 'hydraulic explosion'. Such an explosion releases the energy stored both in the walls and in the liquid. High-pressure jets which may cause serious injury can be discharged, and parts of the vessel may become missiles. For a detailed account of the hazards of hydraulic testing, see Dooner and Marshall[14].

2.5.4 Releases of liquefied vapours

There have been many very serious incidents in the process industries resulting from the loss of containment of liquefied vapours. Because of its great importance, this subject is treated here in detail.

42

In this section the nature of liquefied vapours is discussed, and particularly their behaviour when containment pressure is reduced. In the context of process safety this means that the pressure falls from the containment ('storage') level to the atmospheric level (about 1 bar absolute). This leads to a phenomenon known as 'flashing', in which a fraction of the liquid phase is vaporized.

Two differing circumstances are recognized in which flashing may take place and a model is put forward for each. Using ammonia as an example substance, the methodology by which the flashing fraction may be calculated for each of the two models is demonstrated. From this value the volume of vapour released from a given mass of liquefied vapour may be estimated. The specific energy released by flashing can also be estimated.

Gases and vapours

The vapour phase is a sub-set of the gas phase. All substances which can exist as a gas also have a vapour phase. A vapour is a gas which is below its critical temperature — that is, the highest temperature at which liquid and gas can be in equilibrium with each other. Only below this temperature can the gas be liquefied by pressure alone. Vapours also exhibit a critical pressure, which is their vapour pressure at their critical temperature.

A liquefied vapour system is thus one in which vapour and liquid are in equilibrium at a temperature between the atmospheric pressure boiling temperature (*normal boiling point* or T_{BN}) of the liquid and its critical temperature T_C. Some liquefied vapour systems are at ambient temperature as, for example, storage systems for ammonia, chlorine and propane. Others are above ambient temperature as, for example, steam systems. There is no basic difference in thermodynamic behaviour between the two kinds of system.

It should be noted that liquefied vapours stored at ambient temperature are often referred to as 'liquefied gases'. For example LPG means 'Liquefied Petroleum Gas'. As explained above, this is scientifically inappropriate, as they are actually liquefied vapours. The term 'liquefied gases' is here reserved for liquids with a critical temperature below ambient which are kept at, or around, their normal boiling points by means of refrigeration. This subject is discussed in Sections 2.5.5 and 2.6 (pages 52 and 57).

Hydrocarbons may be classified according to the number of carbon atoms in the molecule as follows:

- one carbon atom (methane): this is handled as a refrigerated liquefied gas;
- two carbon atoms (ethane, ethene): these are borderline cases and are usually handled as refrigerated liquefied gases;
- three and four carbon atoms (propane, butane and corresponding unsaturated compounds): these are handled as liquefied vapours.

43

- five or more carbons (pentane, hexane): these are liquids at ambient temperatures.

Most substances which exist completely in the gas phase at ambient temperature are vapours and may be handled in the liquefied state. Five of them will be discussed in detail, but there are many more, including phosgene, sulphur dioxide, dimethyl ether, ethylene oxide and refrigerants such as Freons.

Table 2.7 sets out the critical temperatures and pressures of the five commonly encountered liquefied vapours. The data are from Kaye and Laby[15]; temperatures are in °C and pressures are in bar absolute. Most organic compounds have a critical pressure which is less than 50 bar.

Flashing

If the pressure is reduced on any system in which a liquid is in equilibrium with its vapour at its boiling temperature, this will cause the liquid to boil without the need for an input of externally supplied heat. This process is described as 'flashing'. The conditions of such a process are essentially adiabatic. It follows from the First Law of Thermodynamics that the enthalpy of vaporization of the vapour must therefore be supplied by an equal reduction of enthalpy of the remaining liquid, resulting in a fall in the temperature of the latter. Thus:

$$\Delta H_1 + \Delta H_v = 0 \qquad (2.2)$$

where ΔH_1 is the (negative) increase in the enthalpy of the liquid and ΔH_v is the increase in the enthalpy of the vapour.

The fraction of the liquid (α) which vaporizes under any given circumstances is a function of the initial and final pressures and of the geometry of the release. The process has long been utilized technologically; for example, it is the basis of most refrigeration cycles.

For flashing to be a hazardous process the initial pressure of the liquid in equilibrium with its vapour must be above atmospheric. If there is then a loss of containment, the pressure of the system will fall eventually to atmospheric and a fraction of the liquid will vaporize.

Table 2.7 Critical temperatures and pressures

Substance	Propane	Butane	Ammonia	Chlorine	Water
Critical temperature (°C)	97	152	132	144	374
Critical pressure (bar)	42.5	38	113	77	221

Physical models of the flashing process

As with other accidental releases, the geometry of the system is a powerful determining factor, so there is no unique model of a flashing process. Two models, both of which assume adiabatic conditions, are considered.

In model 1, it is assumed that a vessel containing a liquefied gas discharges vapour from a leak above the liquid level sufficiently slowly that there is no significant liquid carry-over (entrainment). If the vessel is assumed to be thermally insulated, adiabatic conditions are assured. The vapour at any stage in the process will be in thermal equilibrium with the liquid. Its initial temperature will be that of containment T_S and its final temperature will be its normal boiling point T_{BN}. The temperature of the vapour will thus vary continuously during discharge. Its mean temperature will be the average of these two values.

In model 2, it is assumed that the vessel discharges liquid through a leak *below* the liquid level. [To simplify the treatment, the leak is supposed to be at the lowest point of the vessel. Otherwise the system would conform with model 2 until the liquid level fell to the point of leakage, thereafter flashing off vapour and thus conforming with model 1].

Before discharge, the liquid is at its containment pressure and temperature. After discharge, its pressure falls to that of the atmosphere. The liquid is then superheated above its normal boiling point. It will, in consequence, boil with explosive rapidity and its temperature will fall to the normal boiling point. The rapidity of the process ensures adiabatic conditions. It also means that the vapour cloud formed will contain droplets of entrained liquid and therefore the vapour will be in thermal equilibrium with the liquid at its normal boiling point.

The two models differ thermodynamically. In model 1, the mean temperature of the vapour is higher than the normal boiling point of the liquid. In model 2, it is equal to it.

Case histories related to the models

Model 1 seems to conform to the circumstances of the Flixborough disaster, which is described as a case history in Chapter 5 (page 227). Similarly, model 2 seems to conform to the circumstances of the Spanish campsite disaster, also described as a case history in Chapter 5 (page 237). The case history of Feyzin (page 225) seems to have started as in model 2 and ended as in model 1.

Calculation of flashing fraction

The flashing fraction denoted by the symbol α is the fraction of the original mass of the liquid component of a liquefied vapour system which is converted to vapour. It may be calculated, for any given substance, using either model. From this fraction it is then possible to calculate the volume of vapour released per unit mass of the original liquid for either model. [The flashing fraction, α, is sometimes denoted in the literature as the theoretical adiabatic flashing fraction (TAFF)].

In order to facilitate the understanding of these calculations we set out the variables in a standard form in Table 2.8. The symbols have the following meanings:

- T_S and T_{BN} are the containment ('storage') temperature and the normal boiling point, respectively. They apply to both liquid and vapour;
- h_{LS} and h_{LBN} are the specific enthalpies of the liquid at its containment temperature and its normal boiling point, respectively;
- h_{VS} and h_{VBN} are the specific enthalpies of the vapour at the containment temperature, and the normal boiling point of the liquid, respectively;
- h_{VM} is a mean value of the specific enthalpy of the vapour.

All values of specific enthalpy, except h_{VM}, may be obtained directly from tables of thermodynamic properties. The method of estimating h_{VM} will be described later.

The following general equation is applicable to either model:

$$h_{LS} = \alpha h_{VM} + (1 - \alpha)h_{LBN}$$

$$\text{or} \quad \alpha = \frac{h_{LS} - h_{LBN}}{h_{VM} - h_{LBN}} \tag{2.3}$$

It is now necessary to determine an appropriate value of h_{VM} for each model.

In model 1 the most accurate mean value is obtained by treating the vapour as being flashed in a series of increments of varying specific enthalpy and then averaging these. Such a mean value may be obtained from thermodynamic property tables by summing the values at equal intervals of temperature and dividing by the number of incremental steps. This is an application of the trapezium rule which is explained in dictionaries and other reference works on

---

Table 2.8 Variables in a flashing system

Initial conditions: containment pressure P_S, temperature T_S

Liquid	Vapour
h_{LS}	h_{VS}
	h_{VM}
h_{LBN}	h_{VBN}

Final conditions: atmospheric pressure P_A
  normal boiling point T_{BN}

---

mathematics. Somewhat less accurate values are obtained by taking either the specific enthalpy at the mean temperature of the flashing range or the mean of the specific enthalpy of the vapour at storage temperature and at the normal boiling point of the liquid. Example calculations using each of these three values are given below.

In model 2, if it is assumed that the vapour is always in thermal equilibrium with the liquid at its normal boiling point, it follows that its appropriate mean specific enthalpy is that at the normal boiling point of the liquid.

Example calculation for ammonia: model 1 (vapour leak)
Thermodynamic data for ammonia were taken from Rogers and Mayhew[16], interpolated where necessary. The relevant values are displayed in Table 2.9. The quantity h_{VM} has three possible values, as discussed in above:

(1) the incremental mean value, $1445\,\text{kJ}\,\text{kg}^{-1}$;
(2) the value at 8.5°C, the mean temperature of the flashing range (42°C to $-33.35°C$), $1453.0\,\text{kJ}\,\text{kg}^{-1}$;
(3) the mean of the values at 42°C and $-33.35°C$, $(1473.8 + 1400.4)/2 = 1437.1\,\text{kJ}\,\text{kg}^{-1}$.

Equation (2.3) becomes:

$$\alpha = \frac{381.8 - 29.7}{h_{VM} - 29.7} = \frac{352.1}{h_{VM} - 29.7}$$

Then,
for $h_{VM} = 445.0\,\text{kJ}\,\text{kg}^{-1}$, $\alpha = 0.249$;
for $h_{VM} = 1453.0\,\text{kJ}\,\text{kg}^{-1}$, $\alpha = 0.247$;
for $h_{VM} = 1437.1\,\text{kJ}\,\text{kg}^{-1}$, $\alpha = 0.250$.

The discrepancies between these results are clearly negligible. It is recommended therefore that for model 1 (vapour leak), equation (2.3) is applied with

Table 2.9 Variables in calculation for ammonia

Initial conditions: $P_S = 16.42$ bar absolute, $T_S = 42°C$	
Liquid	**Vapour**
$h_{LS} = 381.8\,\text{kJ}\,\text{kg}^{-1}$	$h_{VS} = 1473.8\,\text{kJ}\,\text{kg}^{-1}$
	h_{VM}
$h_{LBN} = 29.7\,\text{kJ}\,\text{kg}^{-1}$	$h_{VBN} = 1400.4\,\text{kJ}\,\text{kg}^{-1}$

Final conditions: $P_A = 1.013$ bar absolute
$T_{BN} = -33.35°C$

h_{vm} evaluated as the mean of the specific enthalpies of the vapour at storage temperature and at the normal boiling point.

It should be noted that, though the figures for the flashing fractions seem to have a high degree of precision, this is accidental because they are derived from thermodynamic tables. In practice pressures may not correspond exactly with the values in the tables. Furthermore the model must be regarded only as an approximation to reality.

Example calculation for ammonia: model 2 (liquid leak)

Substituting the values for ammonia from Table 2.9 into equation (2.3) and evaluating h_{VM} at the normal boiling point:

$$\alpha = \frac{381.8 - 29.7}{1400.4 - 29.7} = \frac{352.1}{1370.7} = 0.257$$

This compares with the most accurate value for α in model 1 of 0.249. The difference between the values of α as between models 2 and 1, for ammonia flashing from 16.42 bar to 1.013 bar, is thus about 3%, which is quite small.

Calculation of volume of vapour for both models

The ultimate volume of vapour released per kilogram of original liquid will be equal to the product of the flashing fraction α (kg vapour/kg original liquid) with the specific volume of the vapour, v_V. The latter depends, of course, on the temperature and pressure — at a typical ambient temperature (20°C) and atmospheric pressure (1.013 bar absolute), it will be (based on the perfect gas law) 1.42 m^3 kg^{-1}.

Thus, in the case of ammonia, flashing to atmospheric pressure at 20°C:

For model 1 $\quad V_R = 1.42 \times 0.249 = 0.354$ m^3 kg^{-1}
For model 2 $\quad V_R = 1.42 \times 0.257 = 0.365$ m^3 kg^{-1}

Calculation of specific energy release

The energy released by a vapour on flashing, and with the capability of doing work on the surroundings, may be expressed by equation (2.4):

$$E_W = \left[\frac{P_1 V_1}{\gamma - 1}\right]\left[1 - \left[\frac{P_A}{P_1}\right]^{\frac{\gamma-1}{\gamma}}\right] \tag{2.4}$$

where,
E_W — energy available to do work
P_1 — initial pressure

P_A — final [atmospheric] pressure

V_1 — initial volume

γ — C_p/C_V [gamma] (C_p and C_v are the molal heat capacities at constant pressure and constant volume respectively).

This equation is an algebraic rearrangement of equation (1.12) given in Baker[17] as being applicable to the energy released by the failure of vessels containing compressed gases. It is assumed that the specific energy is released, with the capability of doing work, by a volume of vapour on flashing from a given containment pressure, is equal to that which would be released by an equal volume of a compressed gas at the same storage pressure. An appropriate notional value of the product $P_1 V_1$ is employed which is calculated on the basis of the ideal gas law:

$$P_1 V_1 = P_2 V_2 (T_1/T_2) = P_A(\alpha m_L) v_{BN} T_S/T_{BN} \tag{2.5}$$

where,

m_L — original mass of liquid

v_{BN} — specific volume of vapour at P_A, T_{BN}

This equation is now adapted to give the specific energy release per 1 kg of liquefied gas — that is, $m_L = 1.0\,\text{kg}$ — so that E_W will become e_W, the specific energy available to do work:

$$e_W = \left[\frac{P_A \alpha v_{BN}}{\gamma - 1} \frac{T_S}{T_{BN}}\right]\left[1 - \left[\frac{P_A}{P_S}\right]^{\frac{\gamma-1}{\gamma}}\right] \tag{2.6}$$

This quantity for ammonia is calculated for the two alternative flashing models using the following data:

$P_A = 1.013 \times 10^5$ Pa; $P_S = 16.42 \times 10^5$ Pa; $v_{BN} = 1.133$ m^3 kg^{-1} (by interpolation from the tables); $T_S = 42°C$ ($\equiv 315.15$ K); $T_{BN} = -33.35°C$ ($\equiv 239.8$ K); $\gamma = 1.31$ (from Perry's Handbook).

For either model, the quantity $[e_W/\alpha]$ may be calculated as:

$$\frac{e_W}{\alpha} = \frac{1.013 \times 10^5 \times 1.133}{0.31} \times \frac{315.15}{239.80}\left[1 - \left(\frac{1.013}{16.42}\right)^{0.31/1.31}\right]$$

$$= 2.348 \times 10^5 \text{ J kg}^{-1} \text{ liquid}$$

Hence for model 1, $e_W = 2.348 \times 10^5 \times 0.249 = 5.9 \times 10^4$ J kg^{-1} of liquefied ammonia, while, for model 2, $e_W = 2.348 \times 10^5 \times 0.257 = 6.0 \times 10^4$ J kg^{-1} of liquefied ammonia.

It may be remarked that the difference between these results is negligible compared with the inherent inaccuracies of the calculation.

Comparative data for various substances

Using the methodology given above for ammonia, similar data have been calculated for other substances over the same flashing range and using model 2. The reference temperature for specific volume and specific energy is 0°C except for steam where it is 100°C. The values quoted relate to 1 kg of liquefied vapour (see Table 2.10).

These energies may be compared with the detonation of trinitrotoluene (TNT), where the specific energy is of the order of 4×10^6 J kg^{-1} (see Section 2.13, page 121). The detonation of TNT is thus 100 times more energetic than the flashing of a liquefied vapour over the range 16 bar to 1 bar.

The power of such releases

In order to calculate the power of such events it is necessary to know their duration. It is known that in the Flixborough disaster, which is described as a case history in Chapter 5 (page 227) and which seems to have conformed to model 1, some 40 tonnes of cyclohexane vapour escaped from a reactor train in around 45 seconds. The reactor train contained approximately 120 tonnes of liquefied vapour at ca. 10 bar absolute.

The hazards of liquefied vapours

The hazards which are realized by the loss of containment of liquefied vapours depend in part upon the chemical nature of the released vapour. They may be divided into a number of classes as listed below:

(1) Primary pressure hazards are the direct effects of the loss of containment: they are essentially independent of the nature of the vapour. [Secondary pressure effects that may result from the chemical reactions involved in category (3) below are discussed in that context].
(2) Thermal hazards are discussed in Section 2.6 (page 57).

Table 2.10 Comparative data

Property	Substance			
	Ammonia	**Chlorine**	**Propane**	**Steam**
α	0.249	0.310	0.520	0.195
v_R [m^3 kg^{-1}]	0.339	0.098	0.265	0.332
γ	1.31	1.355	1.13	1.324
e_W [10^4 J kg^{-1}]	6.0	1.6	6.4	4.3

(3) Flammable and explosive hazards are discussed in Sections 2.8 to 2.11 of this chapter (pages 80–115).

(4) Asphyxiating and toxic hazards are discussed in Chapter 4.

Primary pressure hazards

The nature of the primary pressure effects depends on the speed and geometry of the release. The most serious case is that of the catastrophic disintegration of the containing vessel. In such circumstances cracks may propagate with the speed of sound in the metal — for steel this speed is around 5000 m s^{-1}. Thus on the assumption that a crack would have to be propagated over a distance of, say, 20 m, a road tanker could fail catastrophically in about 0.004 seconds.

There have been several examples of road tankers disintegrating and portions travelling distances of as much as 500 metres before coming to rest. This is brought about by the reactive forces as the portions discharge their contents and are propelled like rockets. There may also be local blast effects which knock down walls and buildings. The case history of the Spanish campsite disaster in Chapter 5 (page 237) illustrates this.

The BLEVE scenario

A particular sequence of events which may result in serious harm is commonly described as a 'boiling liquid expanding vapour-cloud explosion', usually denoted by its acronym BLEVE. As noted by IChemE (Jones[2]), this term is frequently used in an imprecise manner, but used in its strict sense it has a definite meaning.

A BLEVE may occur when a storage tank containing liquefied vapour receives thermal energy of great intensity, for example, by being engulfed in a conflagration. This may cause the internal vapour pressure to rise, eventually forcing the relief valve to open. The subsequent course of events is determined by the existence of two different heat-transfer regimes. Below the liquid level, a high heat-transfer coefficient on the inner surface ensures that the temperature of the tank wall remains little higher than that of the liquid; above it, because of the very much lower coefficient characteristic of the vapour phase, the wall temperature rises to a value much nearer to that of the flame.

The tensile strengths of metals fall with rising temperature, and at 650°C structural steel has lost half its strength. As the liquid progressively boils away (the vapour escaping through the open relief valve), its level falls and the area of dry — and consequently hot and enfeebled — wall increases. Eventually, even though the relief valve may keep the internal pressure from exceeding its design value, the walls can no longer withstand this. A bulge develops which eventually becomes a 'petal fracture'. This is followed by an extremely rapid discharge of vapour, which gives rise to a powerful reactive force that may topple the tank or cause it to become airborne and may produce a blast wave, which may be described as a 'physical explosion' (see Section 2.2.7, page 29).

If the escaping vapour is flammable (it must be emphasized that this is not a necessary condition for a BLEVE) there is a high risk of ignition and the generation of a fireball (see Section 2.6, page 57). Two case histories of BLEVEs involving flammable vapours are given in Chapter 5 under Feyzin and Mexico City (pages 225 and 232).

2.5.5 Implosions

Vessels which have not been specially designed as pressure vessels may collapse if they are wholly or partially evacuated. Because the collapse is inwards it is known as an 'implosion', which is the opposite of an explosion. The pressure difference which brings about an implosion is, at maximum, atmospheric pressure.

Implosions may be classified, according to the mode of failure of the collapsing vessel, into two classes — brittle and ductile. In the first, failure is extremely rapid and the collapse is total; in the second, failure is slower and the collapse is only partial, the walls crumpling.

Brittle implosions

Brittle failure is likely to occur with glass vessels. The phenomenon is hard to distinguish from an explosion. The vessel fragments are propelled inwards and although they are likely to collide with other particles in the centre of the space formerly occupied by the vessel, most will continue their flight into the surrounding atmosphere. Brittle implosions are much more common in laboratories and in pilot plants than in full-scale process plant.

Ductile implosions

An important and fairly common class of ductile implosions is that of the failure of atmospheric pressure storage tanks, which is a fairly common occurence.

Consider a storage tank containing a liquid. Suppose that the space above the liquid is filled with a gas, which could be air or nitrogen, and that the gas pressure is atmospheric. Under normal circumstances, if a given volume of liquid is pumped from the tank, and an equal volume of gas is sucked in through a venting system, the pressure in the gas space will remain constant.

If, however, there is partial or total failure of the venting system, then, as liquid is pumped out, the pressure in the gas space will fall below atmospheric. A partial vacuum will thus be created. The extent to which the pressure falls will be determined partly by the geometry of the system and partly by the type of pump employed. A major factor in the geometry of the system will be the degree to which the tank was originally filled. With a full tank the original gas volume would be small and the pumping out of only a relatively small volume of liquid would produce a considerable drop in pressure.

The stresses involved

The storage tanks in question are relatively thin-walled and their wall thickness is primarily determined by considerations of rigidity to enable them to support the weight of the roof without buckling, and to withstand strong winds. Wall thicknesses determined in this way are amply sufficient to withstand the hydraulic pressure exerted by the liquid contents.

Suppose that, because of a venting failure, the pressure inside a tank fell by 0.1 bar. The effect of this would be to increase the downward stress exerted on the walls by the roof by a factor of perhaps 50 or more. This would far exceed any safety factor employed in designing the walls and they would buckle.

A differential pressure force acting radially inwards on the walls would also cause them to crumple, though below the liquid surface hydraulic forces would tend to counteract this. The diminution in internal volume produced by the crumpling would be equal to the volume of liquid which had been pumped out. In many cases tanks have failed so badly from this cause that they have had to be scrapped.

2.5.6 Releases of compressed gases

Compressed gases may be stored in permanently installed storage tanks or they may be delivered in cylinders. Permanent systems may be used where gases are generated and stored *in situ*, as with compressed air. As wall thicknesses have to be increased in proportion to the diameter of a storage vessel containing a compressed gas, it is usually not feasible to store compressed air at high pressures. A pressure of 16 bar absolute, which has been used earlier for calculations on liquefied vapours, would also be appropriate here. A calculation for the specific energy released by compressed air at 16 bar is given below.

All commercially important gases are available from specialist suppliers and are delivered in cylinders. These vary in size from those which require special handling equipment to those which may be handled manually. The safety precautions to be followed when handling such cylinders are set out in the suppliers' safety manuals. Some are general and some are related to the particular gas.

Calculation of specific energy

The specific energy available for doing work from the rupture of a vessel at 16 bar absolute may be calculated from equation (2.4), using the following data for air at STP:

$$\text{Specific volume} = 0.773 \text{ m}^3 \text{ kg}^{-1}; \quad \gamma = 1.402$$
$$\text{then } e_W = 1.06 \times 10^5 \text{ J kg}^{-1}$$

This may be compared with the blast energy released by 1 kg of TNT, which is ca 4×10^6 J kg^{-1}. The detonation of 1 kg of TNT is thus 40 times as energetic as the energy release from 1 kg of air at 16 bar absolute.

Calculation of specific power

The following calculation does not pretend to be accurate, but should give an idea of the order of magnitude of the power associated with the release of energy from compressed gas.

The duration of the event may be calculated by supposing that, at the moment of disintegration of a vessel containing a compressed gas, the gas just inside the container wall has zero velocity. After disintegration, it will accelerate. It is assumed that it reaches the velocity of sound and then decelerates to zero velocity at a point at which its pressure has fallen to atmospheric. The mean velocity is taken therefore as half the speed of sound and the distance travelled as equal to the difference between two radii — one, that of a sphere which would contain the gas at the original pressure, and the other, that of one which would contain the gas at atmospheric pressure.

If 1 kg of air is taken, the radius of a sphere containing it at 16 bar $= 0.22$ m and that of a sphere containing it at 1 bar $= 0.56$ m. The difference in radii is 0.34 m. The velocity of sound is 331 m s^{-1} and half of this is 165 m s^{-1}. The duration of the pulse is thus ca. $0.34/165 = 0.002$ second. If the specific energy calculated above, which was 10^5 J kg^{-1}, is divided by the duration of the event, the power is ca. 5×10^7 W kg^{-1}.

2.5.7 Releases of liquefied gases

In this section the hazards of pressure energy releases which may arise in the handling of liquefied gases are discussed. As explained earlier, a liquefied gas is a gas which is maintained as a liquid by refrigeration and cannot be liquefied by pressure alone at ambient temperature. Such liquefied gases are often termed 'cryogenic liquids' or 'cryogens', and the technology of making them is called 'cryogenics'.

There are other hazards associated with the handling of these gases which are discussed elsewhere. Thus, hazards which arise from their low temperature are discussed in Section 2.6 (page 57). The most important of the liquefied gases are (1) methane which is used as a fuel gas and (2) the air gases, oxygen, nitrogen, argon and liquid air itself, which are widely used in the process industries. [For a fuller account of these, and other liquefied gases, see Shreve's *Process Industries*[18]].

The salient properties of these, and other gases, are set out in Table 2.11.

The boiling temperature and critical temperature of natural gas are higher than those of methane because of high-boiling impurities.

The handling of liquefied gases

The storage of liquefied gases requires effective thermal insulation. This is usually achieved by the use of double-walled containers in which the intervening space is either evacuated (such containers are thus giant Dewar flasks) or filled with high-grade thermal insulating material. For example tens of millions of tonnes of liquefied natural gas, which is substantially methane, are transported annually in such containers in dedicated ocean-going ships.

Inevitably some boil-off occurs. This may be recycled to the refrigeration system or used in the process for which the gas is intended, or, in the case of ships, as fuel. Clearly, any failure of this venting system would lead to pressurization of the container, with serious results.

Behaviour on spillage

As the surroundings are very hot compared with the liquefied gas, one might expect vaporization to be extremely rapid. However, as is explained in standard texts on heat transfer, the rate of heat transfer to boiling liquids is not a linear function of temperature difference. The highest rate of boil-off for liquid nitrogen, for example, occurs at temperature differences of 10–30°C. There is a minimum rate of boil-off at around 50°C (known as the Leidenfrost point) and after that the boil-off rate slowly increases with increasing temperature difference.

Table 2.11 Some properties of liquefied gases

		Hydrogen	Nitrogen	Air	Argon	Oxygen	Methane
Normal boiling point	K	20	77	83	87	90	109
	°C	−253	−196	−190	−186	−183	−161
Critical temperature	K	33	126	132	151	154	191
	°C	−240	−147	−141	−122	−119	−82

The problem arises because of a vapour blanket being formed which reduces heat transfer. This can easily be seen if water is run on to a red-hot surface. So, when the liquefied gas is first spilled, the surroundings are so hot relative to the liquid that vaporization is slow. But the surroundings then cool, and the temperature difference falls with consequent increase in the boil-off rate. Higher rates of boil-off are achieved when the surroundings are thoroughly cooled.

Rapid phase transitions

There are a number of circumstances in which contact between a volatile liquid and a liquid or solid at a very much higher temperature can give rise to a purely physical explosion known as a 'rapid phase transition' or RPT. Vaporization may occur so rapidly that significant overpressures are produced, as described by Phillips[3].

Contact between cryogenic liquids and water as, for example, when liquid methane is spilled on to the sea, may give rise to the phenomenon. A possible manifestation occurred in the Cleveland, Ohio incident (see case history in Chapter 5, page 222).

Other pressure effects

If a liquefied gas is stored in an unvented vessel, the inevitable vaporization will lead to a pressure build-up which eventually causes the vessel, no matter how stoutly constructed, to explode. Spilled liquefied gases exhibit the same hydraulic effects as any other spilled liquids and will do damage on that account to anything which may obstruct their flow.

Comparison with liquefied vapours

The major difference between the flashing of liquefied gases and the vaporization of liquefied vapours is that the latter is an adiabatic process and therefore requires no input of heat from the surroundings. The rate at which liquefied gases generate gas on being spilled is determined by the rate at which latent heat is supplied by the surroundings. This is many orders of magnitude slower than the flashing of spilled liquefied vapours. The contrast is vividly illustrated (Marshall[12]) by the case histories of Cleveland and Spanish campsite disaster (see Chapter 5, pages 222 and 237). In the former, 128 fatalities resulted from a spillage of 3000 tonnes of hydrocarbon, whereas in the latter a spillage of only about 20 tonnes caused 215 fatalities.

2.6 Thermal energy releases

This topic is discussed under three main headings:

(1) mechanisms of transfer of thermal energy;
(2) releases of hot materials;
(3) releases of cold materials.

Effects on people, buildings and equipment are discussed in Chapter 4.

The Joule-Thomson effect (the change in temperature which occurs when gases expand adiabatically and irreversibly, as from a leak in a pressurized system) is not discussed as the increase or decrease in temperature due to this effect is likely to be less than 10 K.

2.6.1 Mechanisms of transfer of thermal energy

We have adopted the customary classification of the mechanisms of heat transfer, namely conduction, convection and radiation. It would be inappropriate to include a comprehensive account of these mechanisms, and we will restrict the discussion mainly to a brief qualitative overview. For a quantitative presentation of the theory and mechanisms of heat transfer, readers are referred to Perry's Handbook or to the many specialized texts. Thermal radiation will be treated quantitatively to some degree as this is needed for the understanding of some of the phenomena to be described.

A major difference between the systems with which process engineering is concerned and the systems being discussed here is that heat transfer in the former case proceeds almost entirely *within* the equipment, whereas the heat transfer discussed here occurs *externally* to the equipment.

Conduction

Conduction is the non-radiative transfer of thermal energy through a medium without transfer of mass. It may occur entirely within a phase or across phase boundaries. In the context of the present section, conduction plays an important role in the transfer of thermal energy between solids and fluids and between one fluid and another.

Convection

Heat transfer by convection is a process whereby heat is transferred within a fluid by the motion of the fluid. Convection may arise in a number of ways. In the case of thermal energy release in the open air, and in the absence of wind, convection is caused solely by differences in the buoyancy of the different

57

regions of the fluid which arise as a consequence of the release. This is usually termed *natural convection*.

Buoyancy, which may be positive or negative, results from differences in density between one region of a fluid and another. This difference in density may arise from differences in composition or in temperature or some combination of the two. If such a region is of lower density than its surroundings it will tend to travel upwards and may be regarded as possessing *positive* buoyancy. If it is of higher density it will tend to travel downwards and may be regarded as possessing *negative* buoyancy.

A flame is an important example of a gaseous region possessed of positive buoyancy. It may, on account of its temperature, have a density which is as little as a fifth of the density of the surrounding air. The vapour arising from the boiling of a liquefied vapour or liquefied gas will form a gaseous region possessed of negative buoyancy. Oxygen boiling from liquid oxygen has a density more than three times that of air at ordinary temperatures.

Generally speaking, open-air spillages occur in the presence of wind, and this acts as an agency of convection. Though wind is a *natural* phenomenon, it would be misleading to speak of it as *natural convection* because the temperature gradients from which it arises are external to the system under consideration. It is referred to in this text as *wind convection*.

Both natural convection and wind convection are vector quantities, but whereas the direction of natural convection is vertical, the direction of wind convection is horizontal. The resultant direction depends upon their relative velocities. In the process industries convection may be brought about mechanically as, for example, by means of a pump or fan, in which case it is termed *forced* convection. Forced convection of this character, though it is a very important heat transfer mechanism in the process industries, is not central to the present discussion.

Radiation

Thermal radiation forms part of the spectrum of electromagnetic radiation. It is characterized by wavelengths of 10^{-3} to 10^{-6} metres (0.5×10^{-12} to 10^{-15} Hz). The transfer of thermal energy by radiation is governed by the well-established Stefan-Boltzmann Law. This Law is represented by the following equation:

$$\phi_R = \sigma[(\varepsilon_E T_E^4) - (\varepsilon_A T_A^4)] \tag{2.7}$$

where,

ϕ_R — net flux of thermal radiation $[W\,m^{-2}]$

σ — Stefan–Boltzmann constant $[= 5.67 \times 10^{-8}\,W\,m^{-2}\,K^{-4}]$

$\varepsilon_E, \varepsilon_A$ — emissivities of emitter and absorber respectively [dimensionless, ≤ 1.0]

T_E, T_A — temperatures of emitter and absorber respectively [K]

The emissivity is the ratio between the power emitted and that which would be emitted by a 'black body' at the same temperature. The higher the temperature, the more dominant is radiation as the principal mechanism of thermal energy transfer.

2.6.2 Releases of hot liquids

The effects of hot liquids are dependent upon their temperature and flow rate. At the lower end of the temperature range, the hot liquid most likely to be encountered is hot water from steam systems. At the middle of the temperature range are a variety of substances which may be used to maintain temperatures in reactors above those for which it is practical to use steam (in the region of 350°C). These include thermally stable organic substances, silicon compounds, molten inorganic salts and molten metals. The substances concerned, and the ranges over which they are used, are discussed in Section 9 of Perry's Handbook. The spillage of such materials may harm materials of construction and may cause fires. At the higher-temperature end of the range of hot liquids are molten metals such as copper, aluminium, brass and steel.

2.6.3 Releases of hot gases

The nature of flames

'Flame' is defined as a hot, more-or-less luminous, mass of gas. Though it is possible in principle to produce such a mass by, say, electrical heating, flames commonly encountered arise from combustion. They can, however, arise from other redox reactions (defined in Section 2.7, page 67). These reactions are discussed in later sections of this chapter, especially in Section 2.9 (page 92).

Some flames are much more luminous than others. Hydrogen flames are barely luminous, whereas hydrocarbon flames are usually highly luminous. Their luminosity arises from free radicals and from minute particles of unburned carbon. When the flame cools it becomes smoke, while the carbon particles become soot.

For any flammable mixture there exists in principle a 'theoretical' flame temperature, which is the temperature that it would reach if burned completely under perfectly adiabatic conditions. Such temperatures are never attained in the open air. For commonly encountered flammables the maximum attainable flame temperatures in air are of the order of 1000 to 1200°C, but they may be appreciably higher for the large, highly turbulent, flames which arise from pool fires (Section 2.6.4) and from fireballs (Section 2.6.5, page 62).

Thermal balances around flames in the open air

Heat is transmitted from flames to their surroundings by two mechanisms — radiation and convection. It is not possible to apply the Stefan-Boltzmann Law (equation (2.7)) with a high degree of accuracy to radiation from flames in the open air because of uncertainties with the variables, as discussed below. Convection results eventually in mixing with the surrounding atmosphere.

At high source temperatures radiation is the dominant mode. Due to its fourth-power dependence on the absolute temperature of the emitter, rates of emission are very high and the value of the rate of emission from the absorber can often be neglected. As the flame cools, the rate of emission from the emitter falls rapidly. Eventually, mixing with the surrounding atmosphere becomes the predominant mode of cooling of open-air flames.

Types of flame

Flames vary in their characteristics, for example in their shape and in their duration, and it is not practicable to attempt to discuss all the different types of flame which may be encountered.

Two main types of flame are described which are at opposite ends of a spectrum — those arising from pool fires and fireballs. Two other types of flame also occur from time to time which do not require detailed discussion. A combustible material emerging from a vessel under pressure may entrain air to produce, on ignition, a localized *jet flame*. A flame resulting from the ignition of a cloud which has drifted some distance from the point of release and has become mixed with atmospheric air to a degree sufficient to constitute a flammable mixture is called a *flash fire* — such a flame is likely to propagate rapidly back to its source[2].

2.6.4 Flames from pool fires

Sources of pool fires

A pool fire may arise from the ignition of a spillage of flammable liquid on to the ground where the shape of the resulting pool will be determined by the contours of the ground. It may occur after a spillage of flammable liquid into a *bund*, which is a walled enclosure or pit designed to limit the spread of spilled materials. It may also occur in a store tank which has lost its roof as, for example, through an explosion.

The duration of pool fires

This depends on the depth of the spillage: the shortest duration tends to occur in spillages on the ground, when the duration may only be minutes. On the other hand, in large roofless storage tanks, pool fires have burned for days.

The shape of flames from pool fires

When the pool is approximately circular, the flame approximates to a cylinder with a height which is 1.75 to 2.5 times its diameter. In the presence of wind convection it will lean, the deviation from the vertical being a function of the wind velocity. Wind also produces *flame drag* or *spill-over*. This is shown in Figure 2.1.

Thermal energy release

Pool fires have been extensively studied in field trials, where the burn-up rate has been calculated from the rate at which the fuel was consumed. There are uncertainties about how far combustion is complete in such flames. Certainly where the fuel contains three or more carbon atoms in the molecule it tends to be smoky, indicating incomplete combustion. A figure of 10^5 watts per m^3 of flame volume has been suggested for the power of pool fire flames.

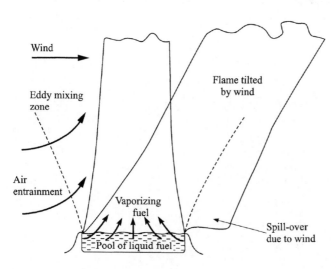

Figure 2.1 Sketch of a pool fire (adapted from Figure 8.4 of Marshall[20])

As with the fireballs discussed below, there seems to be general agreement that pool fire flames radiate about 0.3 of their thermal energy, the remainder being convected into the atmosphere above.

The Major Hazards Assessment Panel[21] suggests $200 \, \mathrm{kW \, m^{-2}}$ as a limiting value for the surface emissive power for large-diameter pool fires. If this value is substituted into the Stefan–Boltzmann equation (equation (2.7)) assuming an emissivity of 1 (black body) and neglecting the back-radiation term, it is found that this corresponds with a mean surface temperature of $1370 \, \mathrm{K}$ (about $1100 °C$). For further information on pool fires, see Section 2.9 and Marshall[20].

2.6.5 Fireballs

Jones[2] gives the following definition:

> **Fireball** — a fire burning sufficiently rapidly for the burning mass to rise into the air as a cloud or ball.

We would describe a fireball as a transient flame which is more or less spherical in shape (a rough sketch is given for illustration in Figure 2.2). This contrasts with the flame of a pool fire, which is typically cylindrical and is of long duration.

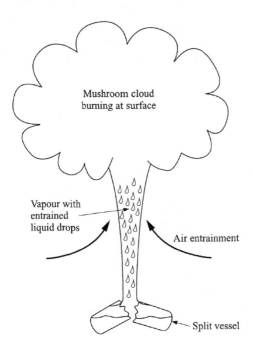

Figure 2.2 Sketch of a fireball

Fireballs may arise from the ignition of a rapidly formed cloud of flammable vapour. There have been many cases of fireballs following a BLEVE scenario when a flashing vapour which is flammable is ignited (see also Chapter 5, Feyzin, page 225).

The physics of fireballs

In order to predict the dose of thermal radiation received by a hazard receptor from a fireball, such parameters as its radius, its surface temperature and emissivity, and its duration must be known. However, these are difficult to calculate and any such calculations have a low level of accuracy.

The correlations presented here indicate the approximate magnitude of these variables. They have been derived from studies of actual incidents, laboratory experiments, field trials and theoretical analysis. These correlations are analysed in Marshall[20]. Important papers on the subject are those of Roberts[22] and Moorhouse and Pritchard[23].

The correlations presented approximate most closely to fireballs formed from hydrocarbons burning in air, which are the most likely ones to be encountered. Fireballs involving hydrogen may, on account of its high reactivity, deviate markedly from these correlations.

The radius of a fireball

Based upon studies of the literature, the following approximate correlation is proposed for the radius of a fireball in metres:

$$R = 28 \times M^{0.333} \tag{2.8}$$

where, M — mass of fuel (typically hydrocarbon) (t).

The constant 28 is not a dimensionless number, but has dimensions $LM^{-0.333}$ (equivalent to specific volume$^{0.333}$). Thus $(28 \times M^{0.333})$ has the dimensions of length.

The catastrophic failure of a propane storage of a design capacity of ca. 300 tonnes could give rise to the ejection of 50 tonnes of vapour which might, if ignited, in some circumstances give rise to a 50-tonne fireball. For such a fireball:

$$R_{(50)} = 28 \times 50^{0.333} = 28 \times 3.68 = \text{ca. } 100 \text{ m} \tag{2.9}$$

where, $R_{(50)}$ — radius of a 50 tonne propane fireball (m)

It would thus have a radius comparable with the length of a football field.

63

The duration of a fireball

There are three main phases in the development of a fireball. The first phase, for a vapour cloud at ground level, is from ignition to lift-off; the second is from lift-off to full development and the third is from full development to dying away.

In the case of a vapour cloud generated by the flashing of a liquefied vapour, if the cloud did not ignite it would sink to the ground. Where it ignites in mid-air, phase one is probably very short and can be ignored.

Based upon High[24] as modified by Marshall[25], a correlation which would cover phases two and three is as follows:

$$T = 3.8 \times M^{0.333} \tag{2.10}$$

where,

T — duration of fireball (s)

M — mass of fuel (t)

The constant 3.8 includes within it factors for specific volume and for velocity, so that the quantity $3.8 \times M^{0.333}$ has the dimensions of time.

For a 50-tonne fireball:

$$T_{(50)} = 3.8 \times 50^{0.333} = 3.8 \times 3.68 = 14s \tag{2.11}$$

The power of a fireball

It is clear from the above discussion that the power of a fireball will start from zero, rise to a peak and then decline again to zero. It is not practicable to seek to do other than ascribe a mean value to its power.

The mean power of a fireball is equal to the product of the specific enthalpy of combustion and the mass of fuel, divided by the duration of the fireball. This may be evaluated as follows:

$$P_T = [M \times (-\Delta H_c)]/[3.8 \times M^{0.333}] = 0.26(-\Delta H_c) \times M^{0.666} \tag{2.12}$$

where,

P_T — mean total power of fireball (W)

ΔH_c — specific enthalpy of combustion (J/t) (a typical value is -4.8×10^{10} J/t)

M — mass of fuel (t).

However, less than half of this power is emitted as radiation, the remainder being convected as hot gases into the upper atmosphere. A value of 0.3 put forward by Roberts[22] and Moorhouse and Pritchard[23] for the fraction radiated has been accepted (and thus 0.7 for the fraction convected). The fraction radiated was estimated from a study of the surface temperatures of pool fires and fireballs.

Thus the radiative power of a fireball is given by:

$$P_R = 0.3 \times 0.26\,(-\Delta H_c) \times M^{0.666} = 0.078 \times (-\Delta H_c) \times M^{0.666} \qquad (2.13)$$

For a 50-tonne propane fireball:

$$P_{R(50)} = 0.078 \times 4.8 \times 10^{10} \times 13.5 = \text{ca. } 5 \times 10^{10}\ W \qquad (2.14)$$

where, $P_{R(50)}$ — radiative power of a 50-tonne fireball.

This radiative power may be compared with the mean electric power generation of the UK which is ca. 3×10^{10} W.

The radiative flux

In calculating radiative flux we find it useful to accept the assumption that a fireball may be treated as a point source radiating uniformly in all directions.

In this case the radiative flux (power per unit area perpendicular to the direction of the radiation), at a distance r from this source, may be evaluated by dividing the radiative power by the surface area of a sphere of this radius. It should be noted that the calculation is valid only if r is equal to or greater than R, the radius of the fireball. At $r = R$, the radiative flux is that at the surface (S) of the fireball. Thus:

$$\phi_{RS} = P_R/(4\pi R^2) \qquad (2.15)$$

where, ϕ_{RS} — radiative flux a surface of fireball (W m^{-2})

For a 50-tonne fireball at a distance of 103 metres from the centre — that is, at the surface of the fireball — the radiant flux would be:

$$\phi_{RS(50)} = 5 \times 10^{10}/[4\pi \times 103^2] = 3.8 \times 10^5\ \text{W m}^{-2} = \text{ca. } 4 \times 10^5\ \text{W m}^{-2} \qquad (2.16)$$

where, $\phi_{RS(50)}$ — radiant flux at the surface of a 50-tonne propane fireball (W m^{-2}).

The surface temperature of a fireball

This may be derived from the Stefan-Boltzmann equation:

$$\phi_{RS} = \sigma[\varepsilon_E \times T_E^4) - (\varepsilon_A \times T_A^4)] \qquad (2.17)$$

The surface of the fireball may be approximated to a 'black body', so that, taking $\varepsilon_E \simeq 1.0$ and the term $(\varepsilon_A \times T_A^4)$ to be negligible in comparison with $(\varepsilon_E \times T_E^4)$:

$$\phi_{RS} = \sigma T_E^4 \qquad (2.18)$$

or

$$T_E = (\phi_{RS}/\sigma)^{0.25} \qquad (2.19)$$

For a 50 tonne-propane fireball:

$$T_{E(50)} = (7 \times 10^{12})^{0.25} \cong 1600 \text{ K} \qquad (2.20)$$

Thus the surface temperature of the 50-tonne propane fireball is about 1600 K or 1300°C.

Some general points on fireballs

The figures calculated are approximations and depend upon the assumptions which are made. However, the assumptions must interlock and are only variable within limits. Taken in combination they must conform with the First Law of Thermodynamics.

To summarize, Table 2.12 presents the approximate values which were calculated for a 50-tonne propane fireball. These values give a good indication of the characteristics of a large fireball.

2.6.6 Releases of cold materials

Comparisons with climatic conditions

The lowest recorded temperature in the UK is around $-20°C$, but much lower temperatures are common in continental regions such as the USA and Russia. These temperatures are comparable with the normal boiling points of some liquefied vapours but are much above the normal boiling points of the liquefied gases.

Low temperatures associated with liquefied vapours

The fall in temperature associated with the flashing of liquefied vapours was discussed in Section 2.5 where it was shown that temperatures as low as $-50°C$ may be attained in some liquefied vapours by flashing down to atmospheric

Table 2.12 Approximate characteristics of a 50-tonne propane fireball

Radius	100 m
Duration	14 s
Radiative fraction	0.30
Mean radiative power	5×10^{10} W
Radiative flux at surface	4×10^5 W m^{-2}
Surface temperature	1600 K (1300°C)

pressure. In special circumstances, as, for example, if a liquefied vapour is run into an evacuated vessel, temperatures much below the normal boiling point may occur during flashing.

Reference was made in Section 2.5 to the tendency of flashing liquids to entrain liquid droplets into the vapour phase. These droplets may evaporate in contact with the atmosphere in a similar way to evaporation in a cooling tower. This effect has been suggested as an explanation of why the vapour cloud from flashing ammonia, which should be buoyant, sometimes behaves as if it were heavier than air. An example of this occurs in the case history 'Houston' in Chapter 5 (page 229).

Low temperatures associated with liquefied gases

Such liquids are sometimes termed 'cryogenic liquids' (or 'cryogens'). There is no precise definition of this term, but it is generally used to identify liquids with normal boiling points of $-130°C$ or below. Cryogenic liquids cannot be stored without material loss except under refrigeration.

Important cryogenic liquids, with their normal boiling points in °C, are: methane (-161), oxygen (-183), argon (-186), nitrogen (-196). Ethene (-104) falls somewhat outside the definition of a cryogenic liquid. However, on account of its low critical temperature it is, like cryogenic liquids, usually handled in a refrigerated condition.

The handling and storage of cryogenic liquids and their behaviour on spillage were described in Section 2.5.7 (page 54). Their effects on materials of construction are described in Chapter 4.

2.7 Chemical energy releases – general principles

2.7.1 Releases of chemicals and chemical energy

The most important realizations of active source hazards in the chemical and process industries are those which release chemicals or which emit energy as a result of chemical reactions. This follows from the nature of the industries, in that they are centrally concerned with the processing and handling of reactive chemical substances.

This section is concerned with the general conditions governing those emissions of chemical energy which have the potential to harm people, property and the environment. Such harm will take place through the transformation of chemical energy into such forms of energy as thermal radiation or overpressure (blast energy).

In order to be able to explain and quantify these phenomena, we shall need to refer to some basic aspects of the science of thermodynamics. It is not our intention to give an extended account of this subject, since students are expected to be studying it in separate courses, with specialist texts.

In this section spillages of chemical substances where there is no chemical reaction at source, and where energy transformations at source are purely physical, are not analysed. The circumstances which give rise to spillages of chemicals have been reviewed in Sections 2.2 (causation and realization) and 2.5 (pressure energy releases). The consequences of chemical spillages are described in Chapter 3 (transmission paths) and in Chapter 4 (hazard receptors).

2.7.2 Energy and power

A minimum requirement for a source to constitute a chemical energy hazard, is that it must have the potential to emit such energy; but not all such energy constitutes a hazard. One criterion is the quantity of energy emitted, which may be too small to constitute a hazard. The other criterion is the *rate* at which energy is emitted — that is, the emissive *power*.

In the following discussion, energy is quantified in SI units as Joules (J) and power as Watts (W) ($J s^{-1}$). Unless the text states otherwise, it is assumed for simplicity that during any given emission its power is constant. The power of an emission is thus the total energy emitted divided by its duration.

To illustrate the significance of power, as opposed to energy, as a determinant of hazard, the example of glucose is given. The catalysed oxidation of glucose in the tissues, at or below 38°C, by oxygen dissolved in the blood stream, is the basis of all animal life. The emission of energy from this source does not have the potential to injure people or property, so this is a non-hazardous process. On the other hand, a dust cloud made up of finely divided glucose in air may explode, causing an over-pressure of several bars and incandescence. Such an event may give rise to human injury and property damage and is therefore a hazard. Yet, as will be shown, the specific *energy*, the quantity of energy emitted per unit mass of glucose oxidized, is the same in both cases (about $15 kJ kg^{-1}$). In fact, there is a small variation due to the different end-states of the reaction products, so that the energy emission of the slower process actually exceeds that of the faster one, but this difference is negligible in the context.

Where the cases differ is in their specific *power* — that is, power per kg of the emission. This results from the difference between the number of molecules which are oxidized in unit time per unit quantity of glucose in each of the two cases.

In the first case energy is released slowly and the animal's cooling system is adequate to prevent any dangerous rise in temperature. In the second case, the dust cloud, the energy is released too rapidly for cooling to prevent the evolution of high temperatures.

The reactions examined in Sections 2.8 to 14 are ranked according to their specific power — that is, power per unit mass of the reactants. The specific powers of these reactions range over many orders of magnitude. The reactions of lowest power are discussed in Section 2.8 (page 80) and those of highest power are discussed in Section 2.13 (page 121).

In this chapter the factors determining the energy associated with chemical reactions which may give rise to energy emissions are examined. The factors which determine the power of such emissions are then discussed.

Note that, though thermodynamics is the science which determines the energetics of chemical reactions, it can play no part in the analysis of the rates of reactions, and hence of their power, since it takes no account of the dimension of time.

2.7.3 Thermochemistry

As discussed above, a key element in the assessment of the hazard associated with the emission of chemical energy is the evaluation of the specific energy emitted. Without this information the specific power, which is the index of hazard, cannot be estimated.

This subject is discussed only in the context of reactions which are completed according to known stoichiometric equations. Therefore, only the application of the First Law of Thermodynamics to emissions of chemical energy is considered. The branch of thermodynamics which enables specific energy released by chemical reaction to be calculated is thermochemistry.

The nature of chemical energy

Chemical reactions are invariably accompanied by substantial energy changes which may exert large effects, not only on the reacting materials themselves but also, potentially, on their surroundings.

These energy changes are evaluated by the methods of thermodynamics, though that science, having been developed originally for the study of steam cycles (which do not involve chemical reactions), has little to say about their precise nature. For the purposes of this book, they are represented as *transformations* between *chemical* energy (associated with the electron motion involved in chemical bonds) and *thermal* energy (associated with the motion of molecules), which is related to the temperature of the system. Whether these changes result in the transfer of energy as heat or work between the system and its surroundings depends on the circumstances of the particular process.

69

The thermodynamic property which is universally used as the measure of the thermal effect of a chemical reaction is *enthalpy*, but it should be noted that a 'chemical' enthalpy change due to reaction will not necessarily alter the enthalpy of the system as a whole — this will depend on the total energy balance.

The standard enthalpy of reaction

Stoichiometric chemical reactions can be defined by a generalized equation of the following form:

$$\sum_{j=1}^{N_j}(v_j \times A_j) = 0 \qquad (2.21)$$

where A_j is a mole of species j (mol) and v_j is the *stoichiometric coefficient* of species j (dimensionless) and N_j is the total number of chemical species involved. By convention, v is negative for reactants and positive for products.

The enthalpy change of any reaction varies with temperature and pressure. To simplify the compilation of data, a *standard enthalpy of reaction*, ΔH_R^0, is defined as the amount of heat absorbed when the reaction, as defined by a stoichiometric equation, is carried out isothermally and isobarically with all the reactants and products in their *standard* states, to the *extent* of one mole. The extent of reaction (sometimes called the reaction co-ordinate) is defined as $\xi = (\Delta n_j/v_j)$, where Δn_j is the amount of any species j produced in the specified reaction (in mol) and v_j is the stoichiometric coefficient of species j in the same reaction (if j is a reactant, both numerator and denominator are negative).

The standard state for this purpose is defined in terms of a standard pressure p_0 [traditionally 1 atmosphere (1.01325 bar), now changing to 1.00 bar to conform with the SI] and the natural state of aggregation of the respective chemical species at this pressure and at the reference temperature T_0 [usually 25°C (298.15 K)]. For example,

$$CO(g) + \frac{1}{2}O_2(g) \rightarrow CO_2(g): \quad \Delta H_{R^{298}}^0 = -283.0 \text{ kJ mol}^{-1}$$

Note that data in the literature are often in c.g.s units (calories mol^{-1}).

It follows from the above definition that ΔH_R^0 is *negative* for exothermic reactions, which release chemical energy, and *positive* for endothermic reactions, which absorb it. If this is at first glance counter-intuitive, it may perhaps be better understood by visualizing, for example, a standard exothermic reaction as taking place in two stages. In the first stage, the conversion of chemical to thermal energy causes the temperature of the system to rise. In the

70

second stage, the system is restored to the standard temperature by transferring energy (as heat) to the surroundings.

Evaluation of the standard enthalpy of reaction

The number of possible reactions is infinite, so it is quite impossible to tabulate — let alone to determine experimentally — values of ΔH_R^0 for all of them. Instead, data are tabulated for a limited number of special reactions, and required values are calculated from these. For this purpose, use is made of Hess's Law of Constant Heat Summation, which states that:

'The standard enthalpy of a reaction is independent of the path of the reaction, depending only on the initial states of the reactants and the final states of the products.'

This empirical law is a corollary of the First Law of Thermodynamics, and of the definition of enthalpy as a *state* — not a *path* — function.

ΔH_R^0 can therefore be determined for a particular reaction by representing the reaction as proceeding through a series of steps (whether these are actually possible or not) for which the values of ΔH_R^0 are known, and adding these algebraically.

Example: Calculate ΔH_R^0 for reaction (a), given (b) and (c):

(a) $C(\beta)0 +$	$O_2(g) = CO_2(g)$		
(b) $C(\beta) +$	$\frac{1}{2}O_2(g) = CO(g)$	$\Delta H_R^0 =$	$-110.5 \text{ kJ mol}^{-1}$
(c) $CO(g) +$	$\frac{1}{2}O_2(g) = CO_2(g)$	$\Delta H_R^0 =$	$-283.0 \text{ kJ mol}^{-1}$
(a) = (b) + (c) $\therefore$ for (a):		$\Delta H_R^0 =$	$-393.5 \text{ kJ mol}^{-1}$

β means 'graphite'.

This is a simple example — the 'fictitious' reaction path that must be used is sometimes less direct, but the basic principle involved is very straightforward.

Standard enthalpy of formation

It follows from Hess's Law that, for a reaction specified by equation (2.21):

$$\Delta H_R^0 = \sum_{j=1}^{N_j}(v_j \times \Delta H_{fj}^0) \qquad (2.22)$$

where ΔH_{fj}^0 is the *standard enthalpy of formation* of participating species j from its constituent elements — that is, the heat absorbed when the formation reaction occurs under standard conditions). It is implicit in this definition that *elements in their standard states have zero standard enthalpy of formation.*

The reactions (a) and (b) above are examples of *formation* reactions. ΔH_{fj}^0 has been measured directly or indirectly for many compounds, and is widely tabulated. There are extensive data in the CRC Handbook (Series)[26] and in Kaye and Laby[15]. Thermochemical data for some commonly encountered substances are given in Atkins[27].

Standard enthalpy of combustion

Frequently, the ideal formation reactions on which ΔH_{fj}^0 is based cannot be carried out in practice, and ΔH_{fj}^0 cannot therefore be directly measured. In such cases, it (or ΔH_R^0 directly) must be deduced from data on other reactions.

Most organic and some inorganic compounds can be burned with oxygen. The heat absorbed by this reaction under standard conditions is called the *standard enthalpy of combustion, ΔH_c^0* (it is always negative, of course!).

This quantity is intrinsically important, but it is also fairly easily measured (by calorimetric techniques) and therefore constitutes a valuable building block for determining enthalpies of reaction. The standard enthalpy of combustion is tabulated for many compounds (see the above-mentioned sources). For example, for methane:

$$CH_4(g) + 2O_2(g) = CO_2(g) + 2H_2O(l) \qquad \Delta H_c^0 = -890.99 \text{ kJ mol}^{-1}$$

Clearly, there is a presumption that the reactant of concern is completely burned. ΔH_c^0 depends on the final states of the products. For tabulation, these are standardized as follows: $H_2O(l)$; $CO_2(g)$; $N_2(g)$; $HCl(aq.)$; $SO_2(g)$.

An alternative expression for the standard enthalpy of a reaction is then:

$$\Delta H_R^0 = -\sum_{j=1}^{N_j}(v_j \times \Delta H_{cj}^0) \qquad (2.23)$$

Example

Methane is reformed with steam according to the equation:

(a) $\quad CH_4(g) + H_2O(g) = CO(g) + 3H_2(g)$.

Determine the standard enthalpy of reaction, using standard heats of combustion and any necessary additional data.

Solution

Three of the species involved in reaction (a) are combustible; their combustion equations and standard heats of combustion are as follows:

j				ν_j	ΔH_c^0 (kJ mol^{-1})
(b) $CH_4(g) +$	$2O_2(g)$	$= CO_2(g) +$	$2H_2O(l)$	-1	-890.95
(c) $H_2O(g)$		$=$	$H_2O(l)$	-1	$* - \Delta H_v^0 = \quad -44.00$
(d) $CO(g) +$	$\frac{1}{2}O_2(g)$	$= CO_2(g)$		1	-283.20
(e) $H_2(g) +$	$\frac{1}{2}O_2(g)$	$=$	$H_2O(l)$	3	-286.04

*Note that the *standard* combustion reaction is presumed to produce *liquid* water, whereas the water used in reaction (a) is *vapour*. We therefore need to allow for the *condensation* of water vapour at the standard temperature, and we do this by including the appropriate latent heat value as a 'notional' heat of combustion.

Now substitution into equation (2.23) leads to:

$$\Delta H_R^0 = \{(-1)(-890.95) + (-1)(-44.00) + (1)(-283.20) + (3)(-286.04)\}$$
$$= 206.37 \text{ kJ mol}^{-1}$$

Non-standard conditions
In reality, chemical reactions, especially accidental ones, rarely occur under standard conditions, and the corresponding enthalpy changes are therefore non-standard. However, the aim here is to evaluate *relative* hazards arising from chemical energy, and this can be done satisfactorily simply by comparing the *standard* enthalpies of reaction. Procedures for calculating enthalpy changes for reactions occurring under non-standard conditions are described in text-books on physical chemistry and chemical engineering thermodynamics (see Atkins[27] and Smith[28]).

Bond energies
An alternative, though approximate, technique for calculating enthalpies of reaction is by manipulation of *bond energies*. Standard reference books on chemistry provide data on the energy changes involved in the dissociation (and formation) of bonds. This might suggest that bond energies could be the 'building blocks' of thermochemistry. Unfortunately, for accurate calculations the energy of dissociation of a chemical bond cannot be totally divorced from the general structure of the compound of which it forms part.

For example, the enthalpy of reaction for the formation of methanal from methanol differs from that for the formation of ethanal from ethanol, or for the formation of benzaldehyde from benzyl alcohol, even though the bonds dissociated and formed are the same. In general, the increments of standard enthalpies of reaction of successive members of a homologous series decrease with increase in molar mass, as illustrated in Table 2.13 overleaf.

Table 2.13 Comparisons of bond energies

Reaction	Standard enthalpy of reaction ΔH_R^0 (kJ mol^{-1})
Methanol to methanal	-92.9
Ethanol to ethanal	-68.9
Benzyl alcohol to benzaldehyde	-64.7

Bond energies are, however, useful for approximate calculations. To reduce error, a *mean bond dissociation enthalpy* $[\Delta H_{A-B}^0]$ derived from the bond dissociation enthalpies of a number of related compounds can be used. Such enthalpies are tabulated in reference sources such as Kaye and Laby[15] and CRC[25]. Caution is recommended in the use of this methodology.

The literature of thermochemistry

There are a number of specialized textbooks on chemical thermodynamics and reactor design. There is a discussion of the principles of thermochemistry in volume 18 of McGraw-Hill's *Encyclopaedia of Science and Technology*. These references also provide data on molal heat capacities and molal latent heats which are necessary for the calculation of the heat emitted by chemical reactions at temperatures which differ from the standard temperature of 298.15 K at which standard enthalpies of formation and combustion are usually reported in the literature.

2.7.4 Relationship between type of reaction and specific energy

There are many ways of classifying chemical reactions. However from a process safety point of view, it is useful to distinguish two main types of reaction by their specific enthalpies, using the bond energy concept discussed in Section 2.7.3.

Substitution and synthesis

The first type of reaction has two sub-classes. There are (1) simple substitution reactions and (2) building up, or synthesis, reactions. These are both reactions in which the reactants are ions or molecules, each of which has at least one reactive group. It is the interaction of these reactive groups, with associated chemical bond dissociation and formation, which constitutes the reaction.

Upon completion of the reaction, though atoms or groups have changed places, the original bonding structure remains unaltered. By examining the chemical structures of the products, it is usually possible to deduce that of the reactants. The ionic reactions of inorganic chemistry and most organic synthesis reactions are of this type.

Molecular disintegration

The second type of reaction is one in which the molecular structure is disintegrated — that is, where the basic configuration of chemical bonds of the reactants is destroyed. In such a reaction it is usually not possible to deduce the chemical structure of the reactants by examining the chemical structure of the products. One example of this type of reaction is the combustion of hydrocarbons; another is the detonation of high explosives. Both are associated with temperatures too high for complex molecules to exist.

The two types compared

In the first class of reactions, the energy emitted is related to that associated with the two reactive groups in which bonds may be broken or reformed. If we consider that these reactive groups are attached, say, to organic structures, it will make relatively little difference to the energy emitted whether these structures are simple or complex. The energy of dissociation of chemical bonds is discussed in standard works on thermochemistry.

In such reactions the energy per mole of reactants will vary only slowly with the molar mass of either reactant. The energy per kilogram will, however, be approximately inversely proportional to the molar mass of the reactants.

In the second class of reactions, where the temperature of the reaction is high, all the bonds in the molecule are ruptured. The energy emitted will be proportional to the sum of the products for each type of bond in the molecule of the number of bonds with the corresponding bond energy. In such reactions the specific energy on a molar basis may be regarded as being proportional to the molar mass of the reactants, while the specific energy on a mass basis is nearly constant. These generalizations are ilustrated in Table 2.14. It should be noted that they must accommodate variations of perhaps ± 10%.

It follows that, other things being equal, the reactions with the highest specific energy (expressed as energy per unit mass) are associated with

Table 2.14 Type of reaction and specific energy

Type of reaction	Energy per mole	Energy per kg
Synthesis reactions	constant	inversely proportional to molar mass
Molecular disintegrations	directly proportional to molar mass	constant

reactants of low molar mass. Power being energy divided by time, an analogous table could be drawn up for specific power. It should be noted also that the concentration of active groups is inversely proportional to the molar mass of the reactants. Since the rate of reaction (for a first-order reaction) is proportional to the concentration, it follows that the rate of reaction, other things being equal, is also inversely proportional to the molar mass of the reactants.

Therefore, other things being equal, reactants of low molar mass are both more energetic and react more rapidly than reactants of high molar mass. These factors make them much the more powerful and they therefore present much greater hazards.

2.7.5 Rates of reaction

Thermochemistry enables the energetics of reactions to be calculated but this does not by itself determine whether a particular reaction constitutes a hazard. The example of glucose oxidation, which is hazardous when it occurs as a dust cloud in air but non-hazardous when it occurs in animal tissues has already been noted. The hazards arising from the emission of chemical energy are partly dependent upon the quantity of energy emitted and partly upon the rate at which it is emitted, its power. There is no rule that relates the energy change in a chemical reaction with the rate at which it proceeds. The rates of chemical reactions must therefore be derived empirically.

For a given reaction, there are four major factors which determine the rates of reactions. They are (1) temperature, (2) the concentrations of the reactants, (3) the distribution of the reactants between phases and (4) the presence or absence of catalysts.

The influence of temperature

It is well known that rates of reaction are greatly dependent on temperature. The reaction between hydrogen and oxygen at room temperature is so slow as to be undetectable. Yet the introduction of an electric spark of 10^{-5} J into such a mixture will cause it to explode. The spark produces a highly localized region of high temperature which initiates a self-sustaining (*runaway*) reaction.

A general feature of chemical reactions is that they require energy, their activation energy, to initiate the reaction. Reaction rates generally increase exponentially with temperature according to the Arrhenius equation for the rate constant, $k = Ae^{-E/RT}$, where A is the so-called frequency factor and E the activation energy (both characteristic of the reaction) and R is the universal gas constant.

Typically, a temperature rise of 10°C will increase reaction rates by two to three times. This can be pictured as being associated with the increase in kinetic energy of the molecules with increase in temperature and especially with the increase in the numbers of molecules possessed of more energy than the activation energy of the reaction.

The influence of concentration

It is a basic law of physical chemistry that the rate of a chemical reaction is proportional to a power of the molar concentration of the reacting substances. But this law finds simple application only when applied to reactions which are homogeneous — that is, which take place in one phase.

One aspect of concentration is that it is inversely proportional to the mean distance between atoms/molecules/ions which constitute a reactive system. In a solid the inter-atomic distance or bond length is of the order of 1.5 to 2×10^{-10} m. Bond lengths are of the same order of size as the diameters of atoms. The distance between the centres of two reacting atoms within an individual molecule is of the order of two or three bond lengths.

In contrast, the mean distance between atoms/molecules in a gas at STP is of the order of 3×10^{-8} m, or 200 times as great. However it is not the inter-molecular distance which is of direct significance, it is the mean free path of a molecule. At room temperature this is of the order of 7×10^{-8} m.

In later sections where deflagrations and detonations are discussed, it is convenient to divide reaction systems into rarefied systems, that is those involving gases, and dense systems, which involve liquids and solids. Jones[2] uses the term 'non-dense' where 'rarefied' is used here.

The influence of distribution between phases

The treatment of reaction rates in textbooks of physical chemistry usually assumes that the reactants are in the same phase — that is, the system is *homogeneous*. However, there are many cases in industrial practice where the reactants are in different phases, so the system is *heterogeneous*. In such reactions the rate will also be governed by rates of mass transfer across phase boundaries. The laws of mass transfer are not given detailed treatment in this book, but, certain conclusions drawn from them will be introduced at appropriate points in the discussion.

The influence of catalysts

Catalysis is a well-known phenomenon which does not require detailed discussion here. Catalysts may be both positive and negative. The absence of a negative catalyst (inhibitor or stabilizer) may accelerate a reaction. In accordance with the First Law of Thermodynamics, catalysis can have no influence on the *quantity* of energy emitted by any given reaction, but it profoundly influences the *power*.

2.7.6 Runaway reactions

The circumstance that reaction rates increase exponentially with temperature is one which can lead to a common realization of a chemical hazard. If an exothermic batch reaction is considered in its early stages, there may be a high concentration of reactants. If insufficient cooling is applied the temperature will rise and so will the rate of reaction. These two factors will be interactive and unless suitable action is taken to cool the reacting mass a runaway reaction may ensue. A conflagration is a notable example of a run-away reaction which will be discussed in Section 2.13 (page 121). There may be a further complication if the system contains more than one phase. Rising temperature may also increase the rate of mass transfer across the phase boundaries and hence further increase the rate at which the reaction proceeds.

Due to the importance of runaway reactions, the subject is dealt with in detail in Section 2.8 (page 80) with case histories under the headings Bolsover, Seveso and Bhopal in Chapter 5 (pages 217, 235 and 215).

2.7.7 The initiation of reactions

Initial energy

Reference has been made above to the important role which temperature plays in determining the rate of a reaction and to the fact that reactions require a certain level of energy — the activation energy — to initiate them. Reactions which initiate themselves at, or below, room temperature are rare but clearly are very hazardous. An example is the reaction, when dry, of yellow phosphorus with air. Silane (SiH_4) is also spontaneously flammable in air. Such hazards have to be identified and guarded against.

Heat as a source of activation energy

The most common form of initiation is by the supply of heat from an external source. There are many possible sources. Some mixtures with air — for example, carbon disulphide — may be ignited by an electric light bulb or by a steam pipe. Other sources of initiation energy are flames or the hot surfaces they may produce, electric sparks, other sparks as from grindstones or violent impacts, the heating of machinery parts by friction, and explosions.

The action of catalysts

The introduction of a catalyst reduces the activation energies of specific reactions, and may thus enable a reaction to proceed at a significant rate at a temperature (ambient, for example) at which it would otherwise be negligibly slow. Catalysts provide alternative pathways for the reaction. However, for any given reaction, though a catalyst may increase its rate and hence its power, it cannot alter the *quantity* of energy emitted.

Atkins[27] quotes the decomposition of hydrogen peroxide in aqueous solution. This has an activation energy of $76 \, kJ \, mole^{-1}$, but the addition of a small quantity of iodine reduces it to $57 \, kJ \, mole^{-1}$. This speeds up the reaction at room temperature by a factor of 2000. Platinum black catalyses the reaction between hydrogen and oxygen so that hydrogen ignites at room temperature. Hydrocarbons such as methane can also be ignited at room temperature by suitable catalysts.

Some catalysts, such as dry Raney nickel, which is a spongy form of nickel, ignite in air at room temperature.

Spontaneous combustion

A phenomenon which it is important to recognize is that of slowly initiated spontaneous combustion. This may take the form of a slow oxidation under conditions in which the heat is not adequately dissipated. It can happen when coal is stored in large heaps. An example from outside of the process industries is a haystack fire, which can occur when hay is stacked in a damp condition and a series of micro-biological and chemical reactions eventually raise the temperature to ignition point.

2.7.8 Characteristics of the reactions selected

Basis of selection of reactions

All chemical reactions involve a change of enthalpy, but in some cases this may be slight and the following discussion is limited to reactions which emit significant quantities of energy with sufficient rapidity to constitute an acute realization of a hazard. (In using the classes set out below as examples, it is not implied that this is an exhaustive list and that types of reactions which are not so listed necessarily either emit only small quantities of energy, or emit it very slowly. Each reaction must be individually assessed).

The reactions discussed in Sections 2.8 to 2.14 have been divided into two main classes. The first class of reactions are those which, though they may give rise to significant hazards, cause adiabatic temperature rises that are not sufficient to produce incandescence. This class, which includes neutralizations, hydrations, condensations and polymerizations, will be discussed in Section 2.8 (page 80). It is the least powerful class of hazardous reactions.

The second class consists of those reactions which are capable of producing incandescence. Such reactions, if they involve more than one species, are almost exclusively *redox* reactions.

Redox reactions

The terms *oxidation* and *reduction* were originally restricted to reactions in which oxygen was added to (oxidation), or subtracted from (reduction), a molecule. Today they have a much wider meaning incorporating reactions in which there is an exchange of electrons. The acceptor atom, molecule, or ion is the oxidizing agent; the donor atom, molecule, or ion is the reducing agent.

Reduction and oxidation occur simultaneously and this is emphasized by the term *redox* which is widely used to describe such reactions. Common reducing agents are hydrogen, the metals, carbon, coal, hydrocarbons, and materials containing cellulose, such as wood and cotton. Reducing agents which are commonly used to generate heat are termed 'fuels'. Common oxidizing agents are air, the halogens, nitric acid, nitrates, chromates, chlorates, permanganates, hypochlorites and peroxides. Many, though not all, possible combinations of reducing agents with oxidizing agents will give rise to the emission of energy under suitable conditions. Such emissions, when uncontrolled, constitute process hazards.

A special category of redox reaction may occur *within* a molecule in which both the oxidizing and reducing elements are present. Propellants and most explosives exhibit reactions of this character. They will be discussed at appropriate points below. The most commonly encountered redox reactions are those involving combustion, which are among the most energetic of all chemical reactions.

2.8 Runaway reactions

2.8.1 Introduction

Runaway reactions have been the immediate cause of a number of the most notorious chemical process incidents, notably *Seveso* and *Bhopal*, and innumerable minor ones. They have been extensively studied[29,30]. Most recently, they have been the subject of a special publication by the Institution of Chemical Engineers[31]. In the sense that they are related to the most central activity of the chemical process industry, the promotion of *controlled* chemical change, they are perhaps its most characteristic failure event.

The term *runaway reaction* is, surprisingly, not defined by Jones[2], the source which is generally considered to be the most authoritative. For the purposes of this book, therefore, it is defined as 'a chemical reaction process which accelerates out of control in consequence of the release of chemical energy at a rate exceeding that at which it can be removed from the system by the operation of heat transfer'. Strictly speaking, all fires and explosions associated with chemical reactions are covered by the above definition. However, the term is customarily reserved for incidents occurring in vessels in which chemical reactions are being conducted deliberately for manufacturing purposes, or in which the reactants or products of such processes are being stored.

For reasons which are explained below, this section deals only with batch-type reactors. It gives a brief account of the fundamental mechanism of runaway reactions, describes the ways in which such reactions are most commonly brought about and the potentially harmful consequences which may ensue from their occurrence, and gives an indication of the kind of methodology that is employed for evaluating potential runaway reactions to ensure their safe management.

2.8.2 Types of chemical reactor

In the early days of the chemical industry, most reaction processes were conducted in batch reactors, basically because this was the available technology. From the 1930s until almost the present day there has been a tendency to use continuous technology, especially for primary bulk chemicals such as chlorine, ammonia, sulphuric acid and petrochemicals, largely because the increasing scale of operation made it economically attractive to dedicate plant to a single process, but also because it permitted consistent production — both qualitatively and quantitatively — with a minimum of labour. However, there have always been many processes which did not lend themselves to continuous operation, mainly because they were very slow or because the products were required only in small quantities such as could be conveniently produced in multi-purpose batch-type plant.

Currently, there is in the West a strong revival of interest in batch processing associated with the tendency to concentrate on the manufacture of small-output high-added-value products, while 'commodity' production has moved nearer to the raw-material sources in the Middle East and to the rapidly industrializing countries of the Far East[32].

81

There is argument (see Kletz[33] and Sawyer[34]) as to whether considerations of safety generally favour continuous or batch operation — this discussion is deferred until Chapter 6. At this stage, it is necessary only to mention that batch reactors are liable to be used for a variety of different, and in some cases unfamiliar, processes, whereas continuous reactors are typically designed individually for specific processes. Coupled with the fact that batch-type operation generally involves a great deal more human intervention, this results in a much higher incidence of unforeseen events. Since thermal calculations for continuous reactors tend to be incorporated into highly organized design procedures which are too complex for adequate consideration in an elementary text, treatment is given here only to batch-type reactors. Readers are referred, for example, to Westerterp[35] and Fogler[36] for a detailed discussion of continuous reactors.

2.8.3 Elementary theory of runaway reactions

The mechanism which underlies runaway reactions is classically called *thermal explosion*. Its basic concept was first enunciated by van't Hoff in 1884, and was formalized by Taffanel[37]. The elaboration of the original theory is associated primarily with the names of Semenov and Frank-Kamenetskii, and is described in Semenov[38]. Many later authors have reviewed and developed it, notably Boddington *et al.*[39] This simplified presentation relies largely on those of Barnard[40] and Medard[41].

It is supposed that a body of material which is thoroughly mixed and therefore at an uniform temperature, the surroundings of which are maintained at a constant temperature, undergoes an exothermic chemical reaction. The thermal behaviour of the body will depend on the balance between the rate at which chemical energy is being released as thermal energy (which itself is proportional to the rate of reaction) and the rate at which this thermal energy is dissipated by heat transfer to the surroundings. If the former exceeds the latter, the temperature will rise, and vice versa, but if the two rates are equal the temperature will remain constant and a steady state will prevail.

The potential for instability arises from the very different relationships with temperature of the heat release and dissipation rates. The former increases exponentially with absolute temperature as represented by the Arrhenius equation for the rate constant ($k = Ae^{-E/RT}$), while the latter increases linearly (if, with Semenov, perfect mixing of the contents and Newtonian cooling are assumed) with the temperature difference between material and surroundings. If, therefore, the two rates are plotted against temperature, a steepening curve for release and a straight line for dissipation are obtained, which will, in general, intersect at two points (see Figure 2.3).

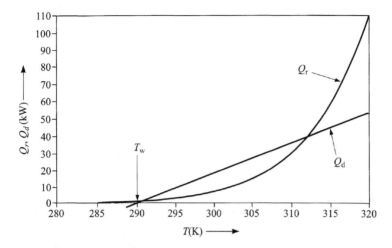

Figure 2.3 Thermal explosion

A qualitative impression of the potential behaviour of the system can be obtained by studying these curves. If the material is initially at the temperature of the surroundings, reaction will bring about a rise in temperature until the lower of the two intersections is reached. At this point, the two rates are equal so that the system may be expected to stabilize. If a transient disturbance causes the temperature to rise further, to some level short of that corresponding to the higher intersection, the temperature will, when the disturbance is removed, fall back to that of the lower intersection. If, however, a more drastic excursion takes the temperature to a level above that of the higher intersection, the system will become unstable and the temperature will continue to rise even after the cause of the disturbance has been removed. Mathematical expressions can be formulated for the two processes as follows:

Heat release:

$$Q_r = rV(-\Delta H_r) = kf(c)V(-\Delta H_r) = Ae^{-E/RT}f(c)V(-\Delta H_r) \qquad (2.24)$$

Heat dissipation:

$$Q_d = US(T - T_w) \qquad (2.25)$$

where
r — rate of reaction $(\text{mol m}^{-3}\text{ s}^{-1}) = kf(c)$ (k is rate constant, $f(c)$ is dependency of rate of reaction on reactant concentration)
V — volume of vessel (m^3)
$(-\Delta H_r)$ — exothermicity of reaction (J.mol^{-1}) (this is temperature-dependent)

83

A and E — frequency factor (s^{-1}) and activation energy $(J\,mol^{-1})$ respectively

T — absolute temperature of the reacting material (K)

U — overall coefficient of heat transfer between vessel and surroundings $(W\,m^{-2}\,K^{-1})$

S — surface area of vessel (m^2)

T_w — temperature of surroundings (K)

The above-mentioned intersections represent the points at which the two expressions are equal, corresponding to a steady-state energy balance. The range of possible behaviours of the system may be illustrated by representing graphically the following variants on the above scheme:

- variation of the reactant concentration c, giving rise to a family of energy release curves (Figure 2.4);
- variation of the surroundings temperature T_w, giving rise to a family of parallel energy dissipation lines (Figure 2.5);
- variation of the heat-transfer conductance US, giving rise to a family of diverging energy dissipation lines (Figure 2.6).

In principle, a critical mixture temperature T_c can be evaluated for the circumstances illustrated in Figure 2.5 by stipulating the equality of the expressions for the release and dissipation rates (equations (2.24) and (2.25)) and also that of their slopes (given by the derivatives with respect to temperature) at the critical condition:

$$Q_d = Q_r, \Rightarrow US(T_c - T_w) = Ae^{-E/RT_c}f(c)V(-\Delta H_r) \qquad (2.26)$$

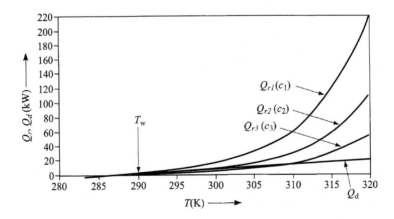

Figure 2.4 Thermal explosion: effect of varying concentration

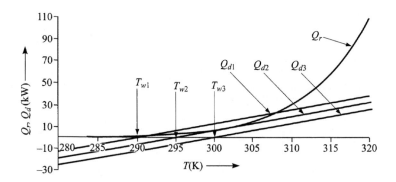

Figure 2.5 Thermal explosion: effect of varying wall temperature

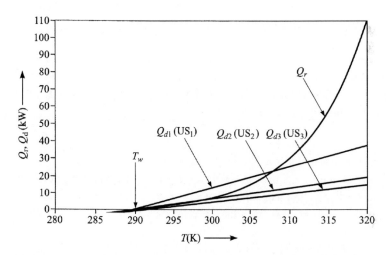

Figure 2.6 Thermal explosion: effect of varying heat transfer conductance

and

$$\frac{dQ_d}{dT} = \frac{dQ_r}{dT}, \Rightarrow US = Ae^{-E/RT_c}(E/RT_c^2)f(c)V(-\Delta H_r) \tag{2.27}$$

Dividing equation (2.26) by equation (2.27), a quadratic equation in T_c is obtained:

$$T_c - T_w = RT_c^2/E \tag{2.28}$$

which has the solution:

$$T_c = (E/2R)[1 \pm (1 - 4RT_w/E)^{1/2}] \tag{2.29}$$

85

The value of the activation energy E is generally[41] within the range 80,000 to 200,000 J mol^{-1}, while the universal gas constant R is 8.3144 J mol^{-1} K^{-1}. For typical values of T_w (say 280 K to 500 K), the root corresponding to the positive sign is absurdly high and relates to a physically unreal situation, so only the root associated with the negative sign needs to be considered. A convenient algebraic approximation to this root gives the expression:

$$T_c - T_w \cong RT_w^2/E \qquad (2.30)$$

At the upper end of the range of values of E, this leads to a critical temperature excess $\Delta T_c (= T_c - T_w)$ of between about 3 K and 10 K, so that the 'leeway' available between the surroundings temperature and the mixture temperature at which runaway could occur may be very small, indicating a requirement for close temperature control. For lower values of E, the system is rather more tolerant, with permissible temperature excesses in the region of 25 K.

The above mathematical analysis has been extended and developed by a number of authors to produce many interesting and useful results. A complete account of these developments is beyond the scope of the present book, but a few important ones are mentioned.

A dimensionless criterion for criticality: effect of scale

Semenov substituted equation (2.30) for T_c in equation (2.26) and, by a process of algebraic manipulation and approximation, arrived at an expression equivalent to the following as a criterion for the avoidance of runaway:

$$\psi < \psi_c = \left(\frac{V}{SU}\right)\left(\frac{AEf(c)(-\Delta H_r)e^{-E/RT_0}}{RT_0^2}\right) = e^{-1}(= 0.368) \qquad (2.31)$$

Equation (2.31) includes the reciprocal of the specific volume of the vessel S/V, reflecting the fact that the rate of heat release is, other things being equal, proportional to the volume of the vessel, whereas the rate of heat dissipation is proportional to its surface area. Assuming a fixed geometry with a variable characteristic dimension r, the former varies as the cube and the latter as the square of r. Hence for geometrically similar vessels, the magnitude of ψ increases with increasing size so that, for a given set of values of the other parameters, there will be a maximum safe vessel size. In practical terms, this means that scaling up apparatus for larger outputs entails increasing the surface available for heat transfer relative to the volume of the vessel (the assumption of temperature uniformity also comes into question — see below).

Departures from the Semenov model

The Semenov model assumes that the resistance to heat transfer between the vessel contents and the surroundings is concentrated entirely at the vessel wall and that, consequently, the temperature of the contents is uniform. This is a reasonable approximation for well-stirred liquid mixtures, especially if they have a fairly high thermal conductivity. For gaseous and other systems which have low conductivity and/or are not well agitated, the approximation breaks down. An alternative model, by Frank-Kamenetskii, in which the resistance to heat transfer is assumed to reside only in the vessel contents (in which heat transfer proceeds solely by conduction) and the wall resistance is neglected, leads to the conclusion that stability is possible only if a 'dimensionless heat release rate' δ does not exceed a critical value:

$$\delta < \delta_c = \left(\frac{r^2}{\lambda}\right)\left(\frac{AEf(c)(-\Delta H_r)e^{-E/RT_w}}{RT_w^2}\right) \qquad (2.32)$$

In this expression, r represents a characteristic length dimension of the body (m) and λ the thermal conductivity of the mixture (W m^{-1} K^{-1}). Values of δ_c have been computed for bodies of certain classical standard shapes (see Table 2.15).

It will be noted that there is a formal similarity between the Semenov and Frank-Kamenetskii criteria, in that they have a common factor incorporating the chemical and thermochemical properties of the system and the wall temperature, and different factors characterizing its heat-transfer properties. These different factors represent the two extremes (0 and ∞ respectively) of the range of values of a dimensionless parameter called the *Biot Number*, $Bi = Ur/\lambda$, which is the ratio of the thermal resistance of the bulk of the reacting mass to that of its surface. Boddington[39] has calculated values of the critical parameters for bodies of a number of other shapes and also for heat-transfer regimes intermediate between these extremes.

Table 2.15 Values of δ_c and ΔT_c for various vessel shapes

Shape of vessel	Characteristic dimension, r	δ_c	ΔT_c
Infinite slab	Half-width	0.88	$1.20RT_w^2 E^{-1}$
Infinite cylinder	Radius	2.00	$1.37RT_w^2 E^{-1}$
Sphere	Radius	3.32	$1.60RT_w^2 E^{-1}$

Conclusions from the theory

There are too many uncertainties in the various chemical and thermal parameters to allow engineers to depend solely on theoretical calculations of the kind discussed above for the design and operation of reaction systems, and a brief account of some of the semi-empirical techniques which are available for the evaluation of potential runaway reactions is given below. However, there is abundant evidence in the literature that the results of the theory are *qualitatively* correct and provide an indispensable guide for these methods. In particular, they draw attention to the roles of vessel geometry and of heat-transfer characteristics (including agitation), and demonstrate the very narrow margins within which many exothermal reactions, both intentional and accidental, must be controlled.

2.8.4 How runaway reactions occur

The operation of chemical reactors

Typical batch-type reactor installations are described by White[42] and by Barton and Rogers[31] (see Figure 2.7). Operation may be in either batch or semi-batch

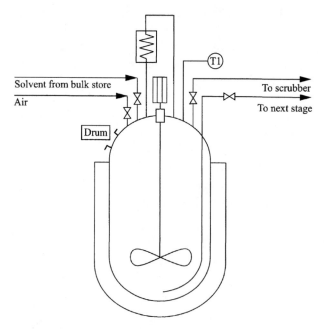

Figure 2.7 Batch reactor (Source: J. Barton and R. Rogers, 1997, *Chemical Reaction Hazards* (IChemE, UK), page 127)

mode. In the former, the whole charge is loaded from the start, which is appropriate for reactions that do not pose difficult problems of temperature control — that is, they are either endothermic or weakly exothermic. In the latter, one or more of the reactants may be supplied instantaneously and the last over an extended period, so that the heat evolved may be dissipated without requiring an excessively large cooling system — this technique is employed for more strongly exothermic reactions. The more hazardous types of reaction obviously belong in the second category.

Usually, either an external 'jacket' or 'limpet coil' or an internal coiled tube is provided, enabling the mixture to be heated by steam or a commercial heat-transfer medium to a temperature at which the desired reaction proceeds at a reasonable rate and permitting the introduction of cooling water to control any tendency for the temperature to 'run away'. Sometimes one of these devices is reserved for emergency use in case a 'runaway' should commence.

It is common practice to provide a reflux condenser to enable a desired product to be preferentially removed while reactants are returned 'to the pot'. This also serves as a device for removing surplus heat from the system (as latent heat of vaporization).

Common causes of runaway reactions

Barton and Nolan[43] carried out an investigation into the circumstances and causes of 189 runaway reactions in the UK during the period 1962–1987 (in 20 cases the data were insufficient to allow 'prime causes' to be identified). The results are summarized briefly in Table 2.16 overleaf.

It will be apparent that there is a large number of potential causes of 'runaway'. If the thermochemistry and the heat-transfer properties of the materials involved are well known, it is not too difficult to design a system with adequate provision for heat dissipation, for proper regulation of reactant and catalyst charging and for control of the reaction mixture temperature, though it remains necessary, by means of appropriate protective devices and very rigorous procedures, to guard against many possible kinds of equipment or services failure and maloperation.

The main difficulty is that, while a process may be designed to follow certain chemical paths, the nature of chemistry is such that innumerable alternatives, some readily predictable but others less so, may come into play under specific conditions of composition and temperature. Thus a process which is eminently safe as long as it proceeds along the intended lines may go disastrously wrong as the result of a quite minor deviation from the design conditions. The Seveso incident (see Chapter 5, page 235) involved the occurrence of totally unexpected side-reactions at a time when the nominal process was nearly complete

Table 2.16 Prime causes of runaway reactions

Type of 'prime cause'	No. of incidents	%
Process chemistry		
Reaction chemistry and thermochemistry (inadequate study and/or provision for the thermochemical characteristics of the system)	34	20
Raw material quality control (contamination — mainly with water)	15	9
Plant design and operation		
Failure of temperature control	32	19
Agitation (inadequacy or failure of equipment, power failure or operator error)	17	10
Mischarging of reactants or catalysts (wrong materials, quantities, proportions, rates or timing)	35	21
Maintenance (leaks, blockages, residues, water in lines)	25	15
'Human factors' (other operator errors)	11	6
Total	169	100

and ostensibly arrested. Equally, the accidental ingress of an apparently innocuous material such as water into a storage vessel containing a reactive substance can lead to a catastrophic runaway, as in the tragic example of Bhopal (see Chapter 5, page 215). In both these cases, disaster resulted not from the loss of control of intended reactions, but from the unplanned and unforeseen occurrence of others.

2.8.5 The effects of runaway reactions

The rapid rise of temperature associated with a runaway reaction leads almost invariably to the evolution of gas at a rate far higher than under design conditions. This results in foaming and in a rapid pressure rise in the vessel.

Given some over-design of the vessel, it may be possible, by means of prompt emergency cooling, to contain this pressure rise without any ill effect. Otherwise, there will be a failure of containment, of a nature and scale depending upon the thermodynamic and mechanical conditions. If sufficient relief is provided, the integrity of the vessel may be preserved, though the release may still be very large. Otherwise, the vessel may fail, perhaps to the point of disintegration, so that the release is even larger and more rapid and the effect is aggravated by the generation of missiles, as well as by the loss of the vessel itself. The physical aspects of pressure-energy releases were discussed in Section 2.5 (page 40). The thermal energy releases which may accompany them were the subject of Section 2.6 (page 57).

The consequences of such a release depend on its scale, on the conditions governing the subsequent dispersion of the released material (covered in Chapter 3), on the nature of the material and on the distribution of potential receptors (see Chapter 4). Some especially significant case histories are included in Chapter 5. For the present, it may be said that the material released as a result of runaway reactions is almost invariably hot and/or noxious in a variety of possible ways (acidic, corrosive, toxic, flammable, explosive) and thus potentially harmful.

2.8.6 Evaluation of reaction hazards

As indicated already, the evaluation of reaction hazards entails both theoretical analysis and empirical investigation. The range of studies required is too extensive and too complex to allow a detailed description here, and the reader is referred to Barton and Rogers[31]. These authors emphasize that there is no single standard procedure because the circumstances and the available information are very variable. However, they do indicate a typical methodology, involving the use of literature data, basic screening tests, isothermal calorimetry for determining kinetic and thermal parameters, adiabatic calorimetry for examining runaway behaviour, and specific measurements for estimating requisite vent sizes etc. A few specially important indicators are mentioned below.

Chemical reactivity

The potential reactivity of the mixture can be estimated, at least qualitatively, from the natures of the chemical groups present. Barton and Rogers[31] list some of the better known examples of unstable groups. A comprehensive listing is provided by Bretherick[44]. Of particular importance in assessing the propensity of an organic compound to decompose is its 'oxygen balance'[31].

Adiabatic temperature rise

This is the rise of temperature that would result from reaction if none of the thermal energy evolved could be dissipated to the surroundings. It is given by $\Delta T_{ad} = -\xi_{max} \Delta H_r / m C_p$, where ξ_{max} is the maximum possible extent of reaction (mol), ΔH_r is the enthalpy of reaction ($J\,mol^{-1}$), m is the mass (kg) and C_p the specific heat capacity ($J\,mol^{-1}\,K^{-1}$) of the reaction mixture (including inert materials). ξ_{max} may be calculated, assuming complete reaction, by reference to the quantities and proportions of reactants present and to the stoichiometry of the contemplated reaction. Strictly speaking, ΔH_r and C_p should be represented by mean values over the temperature range involved.

The estimated value of ΔT_{ad} may be compared with the 'critical temperature excess' $(T_c - T_w)$ (see Section 2.8.3, page 82) to make a rough estimate of the 'hazardousness' of the system.

2.8.7 Conclusions

Runaway reactions are a relatively common event. Their effects are generally less dramatic than those, for example, of thermal releases resulting from the loss of containment of volatile liquids from pressurized storage, because the heats of reaction involved are comparatively small. Nevertheless, they do cause fatalities and serious equipment damage, mainly by the dispersal of noxious materials but also by thermal and mechanical effects. In certain notorious cases they have led to major catastrophes. Their control depends on a proper scientific understanding of their causes, rigorous evaluation and design, and responsible operation — these matters will be discussed further in Chapter 6.

2.9 Deflagrations and detonations – general principles

Deflagrations and, with few exceptions, detonations, are high-energy redox reactions accompanied by incandescence. They fall into the category of those reactions, described in Section 2.7 (page 67) in which the reacting molecules undergo complete disintegration.

Jones[2] gives the following definitions:

Deflagration — the chemical reaction of a substance in which the reaction front advances into the unreacted substance at less than sonic velocity. Where a blast wave is formed which has the potential to cause damage, the term **explosive deflagration** is usually used.

Detonation — an explosion caused by the extremely rapid chemical reaction of a substance in which the reaction front advances into the unreacted substance at greater than sonic velocity.

The above definitions do not specify what constitutes sonic velocity. It is assumed here that this means the velocity of sound, under standard conditions, in the unreacted substance.

Whilst adopting the general definition of deflagration given above, it is convenient to recognize three sub-categories of this phenomenon. These are:

Unconfined deflagration — a deflagration in a system where no significant pressure rise occurs and in which the factors controlling the velocity of advance of the reaction zone are heat transfer and mass transfer.

Confined deflagration — a deflagration in a system where a significant pressure rise occurs and in which the factors controlling the velocity of advance of the reaction zone are heat transfer and mass transfer.

It is not a simple matter to define the terms 'unconfined' and 'confined'. It is better to think of degrees of confinement as lying on a spectrum with the 'unconfinement' of an open plain without obstructions at one end and the 'confinement' of a vessel strong enough to withstand any pressure rise which may occur at the other. 'Unconfinement' as described has little relevance to process plant and many vessels are ruptured by internal deflagrations.

Explosive deflagration — a deflagration in a system where a significant pressure rise occurs on account of the high velocity of advance of the reaction zone and in which the principal factor controlling the velocity of advance of the reaction zone is shock.

This usage calls for a definition of 'shock'. For the present purpose we shall define this as:

Shock — a large and virtually instantaneous — and therefore adiabatic — local compression of the medium in question.

The following terms are used in addition:

Rarefied system — a system predominantly in the gas phase. Gas mixtures, dust/gas mixtures and aerosols may be so described.

Dense-phase system — a system predominantly in the liquid or solid phase.

2.9.1 The three zones

Deflagrations and detonations have common features. In each case there is a heterogeneous reaction system in which there are three zones, an unreacted zone, a reaction zone and a reacted zone. With controlled deflagrations the reaction zone (the flame front) is stationary with respect to the observer. An example is a Bunsen burner. With uncontrolled reactions the reaction zone moves relative to an observer. In the cases of both unconfined and confined deflagrations this zone is the flame front. In explosive deflagrations and detonations it is the shock wave.

2.9.2 Taxonomy

In Table 2.17 a taxonomy is presented based upon the definitions given above.

Table 2.17 A taxonomy of deflagrations and detonations. Common basis: heterogeneous systems with three zones

Class	Velocity	Pressure rise	Controlling mechanism
Unconfined deflagration	<sonic	not significant	heat and mass transfer
Confined deflagration	<sonic	significant	heat and mass transfer
Explosive deflagration	ca. sonic	several bars	shock
Detonation	>sonic	extreme	shock

2.9.3 The consequences of deflagrations and detonations

Mechanisms

Deflagrations and detonations cause harm principally by either or both of two forms of emission: (a) thermal radiation and (b) pressure energy. Some aspects of these types of emission have been discussed in Sections 2.5 and 2.6 and are considered further below. At this point it will be helpful, to facilitate comparison, if the definitions of two parameters are quoted[2] relating to emissions of pressure energy (other relevant parameters will be defined at the appropriate place):

Overpressure — for a pressure pulse (*blast wave*), the pressure developed above atmospheric pressure at any stage or location.

Peak positive overpressure — the maximum overpressure generated.

The significance of these terms will be better appreciated against the background of a description of the phenomenon of the blast wave. The following is a slightly edited extract from a report published by the Health and Safety Commission[45]:

'**Blast wave** When an explosion occurs*, the gases formed as a result of the reaction (whether from gaseous or non-gaseous reactants) are suddenly at high temperature and high pressure relative to the surrounding atmosphere. They therefore expand rapidly, driving before them the air they displace, and

---

*In the context of the more recent nomenclature defined above, we would now say 'an explosive deflagration or a detonation'.

initiating a pressure pulse which travels outwards, at first with a velocity comparable with that of the expanding gases and afterwards more slowly, eventually degenerating into a sound wave. This pressure pulse is commonly described as a *blast wave* or *shock wave*. As it travels outwards its shape (i.e. the pressure/time relationship as it passes a particular point in space) changes. For the cases with which we are concerned, however, it may be assumed that this pressure/time relationship is of the form shown in Fig. 3.1: a very sudden rise at time t_a ('over' atmospheric pressure) to some value p_{max} (the peak positive overpressure), followed by a fairly steady decline to zero in time T^+, called the *duration*, and thereafter to a smaller negative value of longer duration. The areas $\int (p) \mathrm{d}t$ in the intervals under this curve before and after $t_a + T^+$ are called respectively the *positive* and *negative impulses*. The algebraic sum of these areas is usually very small, approximating to zero. For the cases with which we are concerned (though not for all) it may be assumed that the cause of damage is the *positive* overpressure phase, and the abbreviated term *impulse* often refers just to this phase.' Further discussion of blast waves is deferred to Chapter 3.

Capacity for inflicting damage

For a given mass of reactant, detonations and deflagrations of gas/air mixtures emit the same quantity of energy. However, the former are more damaging for two reasons:

(a) they emit their quantum of energy in a much shorter time, thus exhibiting higher levels of *power*;
(b) they give rise to higher *peak positive overpressures*.

2.9.4 Interchangeability of mode

Any given reaction may, in principle, take place in any of the four modes. Thus coal can undergo unconfined deflagration in a furnace, it can undergo a confined deflagration (dust explosion), it can take part in an explosive deflagration in a coal mine gallery and, under extreme circumstances, such an explosive deflagration may escalate into a detonation.

Thus, whether a reaction falls into one or other of the above categories depends not only upon the nature of the reactants, but also partly upon the mode of initiation and partly upon the geometry of the system (see definition of geometry in Section 2.1, page 26).

In Section 2.14 (page 128), a table of comparisons of the various modes of deflagration, together with detonations, is provided. This compares such characteristics as flame velocity, energy release and power.

2.10 Chemical energy releases – unconfined deflagrations

2.10.1 Definitions

Unconfined deflagration

Unconfined deflagration has been defined in Section 2.9 (page 93). Other modes of deflagration are discussed in later sections. What constitutes confinement, or lack of it, is a matter of degree. Even the open air has one solid boundary, the surface of the ground. Though a furnace has boundary walls, its flue will be of such a cross-section as to allow the reaction products to escape with negligible pressure rise under normal conditions.

Combustion and fire

Many pairs of words of similar meaning in the English language have one of the pair derived from Anglo-Saxon and the other from Latin. The Anglo-Saxon word is the one in common use, whereas the Latin word is the one used by scientists. There are advantages in using Latin-based words as they generally have more precise meanings. This is true of the pair of words *fire* and *combustion*: *fire* is of Anglo-Saxon origin, and *combustion* of Latin origin.

The term 'combustion' is used to mean an exothermic redox reaction in which gaseous oxygen is the oxidizing agent, whether mixed with nitrogen, as in air, or in the pure form. The theoretical foundations of combustion are discussed in Medard[41].

We have avoided the word 'fire' as far as possible and have instead used the Latin-based word 'conflagration' to mean the phenomena associated with uncontrolled, run-away combustion reactions involving, usually, incandescence and the emission of smoke. Tuhtar[46] analyses the phenomena associated with conflagrations.

The terms *burn* and *burning*, which are also of Anglo-Saxon origin, have meanings which are sometimes interchangeable with *combustion* and sometimes with *fire*. They are used in this section of the book where the use of the terms combustion or fire would be clumsy or inappropriate.

Flame

The combustion reactions with which this section is concerned are accompanied by flame. *Flame* is defined in OCDC as 'a hot luminous mixture of gases undergoing combustion. The chemical reactions in the flame are mainly free radical chain reactions and the light comes from fluorescence of excited molecules or ions or from incandescence of small solid particles such as carbon'. Flame is thus one of the three zones of a deflagration — the reaction zone.

It is assumed in this chapter that flames can arise both from combustion, as previously defined, and from other redox reactions which produce incandescence. There are also such things are 'cool flames', though these are not commonly encountered. The phenomenon is described in Stull[47], and in Medard[41].

2.10.2 Redox reactions and deflagrations

Varieties of redox reactions

There are a vast number of possible redox reactions. Though only those which fall into the category of combustion reactions are likely to be encountered by the general public, it is necessary for process engineers to be continually alert for less commonly encountered redox reactions, bearing in mind that many oxidising agents other than oxygen may be utilized in the process industries (some of these may be liquids or solids).

In general, reducing agents are so widely distributed that, in assessing the hazards of non-combustion redox reactions in any particular process, the most useful initial approach would seem to lie in identifying the presence of potential oxidizing agents as well as gaseous oxygen.

Enthalpies of redox reactions

Redox reactions can be associated with differing levels of enthalpy of reaction. For example the reaction of carbon with steam has a positive enthalpy of reaction so it is endothermic. It cannot therefore take place spontaneously. Other redox reactions, such as those between hydrocarbons and air or oxygen, have negative enthalpies of reaction — that is, they are exothermic and can take place spontaneously.

These latter are among the most energetic reactions commonly encountered in the chemical and process industries. The adiabatic temperature rises accompanying the combustion of hydrocarbons with air are of the order of 2000 K. In some less commonly encountered redox reactions they exceed 3000 K.

Rates of redox reactions

Redox reactions vary greatly in their rates. Some are very slow — reference has been made above to how slowly the rusting of iron proceeds even though the reaction is highly energetic. Some take place spontaneously at room temperature but form adherent layers of reaction products which block further reaction (see below).

Slow redox reactions are the basis of animal life. A human being at rest emits heat at the rate of around 70 W, or 1 W per kg of body weight. This heat is derived from the oxidation of sugars catalysed by enzymes and takes place at a temperature of ca. 40°C.

But some redox reactions are very rapid. In the extreme case, the intra-molecular ones which take place in the detonation of some explosives may have durations measured in microseconds per tonne of reactant.

Redox reactions and the periodic table

Chlorine is an important oxidizing agent. In fact all the elements in Group 7 of the Periodic Table (the halogens) are oxidizing agents, though their oxidizing properties diminish with increasing atomic number. In Group 6 only oxygen and sulphur have significant oxidizing properties. The most powerful reducing agents among the elements are hydrogen, carbon and certain metals. Redox reactions between hydrogen and the lower members of Groups 7 and 6 are highly energetic. Some of the reactions of carbon with oxidizing agents are also highly energetic.

As noted, there are factors other than heat releases which determine hazard. For example, the reaction between aluminium and oxygen is highly energetic but aluminium is used as a material of construction because, though it reacts with oxygen at room temperature, the oxide layer that is formed is adherent and blocks further oxidation. However, if the aluminium is in a sufficiently fine state of subdivision, the reaction may be very rapid — this coupled with the high energy release makes it very hazardous.

Preconditions for hazardous redox reactions

For a redox reaction to be hazardous certain preconditions must be met. These are:

(a) A reducing agent and an oxidizing agent must both be present;
(b) The reaction must have a negative enthalpy (it must be exothermic);
(c) Its rate must be sufficiently high that the heat emitted is not readily dissipated — that is, there is a supply of initiating energy to enable it to achieve its threshold initiating temperature;
(d) Where the reactants are gaseous they must be present within certain limits of concentration.

2.10.3 Conditions for deflagrations without rise in pressure

Redox reactions in which heat is emitted generally give rise to some increase in pressure in the system in which they occur. However, in the conditions with which we are here concerned this pressure rise is small, say of the order of millibars.

2.10.4 Combustion

Controlled and uncontrolled combustion

The technology of *controlled* combustion is one of the basic foundations of present-day civilization and is studied in the subject areas of energy technology or fuel technology which are concerned with subjects such as steam raising and the principles of internal combustion engines.

This book is concerned, among other matters, with the hazards associated with *uncontrolled* combustion. Much of the science which is needed to understand these processes is, however, derived from the study of *controlled* combustion, and it seems to be useful to consider some of this as an introduction to the hazards of concern.

Pre-conditions for a combustion reaction

As a form of redox reaction, combustion must conform with the general conditions for redox reactions set out earlier. Thus, for combustion to proceed:

(a) there must be a supply of reducing agent (fuel);
(b) there must be a supply of oxygen (usually in the form of air);
(c) there must be a source of ignition energy sufficient to initiate the reaction;
(d) the combustion reaction must be exothermic;
(e) in the case of combustion reactions involving gases and vapours, the reactants must be present at levels of concentration lying between values known as 'flammable limits'.

These conditions are inter-dependent. Thus, the reaction may be initiated by an independent energy source (which may be mechanical, electrical, thermal or chemical) but, such a source is not generally maintained, and the reaction continues only if it is sufficiently exothermic to maintain spontaneously a temperature high enough to sustain it, taking account of heat losses from the reacting mixture to the surroundings. Conditions (a), (b) and (c) are sometimes referred to as 'the fire triangle'. A useful source of information on ignition is Bond[48].

Stoichiometry

Enthalpies of combustion reported in the literature assume that combustion is complete and that the products at 298.15°C are in equilibrium. These assumptions determine the stoichiometry of the reaction.

Uncontrolled combustion processes usually depart from these assumptions. The reactions are seldom complete, as evidenced by the generation of carbon monoxide and by the presence of soot and smoke. Soot is mainly unburned carbon and smoke is usually a complex mixture of compounds having reducing properties. In addition, combustion products such as carbon dioxide, steam and carbon monoxide, which react with each other, are not able to reach equilibrium before they become so cool that reaction practically ceases. The stoichiometry of combustion processes, especially when uncontrolled, can thus only be an approximation[41].

2.10.5 The combustion of substances in massive form

In the examples given below the reducing agent is assumed to be in the macrocosmic or massive form, that is in a size visible to the naked eye.

The combustion of coke and coal

The rate of combustion of coke and coal is governed by the rate at which air is supplied and hence its velocity relative to the surface of the material. This is an application of the laws of mass transfer which have been referred to in Section 2.9. The greater the relative velocity the more rapidly the products of combustion, which would otherwise inhibit further reaction, are swept away. This can be represented by saying that the thickness of the *boundary layer* between the substance undergoing combustion and the unreacted air is minimized. Very high temperatures, 1500°C and higher, are possible with high air velocities.

The ignition temperature of coke is around 500°C and this is the minimum temperature at which a self-sustaining reaction may be achieved. It is usually described as 'red heat, barely visible'. Combustion takes place at the surface of the coke to produce carbon monoxide which then burns to form carbon dioxide. If the air supply is inadequate the carbon monoxide may not be burned off and it becomes a toxic hazard.

Though bituminous coals, depending on their classification, contain 80 to 90% carbon, the reactions which take place during combustion are complex. Coal has an ignition temperature in the region of 425°C, and once a self-sustaining reaction has been achieved the coal substance is broken down (pyrolysed) as the interior of the coal is heated by conduction from the hot surface. This releases 'volatiles', which are a complex mixture including hydrogen and hydrocarbons, both paraffinic and aromatic. The combustion of these volatiles constitutes the flame, which may be luminous. As with the combustion of coke, the rate of combustion of coal is greatly dependent upon the relative velocity of the air.

The specific power of the combustion of a bed of coal, under poor conditions for rapid combustion, is of the order of $-50\,kW\,m^{-3}$ of furnace volume or $-250\,W$ per kg of coal. The burning velocity of coke and coal — the rate at which the flame zone advances into the unreacted mass — can only be given very approximately: it is of the order of 10^{-6} to $10^{-5}\,m\,s^{-1}$.

The combustion of wood

Wood has ceased to be an important material of construction for process plant. However it is still used in scaffolding and staging, in cat-walks, ladders and stairs, in temporary buildings and in furnishings. It is also used as a packaging material. These uses require wood to have a definite geometry for any particular purpose.

The combustion of wood bears some resemblance to that of coal, though wood contains a much higher proportion of volatiles than does coal. Heat conducted into the body of the wood pyrolyses it and a number of volatile and flammable products are released. These include 20 to 40 identifiable products, including benzene, methanol, acetone, cyclopentadiene, methyl benzene (toluene) and methane.

These products burn to give a luminous flame. When the volatiles have been liberated and burned, charcoal remains. This burns slowly compared with fresh wood, and the flame from it is much less luminous. The rate of combustion of a wooden surface is related to its geometry, including its orientation. Vertical surfaces have higher rates of combustion than horizontal ones, because natural convection increases the velocity of the air relative to the surface. The burning velocity of wood is, at least initially, somewhat higher than that of coal but, after charring, is probably similar to that of coke.

The combustion of liquids

Solids may take up a great variety of geometrical configurations and combustion may take place on surfaces with any orientation. But liquids, in a static condition, exist in the form of pools and combustion accordingly can only take place on the upper surface. Combustion under these circumstances is known as a 'pool fire'[2]. Pool fires were discussed in Section 2.6 (page 60), and are described in more detail in Marshall[20].

Matters are different with flowing, jetting or cascading liquids but space does not permit a discussion of these special cases. Where the liquid in a pool is volatile and flammable the air immediately above the pool will contain vapour, prior to combustion. Depending upon the volatility of the liquid, this may constitute a flammable mixture. If the temperature of the liquid is above its 'flash point' it may ignite. *Flash point* is not defined in Jones[2] but OCDC gives it as 'flash point: the temperature at which the vapour of a volatile liquid forms a combustible mixture with air' (in other words, the temperature at which the composition of the equilibrium vapour/air mixture is equivalent to the lower limit of flammability). Flammable limits are discussed later.

The initial stage of the combustion is one which involves two zones, a vapour/air mixture and air. This is a simpler system than the combustion of the pool of liquid and will be described below in the discussion of the combustion of vapour clouds.

During the initial combustion of the vapour/air mixture, heat is transmitted by conduction and radiation into the liquid, which brings about evaporation. A steady state is then reached in which the rate of combustion is in balance with the rate of evaporation. In the case of a pure liquid, in a pool which does not shrink in diameter, the rate of combustion is steady until all the liquid has evaporated.

With liquid mixtures there may be differential evaporation, the evaporation rate falling as the liquid remaining in the pool becomes less volatile. In some cases there is not only evaporation but also decomposition of the liquid (cracking), which is analogous with the emission of volatiles from coal.

Combustible liquids of low volatility, such as lubricating oil, will burn only if external heat is supplied, as by the combustion of other materials in the vicinity. The combustion of a pool of volatile, flammable liquid involves four zones: the liquid, the vapour layer above it, the flame/smoke zone and the surrounding air. The rate of heat release from a pool depends only upon its surface area and not upon its depth. The rate of heat release per unit area in a pool fire is principally determined by the volatility of the liquid. It thus bears an inverse relationship to the boiling point of the liquid (mass transfer plays a role, in that the rate of combustion is also governed by wind speed). A typical figure for the combustion of methanol is $450\,\text{kW}\,\text{m}^{-2}$.

2.10.6 Deflagrations of powders and droplets

These are rarefied-phase reactions.

Surface-to-volume ratio

The principal factor determining the rate of multiphase deflagrations is the surface-to-volume ratio of the reducing agent. In the case of lump coal this is of the order of $60\,\text{m}^{-1}$. It is easily possible, by grinding, to increase this ratio by a factor of 1000 but this does not increase the rate of combustion to the same degree. This is because it is not possible to achieve the same relative velocity with the air since the finer a particle (or droplet), the more it tends, through drag forces, to be carried along with the air.

Practical applications

Fine grinding of coal and atomization of fuel oil considerably enhance the rate of combustion, so most coal and oil used to generate steam are burned in a pulverized or atomized form under unconfined conditions. Generally coal is pulverized so that 75% will pass through a 70-micron sieve aperture. Pulverized coal is highly flammable and behaves much like a liquid in storage.

Heat releases from central station boilers are of the order of 0.2 MW per cubic metre.

2.10.7 Gas-phase deflagrations

Gas-phase deflagrations include all redox reactions in which both the oxidizing and the reducing agent are present in the form of gases or vapours. They are thus rarefied-phase reactions.

Most of the studies in this general field have been conducted in the area of combustion — that is, with air as the oxidizing agent. The principles set out below relate to combustion but are generally applicable to all gas-phase deflagrations. Stull[47], Harris[49] and Medard[41] contain much information which is applicable to the subject matter of this section.

For the purposes of this section no distinction is made between the behaviours of gases and vapours. 'Gas' is the more general term (all vapours are gaseous but not all gases are vapours). The term 'vapour' is used where this is correct and appropriate. The section will be concerned with the combustion of gases capable of forming flammable mixtures with air under conditions of constant pressure. The combustion of such flammable mixtures with appreciable pressure rise will be covered in later sections.

Limits of flammability

All gas-phase redox reactions have limits of concentration beyond which deflagrations will not take place. Combustion reactions form a special case of this.

The deflagration of a flammable gas in air will only take place within its 'flammability limits'. However, the way in which these limits are expressed in the literature, as 'lower' and 'upper' flammable limits, may give rise to the misconception that it is the reducing agent (fuel) which is flammable, rather than the mixture. In fact a jet of air introduced into an atmosphere of, say, methane, will burn in the same way as a jet of methane introduced into an atmosphere of air. A mixture in which the fuel concentration is 'above the upper flammable limit' is usually described as being 'too rich to burn', but it would be equally correct to say that such a mixture will not burn because its oxygen concentration is too low. However, as the expression 'upper flammable limit' is well established, it will be used later.

Data for a number of hydrocarbons in air, expressed in terms of volume percent of vapour in the mixture, are presented in Table 2.18. It should be noted that the data are not precise and depend on the geometry of the system in which the limits are determined.

Certain regularities emerge from this treatment. Table 2.18 shows that in the series ethane, ethene (ethylene) and ethyne (acetylene) the limits widen as the degree of unsaturation and hence reactivity increases.

Table 2.18 Flammability limits of hydrocarbons in air

Compound	Formula	Molar mass $(kg\ kmol^{-1})$	Lower limit (% volume)	Upper limit (% volume)
Hydrogen	H_2	2	4.0	75.0
Methane	CH_4	16	5.0	15.0
Ethyne	C_2H_2	26	2.5	80.0
Ethene	C_2H_4	28	3.0	32.0
Ethane	C_2H_6	30	3.0	12.0
Propene	C_3H_6	42	2.5	10.5
Propane	C_3H_8	44	2.2	9.5
Butene	C_4H_8	56	1.7	9.5
Butane	C_4H_{10}	58	1.9	8.5
Benzene	C_6H_6	78	1.4	7.1
Hexane	C_6H_{14}	86	1.2	7.5

Enhanced oxygen concentrations

The presence of enhanced oxygen concentrations in the atmosphere may present a serious hazard. Such concentrations may arise from spillages of liquid oxygen or, in confined spaces, from leakages from cylinders or hoses; gaseous oxygen is much used in industry for cutting and welding. If evaporation occurs from liquid air, nitrogen is lost more rapidly than oxygen, so the liquid air is progressively enhanced in oxygen content.

Enhanced oxygen intensifies combustion, and materials which are normally regarded as being of low flammability, such as some textiles, may be rendered highly flammable and may readily ignite from sparks (this includes some 'flame-proof' fabrics). Air containing more than 24% oxygen should be regarded as especially hazardous[20].

Accidental releases are not homogeneous

When flammability limits are determined in the laboratory, great care is taken to secure homogeneity of the mixture. When vapour is accidentally released it is impossible to achieve homogeneity, and typically a vapour cloud has three regions of differing composition: a central zone which is usually above the upper flammability limit, a zone surrounding it which lies between the flammability limits and an outer zone which is below the lower flammability limit. The boundaries of these zones change continually with time.

Ignition temperatures

One of the preconditions of combustion is that the temperature of the system should be no lower than its so-called 'ignition temperature'. Medard[41] discusses the factors involved. For many hydrocarbons, whether mixed with air or with oxygen, the ignition temperature falls in the range 225–575°C (see Harris[49]). For paraffins the ignition temperature falls with increasing number of carbon atoms.

Flame speeds

The *flame speed* in a flammable mixture, measured relative to a stationary observer, depends upon (1) the fundamental burning velocity, which is a function of the composition of the mixture, (2) the expansion factor, which is the ratio of the densities of unburned and burned gases, and (3) the geometry of the system. The *(fundamental) burning velocity* is the velocity with which the flame front moves relative to the unburned gas ahead of it.

Harris[49] (Appendix 2) shows how to calculate flame speed. He points out that the calculations may be simplified by making certain assumptions. The expansion factor varies within fairly narrow limits, being 7.4 for methane and 8.0 for hydrogen.

Table 1.2 in Harris gives values for maximum burning velocities and maximum flame speeds. For many hydrocarbons these range between 0.45 and $0.83\,\mathrm{m\,s^{-1}}$ for burning velocity and between 3.5 and $6.5\,\mathrm{m\,s^{-1}}$ for flame speed. Hydrogen and ethyne (acetylene) have much higher values (3.5/28 and $1.58/14.3\,\mathrm{m\,s^{-1}}$).

Ignition sources

Naked flames, electrical sparks, mechanically generated sparks or hot surfaces may initiate the combustion of gas/air mixtures, provided that they have a

105

sufficiently high temperature and adequate mass. Other conditions such as the mixture lying within flammable limits, must clearly be fulfilled. Medard[41], in Tables 10.1 and 10.2, gives minimum energy levels for initiating the combustion of various vapour/air mixtures. These lie in a range from 0.02 mJ for hydrogen to about 1.0 mJ for some organic compounds.

Flash fires

When a cloud of a flammable gas/air mixture is formed it may ignite provided that the conditions described above are met. Under the most typical conditions this leads to a 'flash fire', defined in Jones[2] as 'the combustion of a flammable vapour and air mixture in which flame passes through the mixture at less than sonic velocity such that negligible damaging overpressure is generated' (see note above on the terms 'gas' and 'vapour').

The temperatures developed in flash fires depend upon circumstances but are much below theoretical adiabatic flame temperatures — 700 to 900°C is a useful guide.

As the vapour/air mixture burns, it expands according to the well known Law of Charles which holds that a gas expands by 1/273 of its volume at 0°C per degree of temperature rise. Thus the volume of the combustion products at, say, 900°C would be approximately four times as great as that of the unburned mixture. With a flat 'pancake' cloud the expansion would occur upwards; but clouds of different original geometry may expand laterally to some degree on burning. The combustion products, because of their expansion, are very buoyant relative to the surrounding air. The duration of a flash fire is difficult to predict but may be roughly estimated by dividing the diameter of the cloud by the flame speed of the mixture.

Chapter 5 gives a case history of an exceptionally destructive flash fire under the heading of 'Spanish campsite disaster'.

Fireballs

Under certain circumstances a flash fire may escalate into a 'fire ball'. This is defined in Jones[2] as 'a fire, burning sufficiently rapidly for the burning mass to rise into the air as a cloud or ball'. Fireball formation is favoured by the rapid release of flammable vapour in quantities measured in tonnes. Such circumstances can arise in connection with the rupture after engulfment in fire of containers of liquefied vapours (so-called BLEVEs, described in Section 2.5.4, page 51).

The thermal characteristics of fireballs were discussed in Section 2.6.5 (page 62). Chapter 5 gives examples of incidents which involved fireball formation under the headings of 'Feyzin' (page 225) and 'Mexico City' (page 232).

2.10.8 The unconfined deflagration of propellants and explosives

These are dense-phase reactions.

Definitions

Explosives are defined by PDS as 'substances which undergo rapid chemical change, with production of gas, on being heated or struck'.

Propellant is defined by PDS as 'the explosive substance used to fill cartridges, shell cases and solid fuel rockets'.

The nature of propellants

For a full discussion and description of the many propellants which are used technologically, it is necessary to consult monographs and major encyclopaedias. However the accounts given in Stull[47] and that under 'Explosives and Propellants' in Kirk-Othmer[50], together with Fordham[51] should provide adequate further reading.

Propellants have a molecule which, though stable under ordinary conditions of temperature and pressure, is capable, when heated or subjected to shock, of undergoing an internal redox reaction with the production of gases such as N_2, CO_2 and H_2O. The chemical nature of propellants and their deflagration under confined conditions are briefly discussed below.

Though the handling of military propellants and solid fuels for rockets is a highly specialized branch of the chemical industry, there are some materials more generally used in the process industries which resemble such propellants in their deflagrative properties. These include so-called 'nitro-cellulose', actually nitrates of cellulose, which are manufactured for a variety of uses including the production of lacquers and printing inks (it is the more highly nitrated celluloses that are used as military propellants). For further reading on nitro-celluloses see Medard[41], who gives further references.

The behaviour of propellants on unconfined deflagration

Propellants, because they undergo intra-molecular redox reactions, do not require oxygen for deflagration. Some are oxygen-deficient (they have insufficient oxygen in the molecule to oxidize all the carbon and hydrogen) and these deflagrate more intensely in the presence of air. Typical burning velocities under unconfined conditions are of the order of $0.1 \, \mathrm{m \, s^{-1}}$. In comparing this with the burning velocity of gas/air mixtures, allowance must be made for the much higher density of solid propellants, which means that unit distance travelled by the reaction zone relative to the unreacted zone releases much more energy.

A major difference between the deflagrations of gases and of propellants lies in the relative volumes of the gaseous reacted products. With gaseous reactants the expansion produced by the deflagration is due largely to the increase of temperature; with propellants, there are also solid reactants being transformed by reaction into gases. Thus, a typical propellant will produce about 800 times its own volume of gas at STP, but this will increase at reaction temperature to about 6000 times.

The energy output of the unconfined deflagration of propellants is of the order of 10^5 J per kg and the power is of the order of 10^7 watts per square metre of surface. Thus the energy emitted is appreciably less than with coal, say, but the power is about 100 times greater.

The nature of explosives

Though, strictly speaking, explosives are a general class which also includes the class of propellants, in practice the term 'explosive' is usually restricted to liquids or solids which are readily capable of detonation. As with propellants, for further reading on explosives, Stull[47], Kirk-Othmer[50] and Fordham[51] are recommended.

Explosives resemble propellants in that, with a few exceptions, they also are capable of undergoing internal redox reactions when subjected to heat or to shock. The exceptions are a small class of substances which decompose to yield appreciable volumes of hot gases.

Though, as with propellants, the production of military or commercial explosives is a specialized branch of the chemical industry, some of these substances may be encountered more generally. Trinitrotoluene (which will be referred to below as TNT) may be produced as a by-product of the nitration of toluene for dyestuffs manufacture. The class of organic peroxides, though without military application, may behave similarly to conventional explosives. An important substance which is a fertilizer and, under some circumstances, an explosive, is ammonium nitrate (see Chapter 5 — case history of Oppau, page 233).

The behaviour of explosives on unconfined deflagration

Explosives, on unconfined deflagration, behave in a similar manner to propellants. If they are oxygen-deficient, the presence of air will make them deflagrate more fiercely than otherwise. Their burning velocities and their energy and power emissions are similar to those of propellants.

Ammonium nitrate, even in the pure form, may be ignited to undergo what is called 'cigar burning'. [This is a rather misleading description as cigars need air to burn whereas ammonium nitrate 'burns' without the need for air]. Cigar burning produces nitrous oxide according to the equation:

$$NH_4NO_3 \rightarrow N_2O + 2H_2O$$

Nitrous oxide vigorously supports ordinary combustion and such deflagrations are difficult to extinguish. Large heaps have been known to 'burn' for days. For a case history of an unconfined deflagration of ammonium nitrate which eventually became a detonation, see Chapter 5 — Texas City (page 240).

2.10.9 Conflagrations

The term *conflagration* is used here in its ordinary dictionary sense of a major fire. In the context of chemical and process plant, conflagrations are complex phenomena. They are likely to provide activation energy which may bring about all types of deflagration and even detonations. They may lead to the rupture of pipes and vessels, thus releasing flammable materials to spread the conflagration. They are characterized by flames which may occupy zones many metres thick and possibly a hundred metres or more high.

See Chapter 5 for case histories of 'Cleveland' (page 222), 'Flixborough' (page 227), 'Feyzin' (page 225) and 'Mexico City' (page 232).

2.11 Chemical energy releases – confined deflagrations

2.11.1 The nature of confined deflagrations

Deflagration, unconfined deflagration and *confined deflagration* have already been defined. The definition of *deflagration* requires that the reactions under discussion are heterogeneous, three-zone reactions in which the velocity of advance of the reaction zone into the unreacted zone is less than the velocity of sound in the unreacted zone. For unconfined and confined deflagrations the factors which determine burning velocity are heat transfer and mass transfer.

It is clear that confined deflagrations can give rise to appreciable overpressure and thus it is necessary to explain why they should not be treated as 'explosive deflagrations'. This is because the latter term is restricted to those deflagrations in which (1) the overpressure is a direct consequence of flame speed and (2) the principal factor which governs the velocity of advance of the reaction zone into the unreacted zone is shock transfer. Explosive deflagrations are thus qualitatively different from confined deflagrations.

The physical and chemical mechanisms of the advance of the reaction front in a confined deflagration do not differ from those in an unconfined deflagration. The difference between them lies in the inability of the reacted zone in a confined deflagration to expand freely on account of the confinement.

2.11.2 Confined deflagration of gas/air mixtures

These are rarefied-phase reactions. For a given gas/air mixture, the conditions governing the initiation of a confined deflagration (including such factors as flammability limits, ignition temperature, and ignition energy) are similar to those for an unconfined deflagration.

Flame speed

During the development of a confined deflagration the pressure rises and this can influence burning velocity and flame speed. It will be pointed out later that, under process plant conditions, uncontrolled confined deflagrations do not achieve more than a fraction of the pressure rise which is possible and that therefore the influence of pressure on reaction conditions is seldom important. Harris[49] points out, that over the range 1 to 9 bars increase in pressure, burning *velocity* reduces but, at the same time, because of increased density, the *mass* burning rate increases. This leads to the conclusion that for the same gas/air mixture, the rate of energy emission of a confined deflagration will be higher than that of an unconfined one. Hence confined deflagrations are more powerful than unconfined deflagrations.

Theoretical maximum pressure rise

It is possible to calculate a theoretical pressure rise under adiabatic conditions for any given mixture. However, such calculations assume that combustion is as complete as the composition of the mixture permits, and chemical equilibrium between the products of combustion is achieved and that dissociation is negligible. None of these conditions is completely fulfilled in practice.

On the other hand there is a wealth of experimental data available, suggesting that for many vapours mixed with air a maximum overpressure of 6.5 bar is achieved. Such overpressures are only achieved with uniform mixtures in which the gas concentration is around, or slightly above, stoichiometric proportions. As the gas concentrations approach the flammable limits the overpressures obtainable eventually fall to zero. If the initial pressure in a container subject to a totally confined deflagration is greater than atmospheric, the final pressure reached is proportionately higher.

Pressure rises achieved in practice

The conditions which determine maximum pressure rise are seldom achieved in practice. For example, the vapour/air mixture may not be well mixed. Harris[49] points out that a rich layer of vapour/air mixture may produce an explosion because it has an appropriate composition even though, if the same quantity of vapour had been uniformly mixed with the air in the enclosure, it would have been below the lower flammable limit.

But the most important reason why these theoretical explosion pressures are seldom achieved in rooms or in many kinds of process equipment lies in the inability of the enclosure to withstand more than a small fraction of this pressure rise. Harris[49], Chapter 5, gives values for the failure pressure of common building elements including, for example, glass windows (0.02 to 0.35 bar gauge). Thus failure of structural elements can be initiated at less than 1% of the theoretical maximum explosion pressure rise. In fact the more stout a building, the more severe the damage it will suffer.

Case histories of confined methane/air deflagrations are given in Chapter 5 under 'Abbeystead' (page 212) and 'Staten Island' (page 239).

2.11.3 Confined deflagrations of dust/air mixtures

These are rarefied-phase reactions. They are usually termed 'dust explosions', and are of common occurrence in the process industries. Any process which handles powdered reducing agents is at risk from them. They are especially frequent in the branch of the process industries which handles foodstuffs, including cereals. This is partly because foodstuffs are, by nature, reducing agents. It is also because these industries commonly have to crush and grind materials to render them palatable and have to transport the materials in elevators and various types of conveyors which involve mechanical moving parts.

There is extensive literature on the subject. Eckhoff[52] is a useful source book. It is directed towards the chemical and process industries and contains references to the other principal works on dust explosions. The subject also features in Medard[41] and Stull[47].

Unconfined and confined combustion of dusts

Reference has already been made to the combustion of coal in powdered form. Such combustion takes place under unconfined conditions and the equipment is designed so that the pressure rise is very small. Under confined conditions, however, the combustion of coal dust mixed with air may give rise to severe explosions. Many such explosions have occurred in coal mines.

The agents which may give rise to dust explosions

When mixed with air in a sufficiently fine state of sub-division, and in a suitable concentration, practically every substance which has a negative enthalpy of

111

combustion is capable of giving rise to overpressure. This means that many substances not commonly recognized as being highly flammable may give rise to a dust explosion. Examples of such substances are flour, cocoa and starch. The earliest recorded dust explosion was in a flour mill in Torino (Turin) Italy in 1785.

Though the oxidizing agent is usually atmospheric oxygen, in principle dust explosions could occur in any system in which a finely divided solid reducing agent is dispersed in a gaseous oxidizing agent. Such explosions can be demonstrated in the laboratory, but we do not know of any which have occurred on an industrial scale.

Particle size of hazardous dusts

This varies with the substance. There is usually a critical upper limit such that, if it is exceeded by a substantial fraction of the dust, no explosion will occur. Eckhoff[52] has an appendix containing extensive data on this subject, including notes on the type of pressure vessel used for the testing. The median particle size on a weight basis for many of the materials listed lies in the range of 10 to 100 microns (1 micron or $\mu m \equiv 10^{-6}$ m).

Hazardous concentrations of dust

Eckhoff's tables show that, for many substances, the concentration of the solid material necessary to produce an explosion is in the range of 0.03 to $0.14 \, kg \, m^{-3}$ and that in only a few cases is it as low as $0.014 \, kg \, m^{-3}$. Such concentrations would reduce visibility to a metre or less. Though they may readily be achieved inside of process equipment, such concentrations would be unlikely to occur outside of plant except in special circumstances.

These circumstances arise when a minor explosion occurs inside a building as, for example, when an explosion inside equipment bursts a relief panel and stirs up dust which has accumulated in the building. It is especially dangerous if the dust has accumulated on roof trusses and beams because in this case it cascades down, possibly filling the entire building, and may then explode if it finds an ignition source. It has long been recognized in coal mines that methane explosions could initiate far more destructive coal dust explosions.

Dust explosions, though they require a minimum concentration of dust, are not particularly subject to a limiting upper concentration. This is because the partial volume of the dust is very small. A dust with the same density as water and with a concentration of, say, $1 \, kg \, m^{-3}$, which would be a very high concentration for a dust cloud, has a partial volume of only 0.1%.

Generally, with high concentrations of dust, the heat release is governed by the quantity of oxygen available. If there is more of the reducing agent than is equivalent to the oxygen present it simply remains unburnt. Inside process equipment it is often feasible to prevent explosions by introducing an inert gas such as nitrogen or carbon dioxide. Eckhoff gives a table which shows the minimum oxygen concentration needed to sustain an explosion for various substances. For many common substances the concentration lies between 9 and 14%.

Ignition sources

These may be assumed to be the same as those which are able to initiate gas/air deflagrations. Eckhoff[52] tabulates minimum ignition energies in an Appendix.

Maximum pressure rises

Eckhoff's tables show that the maximum pressure rise in dust explosions tends to be somewhat higher than in vapour/air explosions. It often lies in the region of 8 to 10 bar, with higher values for aluminium (12.5 bar) and magnesium (17.5 bar).

As noted in the discussion on vapour/air explosions, buildings are unable to withstand pressures of this order, though if vented to restrict pressure rise they may survive. Buildings may not avoid serious structural damage even if windows and doors are blown out. Process plant, except for pressure vessels, is likely to suffer severe damage unless vented by the provision of panels which rupture easily in the event of an explosion.

Deflagration of aerosols

Droplets of liquid suspended in air, provided that they satisfy the same criteria as solids, may also deflagrate in a similar way.

Case history

There is a case history of a confined dust explosion in Chapter 5 (Anglesey, page 213).

2.11.4 Confined deflagrations of propellants

The confined deflagration of propellants is a topic where the military significance outweighs its process significance. However, the confined deflagration of propellants has occurred in the process industries. These are dense-phase reactions.

Two case histories are included in Chapter 5 (Castleford, page 220 and Stevenston, page 239).

The nature of propellants

The first propellant was so-called 'gun-powder' or 'black powder'. Its invention preceded that of the gun by several centuries. It seems at first to have been used as a rocket propellant by the Chinese to increase the range of arrows. It was then, and has remained, a mixture of substances in the form of grains. These substances, traditionally, were sodium nitrate (saltpetre), charcoal and sulphur. Later, when guns were invented, the same material was used to accelerate a missile along the length of the barrel.

Propellants today have the same two basic uses: they are used either to propel rockets or in guns to propel bullets or shells. They are often referred to as 'low explosives' because they do not detonate in ordinary circumstances.

Rocket propellants

Rocket propellants can be given only a brief mention: the numerous articles in technical encyclopaedias give further detail. For a short article, see Shreve[19]. They may be divided into two main classes. There are mono-propellants or binary propellants. The former may operate by simple decomposition in the presence of a catalyst — an example is 90% hydrogen peroxide (the decomposition of which is unusual in not being an internal redox reaction).

Usually mono-propellants operate by deflagration with accompanying internal redox reaction. An example is cordite, which is a mixture primarily of nitro-cellulose and nitro-glycerine with a small proportion of petroleum jelly. It was manufactured originally in the form of cords (hence the name). Binary combinations are made of an oxidizing agent and a reducing agent chosen to have a high level of power emission.

Deflagration in rockets is semi-confined. They have a nozzle which constricts the flow of the hot reaction products so that they issue as a high velocity jet.

Gun propellants

Propellants which detonated would be useless in guns as they would burst the gun. There is a considerable variety of gun propellants, ranging from those suitable for hand-guns to those suitable for heavy artillery.

Only cordite is considered here. This has a history, in its various compositions, of more than a century and it was used in the largest-calibre naval guns. In Table 2.19 overleaf, a calculation of the the power of a confined propellant deflagration in a British naval (coastal) gun of a type used in the Second World War, described by Hodges[53], is summarized.

It is seen that the confined burning velocity is perhaps 1000 times greater than that of an unconfined propellant. This is because the burning velocity of propellants is much increased by pressure. The maximum pressure developed in a gun of the type described above is probably of the order of 3500 bar.

Table 2.19 Illustrative calculation of the power of a confined propellant deflagration (cordite in a naval gun)

Data		Calculated parameters	
Bore (m)	0.38*	Acceleration (m s^{-2})	16000
Barrel length (m)	16.15*	Time of travel of shell in barrel (s)	0.04
Muzzle velocity (m s^{-1})	732*	Cross-sectional area of charge (m^2)	0.11
Mass of cordite (kg)	196*	Length of charge (m)	1.07
Density of cordite (kg m^{-3})	1600†	Burning time of cordite (s)	0.02
Energy per unit mass (J kg^{-1})	6 × 10^6‡	Burning velocity (m s^{-1})	49
		Surface per unit mass (m^2 kg^{-1})	0.0066
		Power per unit mass (W kg^{-1})	3 × 10^8
		Power per unit surface area (W m^{-2})	4 × 10^{10}

*Hodges[53]   †estimated   ‡From tables in Kirk-Othmer[50]

However the burning velocity is only about 1% of the detonation velocity of explosives.

The emitted power is proportional to the burning velocity and is thus much higher than it is in unconfined deflagrations. The power is about 1% of that emitted in a detonation, which accords with the burning velocity being only 1% of detonation velocity in a solid.

It should be noted that such a gun emits a jet of high-pressure, incandescent gas at an initial velocity about twice that of sound. Photographs of naval guns firing suggest that the fireball may extend up to 200 metres from the muzzle of the gun. It is clear that such a fireball would be highly destructive were it to come into contact with people or property. The emission also produces powerful reactive forces (recoil). In the conditions of the process industries these could lead to jet propulsion of vessels or containers.

2.12 Explosive deflagrations

2.12.1 Introduction

This section is concerned with deflagrations in which the overpressure arises from the velocity of the flame front and in which the principal factor controlling the reaction rate is shock transfer. In such explosions the flame front and the pressure impulse are coupled together in what is termed a shock wave. The following subjects are discussed:

(1) the factors which lead to explosive deflagrations;
(2) explosive deflagrations of gas/air mixtures;
(3) explosive deflagrations of dust/air mixtures.

2.12.2 Factors which lead to explosive deflagrations

Factors producing acceleration

In the absence of certain factors, an established flame front tends to move at a steady speed. In this model a flame front moving along a horizontal, open-ended, smooth-walled gallery of constant cross-section would maintain a constant speed regardless of the length of the gallery. To use an expression which will be used later, the speed is independent of the L/D [length-to-diameter] ratio of the gallery.

Explosive deflagrations will only occur if factors are present which can produce acceleration of the flame front. Experiments have shown that there are two principal, and inter-related, factors — these are: (1) turbulence, and (2) obstructions.

The influence of turbulence

It is well established that turbulence intensifies both heat transfer and mass transfer and hence increases those reaction rates which are governed by rates of heat transfer and mass transfer. This implies, in the context of flame propagation, that turbulence increases burning velocity and hence flame speed. There seems to be much evidence to confirm this from the field of fuel technology.

The influence of obstructions

It is well known that in fluid flow turbulence may be brought about by abrupt changes in direction of flow and cross-section, and by roughness of duct walls, enhancing resistance to flow.

2.12.3 Explosive deflagrations of gas/air mixtures

These are rarefied-phase reactions.

Explosive deflagrations of gases in long ducts

It has long been recognized that the deflagration of methane in coal mines could give rise to explosions. These occurred in spite of the fact that the flame speed of methane is lower than that of any other hydrocarbon. However, mine galleries were highly obstructed with many changes of direction and cross-sectional area and typically had L/D ratios in excess of 1000.

116

Explosive deflagrations have occurred in the chemical and process industries and elsewhere even though the conditions described in coal mines are not exactly reproduced there. Sewers, for example, have high L/D ratios and, in addition to other conditions which promote turbulence, flowing liquids in them can impart turbulence to gas/air mixtures. There is a case history of a catastrophic series of explosive deflagrations in sewers in Chapter 5 under 'Guadalajara' (page 228).

Explosive deflagrations in the open air

Though the occurrence of explosive deflagrations in the process industries had long been acknowledged, it was until fairly recently assumed that they could only occur in galleries and tunnels with high L/D ratios. The notion that they could occur in the open air was rejected in the belief that, without confinement, any potential overpressure would be dissipated to the surrounding atmosphere.

However, Strehlow[54] pointed out that, whatever theory might have to say, there was incontrovertible evidence that a number of such explosions had actually occurred world-wide. He described them as 'unconfined vapour cloud explosions' or 'UVCEs'.

When a major explosion occurred at Flixborough (UK) in 1974 the Official Inquiry which followed concluded that this explosion was of the nature of those described by Strehlow. After this, Strehlow's concept achieved universal acceptance. A number of case histories — Ludwigshafen (two, page 230), Flixborough (page 227) and Port Hudson (page 235) — are reported in Chapter 5.

The nature of open-air explosive deflagrations

Though such explosions have caused damage over a radius of more than 10 km, there are many marked differences between them and those caused by liquid or solid (dense) explosives.

Perhaps the most striking of these differences is the absence of a crater — though they are able to push whole buildings over, they do not shatter their surroundings. This may be attributed to the low levels of maximum overpressure — a maximum of roughly 1 bar — that they achieve when compared with conventional explosives. Examples of the damage they inflict are given in Chapter 4, Hazards to Property, and in Chapter 5, the case histories of Flixborough (page 227) and Port Hudson (page 235).

Conditions leading to open-air explosive deflagrations

Recognition that such explosions had occurred did not provide an explanation of their cause, and there still remained the paradox of how a flame with a speed

117

of a few metres per second could accelerate up to near sonic velocity in travelling for, perhaps at the most, 100 metres.

An extensive programme of research was instituted on a large scale at a number of centres world-wide and it was concluded that the phenomenon was scale-dependent. Case histories of such explosive deflagrations suggested that a minimum of several tonnes of flammable vapour had been involved in each case. In broad terms, the findings of this research are that such deflagrations can only occur in the presence of obstructions which promote the necessary turbulence[55,56,57,58].

When an advancing flame front has attained a certain level of overpressure, an additional mechanism may play a role. This is the mechanism of reflection from obstructions. When a shock wave encounters a rigid obstacle it is reflected at a higher level of overpressure though with shorter wave length. Thus an array of obstructions may act as a set of pressure amplifiers in series.

It is clear that a site which is capable of giving rise to the release of flammable gases or vapours on a sufficiently large scale to present the hazard of an explosive deflagration is one which is likely to possess such features as columns, pipe bridges and other arrays of piping, as well as supporting structures and buildings. These obstructions create turbulence and amplify overpressure.

Experimental demonstration

In a typical demonstration, a rectangular tunnel of two or three metres height and width and about 50 metres long, with polythene walls, is filled with a well-mixed gas/air mixture. At about 30 metres down the tunnel an array of vertical cylindrical obstructions of about 0.2 metres diameter is placed. A flame is initiated at the end and travels at a steady velocity down the tunnel without disintegrating the walls. On encountering the obstructions the flame undergoes rapid acceleration and the walls are disintegrated. After leaving the array the flame front maintains its velocity but does not accelerate further.

When the experiment is conducted using different gases it seems clear that the reactivity of the gas also plays a role. Unsaturated gases such as ethene are more easily accelerated than, say, methane. This seems to accord with the experience of such explosions. Methane, which is the least reactive hydro-carbon, does not seem to have been implicated in any accidental explosive deflagration.

Nomenclature

To conform with the authors' scheme of classification, the term 'explosive deflagrations of gas/air mixtures' has been used, although this expression is not in use elsewhere. The term generally used today is 'vapour cloud explosion'. This expression avoids controversy as to whether such explosions are semi-confined or unconfined. Jones[2] defines vapour cloud explosion (VCE) as 'the preferred term for the explosion in the open air of a mixture of a flammable vapour or gas with air'.

Energy and power emissions

A rough estimate of the energy and power emissions from an explosive deflagration of a gas/air mixture is put forward, so that its order of magnitude may be compared with those of other deflagrations and detonations. A well studied explosion (Flixborough, UK, 1974 — case history in Chapter 5, page 227) has been taken, and estimates accepted that the cyclohexane vapour/air cloud contained ca. 45 tonnes of cyclohexane. The generally held opinion is accepted, that the energy released by the explosive deflagration of vapour/air clouds is only a fraction of the enthalpy of combustion of the vapour present.

In this case, the 45 tonnes of cyclohexane have been equated with the ca. 16 tonnes of TNT cited in Marshall[20], p. 301 (see paragraph below on TNT equivalence). On this basis some 5.6 tonnes, or 12.5% of the cyclohexane was involved in the explosive deflagration. The duration of the explosive deflagration is judged to be one second, which is consistent with a flame travelling across a cloud of ca. 200 metres diameter at about 2/3 sonic velocity. This assumption makes the power in watts numerically equal to the energy in joules. The energy of the explosion was equal to the detonation enthalpy of 16 tonnes of TNT [$16 \times 4.23 \times 10^9$ J $= 6.8 \times 10^{10}$ J]. Its power, based on a duration of one second, was thus 6.8×10^{10} W.

However, it is also useful for purposes of comparison with other deflagrations and detonations to estimate both energy and power in terms of a unit mass of reactants. It is assumed, based on the Flixborough literature, that the cloud contained 45 tonnes of cyclohexane and that its oxygen equivalent was 154 tonnes, making a total of 199 tonnes of reactants. If the argument above is followed, the quantity of reactants involved in the explosive deflagration was 25 tonnes. Thus the specific energy was 6.8×10^{10} J/$(25 \times 10^3$ kg) $= 2.72 \times 10^6$ J per kg and the specific power was 2.72×10^6 W per kg.

In comparing explosive deflagrations of gas/air mixtures with dense-medium detonations, it should be noted that in an explosive deflagration the flame front has to travel about 100 times as far at about 1/50 of the velocity of a detonation shock wave.

TNT equivalence

A number of investigators have put forward what has been termed 'The TNT equivalent' of such deflagrations. Jones[2] defines it as 'The amount of TNT which would produce the same damage effects as those of the explosion under consideration. For non-dense phase explosions the equivalence has meaning only at a considerable distance where the nature of the blast wave arising is comparable with TNT'. The concept has given rise to controversies which go beyond the scope of this book, but it is obvious that there are considerable difficulties in comparing a rarefied-phase explosive deflagration with a dense-phase detonation. Dense-phase detonations are discussed in Section 2.13.

2.12.4 Explosive deflagrations of dust/air mixtures

Deflagrations in coal mines

This subject has been extensively studied because of its importance for safety in coal mines. Particular circumstances have made coal dust explosions especially devastating. These centre around the existence of very long galleries which connect together the various areas of a mine, but especially the coal face to the shaft. Galleries of five to 10 km are sometimes found. These have L/D ratios of more than 1,000.

The sequence of events is as follows. Ignition of methane at the coal face leads to a local deflagration of gas. A pressure pulse moving ahead of the flame then stirs up dust from the floor and walls of the gallery. The dust then ignites and the deflagration becomes a dust deflagration. The flame becomes turbulent because of the 'roughness' of the walls, roof and floor of the gallery. The unconfined dust deflagration becomes transformed into an explosive deflagration. Eckhoff[52] reports that overpressures of 0.2 to 0.4 bar have been obtained experimentally in a 36-metre gallery.

It must be said that extensive research has brought about a great reduction in the incidence of such explosions in mines. This has been accomplished by suppressing deflagration before it becomes explosive, among other measures.

Explosive deflagrations of dust in process plant

Such explosions are only likely to occur in equipment with high L/D ratios. These could take the form of conveyer systems which, because of moving parts, are likely to provide mechanisms for creating turbulence.

It must be noted that a fully developed explosive deflagration is moving so fast that it does not send acoustic signals ahead of itself such as would, for example, actuate relief panels. Suppression, to be effective, has therefore to operate before the deflagration becomes explosive.

2.13 Detonations

2.13.1 The nature of detonations

Comparison with deflagrations

Detonations resemble all classes of deflagrations in possessing three zones, an unreacted zone, a reaction zone and a reacted zone. They resemble explosive deflagrations in that the transmission mechanism of the reaction is by shock transfer, the flame front being coupled with the pressure front in what is termed a 'shock wave'. However, unlike the shock waves of explosive deflagrations, detonation shock waves travel at velocities higher than that of sound in the unreacted medium. Detonations may occur in rarefied systems (gases) or in dense-phase systems (liquids or solids).

Sonic velocity

Since the criterion of a detonation involves the velocity of sound, this subject must be briefly discussed. The velocity of sound in a given medium, whether gas, liquid or solid, depends upon the elastic constants of the medium and upon the inverse of the square root of its density. The only sonic velocity in a gas which is of significance to this book is the velocity of sound in air. This is usually given, in dry air, as $331\ \mathrm{m\,s^{-1}}$ at 273 K, or about 1/3 of a kilometre per second.

The velocity increases with temperature in the ratio $[T_a/273]^{0.5}$, where T_a is the actual temperature of the air. In organic liquids the velocity is three to four times what it is in air; in solids it is 10 to 20 times the value in air.

2.13.2 Detonations of gas/air mixtures

Theory of detonations

The theory of detonations is concerned with the physics of extreme temperatures and pressures. The theory of detonations, both rarefied and dense-phase, is dealt with in Stull[47], Fordham[51] and in MEST[59]. It may be noted from this theory that the conditions of temperature and pressure under which shock waves are propagated in a detonation differ widely from the propagation of sound waves under standard conditions. The velocity of sound under standard conditions has little meaning in conditions of detonation and therefore it must be taken simply as an index of comparison.

121

Conditions for gas/air detonations

The study of gas detonations has been concerned almost exclusively with mixtures in which air is the oxidizing agent. However, gas-phase redox reactions involving oxidants other than oxygen may also give rise to detonations and process engineers must always be aware of this possibility. A gas/air detonation is a possible escalation of an explosive deflagration. In a long gallery or a pipeline, beyond a certain value of L/D, a detonation may develop.

There is general agreement that the concentration limits for detonations are somewhat narrower than those for deflagrations. Stull[47] gives examples. It seems clear that the risk of detonation is highest when the mixture is of around stoichiometric proportions. Some values given by Stull[47] for detonation velocities of gases in air are shown in Table 2.20.

The peak overpressure developed in a gas detonation exceeds the theoretical adiabatic pressure rise by a factor of two to three.

Table 2.20 Detonation velocities of gases in air

Gas	Velocity ($m\ s^{-1}$)
methane	1540
propane	1730
ethyne (acetylene)	1870
hydrogen	3400

The power of gas detonations

Using propane as an example, the enthalpy of combustion is 5×10^7 J per kg. For a stoichiometric mixture (4%) and accepting Stull's detonation velocity, this gives a specific power of 7×10^9 W.

The detonation of open-air gas/air mixtures

The question of whether the explosive deflagration of open-air gas/air clouds (vapour cloud explosions) can escalate to detonation remains open. Stull[47] cites the Port Hudson incident (see Chapter 5, page 235) as an open-air gas/air detonation. Gugan[60] claims that some of the damage at Flixborough (see Chapter 5, page 227) can only be explained on the basis that much higher levels of overpressure had been generated than would be expected from what we have termed an explosive deflagration. Any attempt to assess these claims would be beyond the scope of this book. Although such escalations cannot be ruled out, they are unlikely to occur in any but the largest of such incidents.

2.13.3 Dense-phase detonations

Significance for the process industries

Although the subject of dense-phase detonations is of great significance for that branch of the process industries which is concerned with the manufacture of military and commercial explosives, the subject of safety in these industries is too specialized for this book to consider in detail. Those interested in further reading in this area will find a concise account of the construction and operation of explosive factories in Fordham[51].

However, there are a number of substances not ordinarily classed as explosives which are handled by the process industries and which are capable of undergoing dense-phase detonation. There is also a substance of great commercial importance, ammonium nitrate, which is used both as a fertilizer and as an explosive (see Section 2.10, page 96).

Classification of dense-phase explosives

The classifications of dense-phase explosives by different authors are sometimes inconsistent. The following categories are adopted for this text:

(a) Low explosives — these operate without detonation. They are propellants which were discussed in Section 2.11.4 (page 113).
(b) High explosives — these exhibit detonation. They may be further subdivided:
  (i) primary or initiating explosives;
  (ii) secondary explosives;
  (iii) tertiary explosives.

High explosives are described in more detail in the reference works already cited.

Primary explosives

There are a large number of chemical substances whose enthalpy of formation is positive — that is, they are endothermic — and which are capable of being detonated by heat or mechanical impact. With a few exceptions they are not of military or commercial importance, largely because they are too sensitive. Some are used as catalysts or as intermediates in chemical reactions, or they may be produced as unwanted by-products or accidentally. Examples of the latter are the copper and silver derivatives of ethyne (acetylene).

For substances to be useful as primary explosives they must be stable under conditions of storage but capable of being detonated by heat or impact. They may also be capable of initiating the confined deflagration of propellants as in hand-gun or rifle ammunition or of initiating the detonation of high explosive in a blasting charge or in a bomb or shell.

The most important primary explosive is lead azide. Mercury fulminate was once important but has largely been phased out. Lead azide is unusual for an explosive in that it is an inorganic compound and does not contain oxygen. Its decomposition, which yields lead and nitrogen, does not constitute a redox reaction. There are other chemical substances which behave in a similar way but most are not practicable primary explosives.

The low values of specific enthalpy of detonation of these primary explosives as compared with those of secondary explosives are related to their high molar mass. See Table 2.21.

An important class of substances which are not manufactured to act as explosives but which are intrinsically explosive are the organic peroxides. These are unstable on account of possessing a $-O-O-$ bond, which if broken is a source of oxygen in a very active form. Their parent compound is hydrogen peroxide which is $H-O-O-H$. It appears (see Bretherick[44], Merrifield[61] and Sax[62]) that hydrogen peroxide cannot be detonated on its own, even above 90%, but is capable of explosion if mixed even with traces of a variety of metals and organic compounds. A number of these compounds can be detonated by heat and shock and some by friction, reaching detonation velocities of about $6000 \, m \, s^{-1}$.

Marshall[20], (Appendix IV) gives further details of this class of compounds, including TNT equivalence, which in some cases is as high as 40%. The properties, hazards, uses and safe handling of this class of compounds are discussed in some detail by Medard[41]. There is a case history in Chapter 5 under 'Organic Peroxides' (page 234).

The nature of secondary explosives

Though it is not true of all dense-phase substances capable of detonation, all those used for military or commercial purposes owe their explosive properties to nitrogen atoms in the molecule.

Table 2.21 Properties of mercury fulminate and lead azide

Substance	Enthalpy of detonation $(J \, kg^{-1})$	Detonation velocity $(m \, s^{-1})$
Mercury fulminate [Hg(ONC)$_2$]	-1.79×10^6	3600
Lead azide [Pb(N$_3$)$_2$]	-1.54×10^6	4500

Figure 2.8 shows the chemical formulae of three types of such molecule. These are: (1) so-called 'nitroglycerin' (actually glyceryl trinitrate), which has three nitrate groups, (2) trinitrotoluene (TNT), which has three nitro- groups and (3) RDX which has three nitro- groups and a six-membered ring in which carbon and nitrogen atoms alternate.

The bonds linking the nitrogen atoms break relatively easily, leaving highly active carbon, oxygen and hydrogen atoms which are separated by distances of the order of only 10^{-10} metres and thus allowing internal redox reactions to take place with extreme rapidity. Table 2.22 sets out the key properties of these three explosives, together with ammonium nitrate, which will be separately discussed. The calculations of specific power were based upon the velocity of detonation and upon the assumptions set out later in this chapter. The time taken to detonate such a charge is of the order of 10^{-5} seconds.

It is instructive to compare the specific power of these detonations with the mean electrical output of the USA and Canada, which is approximately 3.5×10^{11} W (inferred from data for 1990 in Foster[63]).

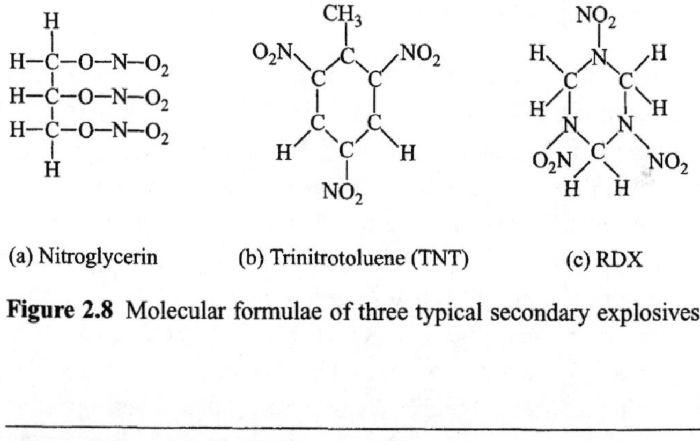

(a) Nitroglycerin   (b) Trinitrotoluene (TNT)   (c) RDX

Figure 2.8 Molecular formulae of three typical secondary explosives

Table 2.22 Properties of some high explosives

Substance	Enthalpy of detonation* $(J\,kg^{-1} \times 10^6)$	Velocity of detonation* $(m\,sec^{-1} \times 10^3)$	Gas released* $(m^3\,kg^{-1})$	Power $(W\,kg^{-1} \times 10^{11})$
Nitroglycerin	−6.29	7.60	0.715	9.6
Trinitrotoluene	−4.23	6.94	0.710	5.9
RDX	−4.54	8.57	0.780	7.8
Ammonium nitrate	−2.63	2.70	0.980	1.4

*These figures are derived from Kirk-Othmer[49] (volume 10).

125

The nature of tertiary explosives

These are substances which, though intrinsically explosive, are very insensitive to shock. When pure they can typically be detonated only by a secondary explosive. Johansson and Persson[64] list three such substances: mono-nitro-toluene, ammonium perchlorate and ammonium nitrate. Sodium chlorate can also be added to this list. Other powerful oxidizing agents may also be candidates for inclusion.

Ammonium nitrate

Though tens of millions of tonnes of ammonium nitrate are used annually as a fertilizer under conditions of safety, ammonium nitrate is also used as an explosive. The detonation of ammonium nitrate is represented approximately by the equation:

$$2NH_4NO_3 \rightarrow 2N_2 + 4H_2O + O_2$$

The following conditions favour the detonation of ammonium nitrate:

(1) admixture with organic substances;
(2) high temperature under confined conditions;
(3) detonation by a secondary explosive.

When mixed with about 5% fuel oil and suitably detonated, ammonium nitrate is widely used as a blasting explosive ('ANFO'). The explosive properties of ammonium nitrate are discussed by Medard[41].

A mixture of ammonium nitrate with TNT has been extensively used as a military explosive under the name of 'Amatol'. Ammonium nitrate is oxygen-rich, whereas TNT is oxygen- deficient. The specific energy release from the mixture is higher on this account than that of either constituent.

There have been a number of incidents in which a large quantity of ammonium nitrate has detonated, as, for example, when heated under confined conditions. Ammonium nitrate is highly hygroscopic and, unless specially formulated, it has a strong tendency to cake. It is essential not to depart from manufacture's instructions when handling it. For case histories see Chapter 5, 'Oppau' (page 233) and 'Texas City' (page 240).

Combustion and detonation: energy releases compared

Some authors claim that the enthalpy of combustion of carbon or hydrocarbons is 10 times the enthalpy of detonation of many explosives. But this is not a valid comparison, as it ignores the fact that oxygen is an essential participant of a redox reaction. When the specific enthalpy of a redox reaction is based on the total mass of the reactants — that is, reducing agent plus oxygen — then the specific enthalpy of such a reaction is only about twice that of the detonation of, say, TNT.

Near-field effects of dense-phase detonations

Though there is no rigid boundary between them, it is convenient to think of there being three concentric zones around a dense-phase detonation.

In the inner zone there is a region of intense pressure of the order of 2 to 3×10^5 bars maximum, with an associated temperature of perhaps 6000 K. This region may be regarded as a plasma consisting of ionized atoms. Only when it expands and cools are the molecules constituting the products formed. The expanding gases radiate outwards, initially at many times the velocity of sound in air. Within the inner zone materials, including any containment, are shattered by this 'wind' and, if the detonation takes place at ground level, the earth is scoured out to form a crater.

This property of shattering is known as 'brisance' from the French *briser* — 'to break'. Explosives vary in brisance; both nitro-glycerin and RDX are more brisant than TNT. It is claimed (Du Pont[65]) that some organic peroxides are brisant. Ammonium nitrate is of relatively low brisance. Brisance shows a general correlation with detonation velocity.

In the next zone, which starts roughly where brisance dies away, the shock wave, which is supersonic relative to air, attenuates into a blast wave which can harm both people and property.

In the third zone, the velocity of the blast wave becomes sonic — it becomes indistinguishable from a sound wave and attenuates according to the inverse square law. The attenuation of blast waves from detonations is further discussed in Chapter 3, which also compares and contrasts blast waves with sound waves. The effects of blast waves upon people and property are discussed further in Chapter 4.

The generation of missiles

Though the materials of which any containment is constructed will be at rest at the moment of a detonation, the 'wind' referred to above will accelerate them. They then constitute *primary missiles*. Although they are only exposed to this wind for a fraction of a second, the wind is so fierce that this short exposure is sufficient to accelerate them to a velocity of thousands of metres per second. However, as the products of the explosion expand, their velocity falls and a time is reached when the missiles are travelling faster than the medium. Thereafter their velocity will diminish as atmospheric drag causes them to decelerate. This phase is discussed in Chapter 3.

As well as accelerating portions of the containment, the 'wind' may also accelerate soil or rock from the ground or detach materials from nearby structures. These will constitute *secondary missiles*. Laws governing the acceleration of missiles are developed in works such as Baker *et al.*[18].

2.14 Deflagrations and detonations – specific power compared

2.14.1 Specific energy

The specific enthalpy changes (based on the mass of reactants) of the reactions for which we have calculated specific power fall in a band between -1.54×10^6 (the detonation of lead azide) and -1.34×10^7 (the reaction between hydrogen and oxygen). For purposes of generalization it is convenient to use typical values of $-10^7 \, \mathrm{J\,kg^{-1}}$ for the combustion of stoichiometric mixtures of many reducing agents in air, and of $-5 \times 10^6 \, \mathrm{J\,kg^{-1}}$ for high explosives.

2.14.2 Calculation of specific power

The specific power of an explosive may be estimated as the product of its specific enthalpy of detonation with the velocity of advance of the reaction front divided by an appropriate characteristic dimension, or

$$P_s = \Delta H_s V_p / L_c \tag{2.33}$$

Dimensionally, $P_s = (E/M) \times (L\theta^{-1})/L = EM^{-1}\theta^{-1}$ (where E is energy, with fundamental dimensions $ML^2\theta^{-2}$).

Though specific enthalpy changes may be extracted from tables of data, specific power thus depends also on a characteristic dimension and hence on the geometry of the system in which the reaction takes place. It is not possible to devise a standard geometry for all systems, but we have sought to produce approximate equivalence of treatment. Thus for confined deflagrations, explosive deflagrations and detonations the characteristic dimension is the radius of the sphere which would contain 1 kg of reactant(s) before reaction.

For unconfined deflagrations it is assumed that the volume of the sphere would increase as a result of the expansion of the products of reaction by a factor of eight, and that hence the radius would increase by a factor of two. This would make the power of an unconfined deflagration half that of a confined deflagration which did not rupture its container.

Table 2.23 Typical parameters of deflagrations and detonations

Description of realization	ΔH_s $(\mathrm{J\,kg^{-1}})$	V_p $(\mathrm{m\,s^{-1}})$	L_c (m)	P_s $(\mathrm{W\,kg^{-1}})$
Unconfined deflagrations gas/air	-10^7	1	2	5×10^6
Unconfined deflagrations dust/air	-10^7	1	2	5×10^6
Confined deflagrations gas/air	-10^7	1	1	10^7
Confined deflagrations dust/air	-10^7	1	1	10^7
Explosive deflagrations	-10^7	2×10^2	2	10^9
Gas-phase detonations	-10^7	2×10^3	1	2×10^{10}
Unconfined propellants	-5×10^6	10^{-2}	5×10^{-2}	10^6
Confined propellants	-5×10^6	5×10^1	5×10^{-2}	5×10^9
Dense-phase detonations	-5×10^6	5×10^3	5×10^{-2}	5×10^{11}

There are no accurate figures for specific power but, by using an approximate value for each group of reactions, it is aimed to indicate the great range in order of magnitude of the power of the redox reactions under consideration. Thus between unconfined gas/air deflagrations and the detonation of high explosives the specific power differs by a factor of 2×10^5. If the comparison is extended to the burning of coal (see Section 2.10.5, page 100), the factor becomes 2×10^9.

Though it would be possible to calculate specific values based upon the data and assumptions set out above, a set of typical values for ΔH_s, V_p and L_c (the characteristic dimension) to give an overview of the order of magnitude of these parameters is displayed. Thus in Table 2.23 the figures in the final column are calculated from equation (2.33), taking the modulus to eliminate the negative sign.

References in Chapter 2

1. Health and Safety Commission, 1979, *Second Report of the Advisory Committee on Major Hazards* (HMSO, London).

2. Jones, D. (ed), 1992, *Nomenclature for Hazard and Risk Assessment in the Process Industries* (IChemE, UK).

3. Phillips, H. (ed), 1994, *Explosions in the Process Industries*. Report of the Major Hazards Assessment Panel (Overpressure Working Party) (IChemE, UK).

4. CCPS, 1989, *Guidelines for Process Equipment Reliability Data with Data Tables* (AIChE (Center for Chemical Process Safety), USA).

5. Green, A.E. and Bourne, A.J., 1972, *Reliability Technology* (Wiley Interscience, UK).

6. Davenport, T., 1991, *A Further Survey of Pressure Vessel Failures in the UK* (Elsevier, UK).

7. Gordon, J. E., 1991, *The New Science of Strong Materials: Or, Why You Don't Fall Through The Floor*, 2nd edn (Penguin, UK).

8. ACDS, 1991, *Major Hazard Aspects of the Transport of Dangerous Substances* (HMSO (Advisory Committee on Dangerous Substances), UK).

9. Lindley, J., 1987, *User Guide for the Safe Operation of Centrifuges* (IChemE, UK).

10. Perry, R.H., Green, D.W. and Maloney, J.O. (eds), 1997, *Perry's Chemical Engineers' Handbook*, 7th edn (McGraw-Hill, USA).

11. Crowl, D.A. and Louver, J.F., 1990, *Chemical Process Safety: Fundamentals with Applications* (Prentice-Hall, USA).

12. Wilkinson, W.L., 1960, *Non-Newtonian Fluids* (Pergamon, UK).

13. Barnes, H.A., Hutton, J.F. and Walters, K., 1989, *An Introduction to Rheology* (Elsevier, The Netherlands).

14. Dooner, R. and Marshall, V.C., 1989, Pressure testing and its hazards, *Loss Prevention Bulletin*, No 86 (April): 5.

15. Kaye and Laby, 1995, *Tables of Physical and Chemical Constants*, Asher, J. (ed.) (originally compiled by G.W.C. Kaye and T.H. Laby), 16th edn (Longman, UK).

16. Rogers, G.F.C. and Mayhew, Y.R., 1988, *Thermodynamic and Transport Properties of Fluids*, 4th edn (Basil Blackwell, UK).

17. Baker, W.E., 1973, *Explosions in Air* (University of Texas Press, UK).

18. Baker, W.E., Cox, P.A., Westine, P.S., Kulesz, J.J. and Strehlow, R.A., 1983, *Explosion Hazards and Evaluation* (Elsevier, The Netherlands).

19. Shreve, R.N., Norris, R. and Basta, N., 1993, *Shreve's Chemical Process Industries Handbook*, 6th edn (revised by N. Basta) (McGraw-Hill, USA).

20. Marshall, V.C., 1987, *Major Chemical Hazards* (Ellis Horwood, UK).

21. Major Hazards Assessment Panel, 1989, *Thermal Radiation Monograph: Calculation of the Intensity of Thermal Radiation from Large Fires* (IChemE, UK).

22. Roberts, A., 1982, The effect of conditions prior to loss of containment on fireball behaviour, *IChemE Symposium Series No 71* (IChemE, UK).

23. Moorhouse, J. and Pritchard, M.J., 1982, Thermal radiation hazards from large pool fires and fireballs — a literature review, *IChemE Symposium Series No 71*, pp. 129–137

24. High, R.W., 1968, The Saturn fireball, *Annals New York Academy of Sciences*, 152 (1) 441–451.

25. Marshall, V.C., 1977, Chemical conurbations, the domino danger, in *Chemical Engineering in a Hostile World, Birmingham, UK, 20 June.*

26. Weast, R.C. (ed), *Handbook of Chemistry and Physics*, CRC Handbook (Series), Cleveland: Chemical Rubber Company (revised annually).

27. Atkins, P.W., 1994, *Physical Chemistry*, 5th edn (OUP, UK).

28. Smith, J.M. and Van Ness, H.C., 1987, *Introduction to Chemical Engineering Thermodynamics*, 4th edn (McGraw-Hill, UK).

29. IChemE, 1981, Runaway reactions, unstable products and combustible powders, *Symposium Series No 68* (IChemE, UK).

30. IChemE, 1987, Hazards from pressure: exothermic reactions, unstable substances, pressure relief and accidental discharge, *Symposium Series No 102* (IChemE, UK).

31. Barton, J. and Rogers, R., 1997, *Chemical Reaction Hazards — A Guide to Safety*, (eds) 2nd edn (IChemE, UK).

32. Anon, 1993, The challenge of Asia, *Economist*, March 13, pp. 25–28.

33. Kletz, T.A., 1993, *Cheaper, Safer Plants or Wealth and Safety at Work* (IChemE, UK).

34. Sawyer, P., 1993, *Computer-Controlled Batch Processing* (IChemE, UK).

35. Westerterp, K.R., Van Swaaij, W.P.M. and Beenackers, A.A.C.M., 1984, *Chemical Reactor Design and Operation*, Student edn (Wiley).

36. Fogler, H.S., 1991, *Elements of Chemical Reaction Engineering*, 2nd edn (Prentice-Hall, USA).

37. Taffanel, J. and Le Floch, G., 1913, *Comptes rendus ac.sc.* 156: 1544; 157: 469.

38. Semenov, N.N., 1959, *Some Problems of Chemical Kinetics and Reactivity*, vol 2, translated by J.E.S. Bradley (Pergamon, UK).

39. Boddington, T., Gray, P. and Harvey, D.I., 1971, *Phil Trans Roy Soc London*, vol 270: 467–506.

40. Barnard, J.A. and Bradley, J.N., 1985, *Flame and Combustion*, 2nd edn (Chapman and Hall, UK).

41. Medard, L.A., 1989, *Accidental Explosions*, 2 vols (Ellis Horwood, UK).

42. White, H.L., 1986, *Introduction to Industrial Chemistry* (Wiley, USA), pp.168–172.

43. Barton, J.A. and Nolan, P.F., 1989, Incidents in the chemical industry due to thermal-runaway chemical reactions, *Hazards X: Process Safety in Fine and Speciality Chemical Plants, IChemE Symposium Series No 115*, pp. 1–17 (IChemE, UK).

44. Bretherick, L., 1995, *Handbook of Reactive Chemicals Hazards* (edited by P.G. Urban), 5th edn, 2 vols (Butterworth-Heinemann, UK).

45. Health and Safety Commission, 1979, *Second Report of the Advisory Committee on Major Hazards* (HMSO, UK).

46. Tuhtar, D., 1989, *Fire and Explosion Protection: A Systems Approach* (Ellis Horwood, UK).

47. Stull, D.R., 1977, Fundamentals of Fire and Explosion, *AIChE Monograph Series, 73(10)* (AIChE, USA).

48. Bond, J., 1991, *Sources of Ignition* (Butterworth-Heinemann, UK).

49. Harris, R.J., 1983, *The Investigation and Control of Gas Explosions in Buildings and Heating Plant* (E & F Spon in association with the British Gas Corporation).

50. Kirk, R.E., Othmer, D.F., Kroschwitz, J.I. and Howe-Grant, M. (eds), 1993, *Kirk-Othmer Encyclopedia of Chemical Technology*, 4th edn (Wiley, USA).

51. Fordham, S., 1980, *High Explosives and Propellants* (Pergamon, UK).

52. Eckhoff, R.K., 1997, *Dust Explosions in the Process Industries*, 2nd edn (Butterworth-Heinemann, UK).
53. Hodges, P., 1981 *The Big Gun* (Conway Maritime Press, UK).
54. Strehlow, R.A., 1973, Unconfined vapour-cloud explosions — an overview, in *14th Int Symposium on Combustion*, The Combustion Institute, pp. 1189–1200.
55. Zeeuwen, J.P., Van Wingerden, C.J.M. and Dauwe, R.M., 1983, Experimental investigation into the blast effect produced by unconfined vapour cloud explosions, *IChemE Symposium Series No 80*, pp. D20–D29 (IChemE, UK).
56. Harrison, A.J. and Eyre, J.A., 1987, The effect of obstacle arrays on the combustion of large pre-mixed gas/air clouds, *Combustion Science and Technology*, 52: 121–137.
57. Van Wingerden, C.J.M., 1989, Experimental investigation into the strength of blast waves generated by vapour cloud explosions in congested areas, *6th International Symposium on Loss Prevention and Safety Promotion in the Process Industries, Oslo, Norway,* June 19–22, 26-1/26–16.
58. Harris, R.J. and Wickens, M.J., 1989, Understanding vapour cloud explosions — an experimental study, *Paper presented to the 55th Autumn Meeting, Institution of Gas Engineers*, 28 November.
59. MEST, 1997, *McGraw-Hill Encyclopedia of Science & Technology*, 8th edn, 20 vols (McGraw-Hill, USA).
60. Gugan, K., 1979, *Unconfined Vapour Cloud Explosions* (IChemE, UK).
61. Merrifield, R., 1988, *Fire and Explosion Hazards Associated with the Storage and Handling of Hydrogen Peroxide*, Report No 19 (Health and Safety Executive, UK).
62. Lewis, R.J. and Sax, N.I., 1996, *Sax's Dangerous Properties of Industrial Materials*, 9th edn (Van Nostrand Reinhold, USA).
63. Foster, J.S., 1993, Global electricity demand and supply trends, in *Power generation choices: Proceedings, International Symposium, Washington, USA, 23–24 September* (PARIS: Organisation for European Co-operation and Development).
64. Johansson, C.H. and Persson, P.A., 1970, *Detonetics of High Explosives* (Academic Press, USA).
65. Du Pont, 1962, *Hydrogen Peroxide in Organic Chemistry* (Du Pont Inc, Electrochemical Dept, Wilmington, USA).

Transmission paths and attenuation

3

3.1 General principles

3.1.1 Transmission paths

In Chapter 1, following Marshall and Ruhemann[1], the concepts of transmission path, attenuation and barrier were introduced. We now present the following definition of the term *transmission path*:

> **Transmission path** — a medium by which, or through which, the harm from a hazard source is transmitted to a hazard receptor.

This definition is equivalent to the biomedical concept of a *vector*. We might well have adopted that term for the present purpose, but for objections arising from its different uses in other contexts such as in mechanics where it is used to describe entities such as velocity, which characteristically have attributes of both magnitude and direction.

3.1.2 Attenuation

In the most general case, harm emitted from a hazard source will, during transmission, diminish in intensity with increasing distance from the source. As indicated in Section 1.2.4 (page 13), this diminution is referred to by the ordinary dictionary word *attenuation*.

Attenuation may be quantified by a dimensionless factor α, defined by equation (3.1):

$$\phi_d = \phi_u(1 - \alpha) \tag{3.1}$$

where ϕ_u, ϕ_d are the upstream and downstream fluxes (of energy or of matter) respectively, and α has a value between zero and 1.0.

Attenuation is almost always a concomitant of transmission by the transmission path, but it may also occur through the intervention of barriers, which are obstructions interposed between the source and a receptor. The suffixes *TP* and *B* are ascribed to the corresponding attenuation factors. If, then, the flux of an emission at the source is ϕ_s, the attenuated flux ϕ at any downstream cross-section of the transmission path will be given by:

$$\phi = \phi_s(1 - \alpha_{TP})(1 - \alpha_B) \tag{3.2}$$

where,

α_{TP} is the factor for attenuation due to transmission paths [number]
α_B is the factor for attenuation due to barriers [number]

The role played by these factors in the assessment of individual risk and societal risk is shown in Chapter 6.

The mechanisms of attenuation differ according to the natures of the emission, of the medium and/or of any barriers. Some of them are very complex and difficult to analyse, especially where mixtures of different substances are involved. There is an extensive literature, most of which is too advanced for detailed discussion in this text (see, for example, Carter[2]). An introductory description of some of these mechanisms is given below.

3.1.3 Amplification

In those cases where the harm results in the realization of secondary hazards, the transmission path may amplify the harm. This is most commonly encountered in the spread of fire. In such cases it is necessary to analyse the resultant harm as a separate and additional realization.

3.1.4 Forms of attenuation

Geometrical attenuation

This book is concerned only with non-coherent radiation; discussion of the behaviour of lasers lies outside its scope.

Consider a system comprising a point source of non-coherent electromagnetic radiation which radiates uniformly in all directions in a medium which is totally transparent to the radiation.

The radiation from such a source is attenuated according to the well known *inverse square* law. If the point source is imagined to be the centre of a number of concentric spherical shells the principle of the conservation of energy implies that the total quantity of radiation energy passing through successive shells is constant. Now the surface area of each successive spherical shell (which is the cross-sectional area of the radiation path) is directly proportional to the square of its radius ($A = 4\pi r^2$). The intensity (radiative flux) ϕ, which is power per unit area, is accordingly attenuated as the square of the radius of the shell; attenuation is thus determined by the *geometry* of the system.

In other circumstances, in which the radiation does not take place uniformly in all directions, for example because of the shape of the source, the geometry of the system is different. The attenuation is then still determined by geometrical factors but the inverse square law may not apply exactly. The discussion of what are termed *view factors* may be found in standard works on heat transfer but it lies outside the scope of this book. A further exception, related to non-coherent radiation, is where wave guides are employed, as in fibre optics.

For most situations in which there are releases of pressure energy of the nature discussed in Section 2.5 (page 40) the inverse square law is approximately applicable. There are, however, some situations involving the release of pressure energy in which the geometry approximates to that of the wave guide. An example of this is the transmission of a blast wave down a pipeline or a gallery.

Attenuation by absorption of energy

When discussing geometrical attenuation *transparency* was referred to. The inverse square law can apply exactly only if the medium is transparent to the radiation. If the medium is not transparent, it will absorb some of the energy transmitted. This causes additional attenuation, and also leads to an increase in the enthalpy of the medium, which is typically manifested as an increase in its temperature.

Attenuation by dilution

This applies to the transmission of thermal energy by convection. Where the medium is hot, as in a flame, dilution with further quantities of the medium at ambient temperature will attenuate its harm by cooling it.

A second case is that of the intensity of the harm being related to the *concentration* of a harmful substance. Dilution of the substance by the atmosphere reduces the concentration, and thus attenuates the harm.

3.1.5 Directions of transmission paths

The atmosphere and radiation

It will be assumed that the radiation of thermal energy is governed solely by the laws of radiation and is independent of the movement of the atmosphere — that is, wind strength and direction.

The atmosphere and blast waves

It will be assumed that wind strength and direction have little effect on the propagation of blast waves.

The atmosphere and gas dispersion

The direction of gas dispersion depends on the direction of the wind and upon the local topography (relief), including plant and buildings.

Water and spilled liquids

This is dependent upon local topography. Spilled liquids will flow under gravity and, if they enter water, will flow along its surface. If the water is moving, they will be conveyed by it.

3.2 The atmosphere as a transmission path

3.2.1 How the atmosphere acts as a transmission path

When assessing the atmosphere as a transmission path, there are four main characteristics to consider:

(1) its transparency to electro-magnetic radiation (this is significant for the transmission of heat radiation);
(2) its elastic properties (these are significant for the transmission of blast waves);
(3) its resistance to the passage of moving objects (this is significant for predicting the ranges of missiles);
(4) its stability and velocity (these are significant for predicting the dispersion of discharged gases or vapours).

3.2.2 Transparency

It is a matter of common observation that the atmosphere displays a great range of transparency to visible light and to thermal radiation. At times the sun shines brilliantly out of a clear sky and at other times it is invisible because of cloud or mist — the intensities of both its light and its heat are diminished.

For similar reasons the radiative flux at a receptor from a pool fire or a fireball may be less than that predicted by the calculations set out in Section 2.6 (page 57) after allowing for geometrical attenuation. However, since this additional attenuation by absorption is so dependent on variable and unpredictable meteorological conditions, it cannot be relied upon, and prudence suggests that one should not make allowances for it when calculating attenuation.

136

3.2.3 Blast waves

A brief introduction to this subject was given in Chapter 2 and is now expanded by a point-by-point comparison of blast waves with sound waves. It is assumed that students have some familiarity with the subject of the propagation of sound waves, and any reader who does not have this knowledge is encouraged to consult an elementary textbook of physics. Blast waves from explosions resemble sound waves in some respects but in other respects they are different. A blast wave from a dense explosive will be contrasted with a sound wave of constant frequency. Blast waves and sound waves lie at opposite ends of the spectrum of intensity. The former attenuate into the latter but obviously the reverse does not occur.

Basic nature

Both are forms of *longitudinal wave motion* — that is, in both cases, the vibration or displacement takes place in the direction of propagation of the waves[3]. In both cases one or more pressure pulses are followed by one or more pulses of rarefaction.

Velocity of propagation

Sound waves propagate at a constant velocity (sonic velocity = ca. $330\,\mathrm{m\,s}^{-1}$ in air at $0°C$) and without displacement of the medium. Blast waves may propagate at a velocity of more than ten times the velocity of sound, and they displace the medium, creating a 'wind'. This wind is extremely destructive: it shatters any containment and the component of it directed to the ground usually scours out a crater.

Amplitude

Blast waves have a vastly greater amplitude than ordinary sound waves (this is measured by their peak overpressure).

Mode of attenuation

The propagation of a blast wave is far removed from being an adiabatic process and hence attenuation exceeds that associated with the inverse square law. The attenuation of sound waves corresponds very closely with adiabatic conditions and is governed by the inverse square law.

The form of the wave

A blast wave consists, essentially, of a singe pulse of pressure followed by a single pulse of rarefaction. A sound wave consists of multiple alternating pulses of pressure and rarefaction. A sound wave with pitch of middle C, sustained for one second, comprises 264 such alternating pulses.

If the pressure of a blast wave is registered at a point of observation and plotted against time, the graph will show an extremely rapid initial rise followed by a much slower falling off to atmospheric pressure and then by a pulse of rarefaction as illustrated in Figure 3.1.

This 'double pulse' is highly asymmetrical. Although in the 'positive phase' the pressure above atmospheric (this is called *overpressure*) may exceed 10^5 bars, clearly, even if the rarefaction were to produce a complete vacuum (which is impossible), the rarefaction could not exceed 1 bar. The form of sound waves, on the other hand, corresponds with simple harmonic motion, the overpressure and the 'underpressure' being equal. This produces a sine curve as shown in Figure 3.2 (note that the pressure axis is to a very much larger scale than that in Figure 3.1 — the numbers are arbitrary).

Blast waves eventually attenuate into sound waves and take on their character. However, because of reflections (echoes), the sound of a distant explosion is extended and becomes a succession of overlapping waves. Thunder is an example of this — it is an explosion produced by an electrical discharge, which at short range registers as a sharp crack but in the distance becomes a prolonged rumble.

The properties of blast waves

A considerable number of characteristic properties are associated with blast waves. These are discussed very thoroughly in Baker[4], and only those which are most important in relation to this subject are considered here, namely *overpressure* and *impulse*.

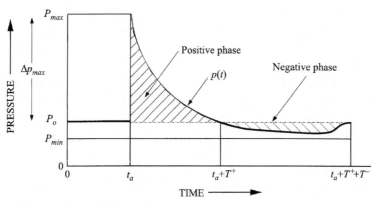

Figure 3.1 A typical blast wave

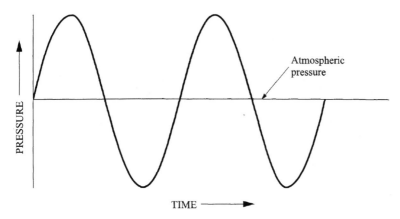

Figure 3.2 The form of a sound wave

Jones[5] defines *overpressure* as follows:

Overpressure — for a pressure pulse [blast wave] the pressure developed above atmospheric pressure at any stage or location is called the over-pressure.

As a measure of *pressure difference*, it has the dimensions of force per unit area ($ML^{-1}T^{-2}$).

Jones[5] also provides subsidiary definitions:

Peak positive overpressure — the maximum overpressure developed is called the peak positive over pressure.

Side-on overpressure — if a pressure-sensitive device which offered no obstruction to the passage of the blast wave were placed in its path (i.e. one which was facing sideways in relation to its advance), the device would record side-on over pressure.

Baker *et al.*[4] give the following definition of *impulse* (expressed in verbal terms):

Impulse — the integral of the pressure/time history of a blast wave. Impulse has dimensions of momentum per unit area ($ML^{-1}T^{-1}$).

Hopkinson's scaling law

This Law[6] enables a number of variables to be plotted against a parameter known as *scaled distance*. These variables include *overpressure* and *impulse*, as defined above. They are very important factors in predicting the harm to people and property arising from explosions, as shown in Chapter 4.

Though very little seems to be known about Hopkinson, or how he arrived at his Scaling Law in 1915, it has proved to be a very powerful correlation. It has been shown to be applicable over an enormous range from a few grams of conventional explosive to megatonne nuclear weapons. Sachs[7] later formulated a more general law by 'normalizing' the parameters to express them in dimensionless form.

Hopkinson's Law has since been rigorously proved, using dimensional analysis, in Baker[4]. The Law makes it possible, for a given dense explosive, to present, in a single curve, the attenuation of the blast for any quantity of explosive. It is also possible to use this curve to predict the attenuation of the blast from a charge of an explosive with a different but known specific blast energy.

Statement of Hopkinson's Law

Jones[5] does not discuss Hopkinson's Law, though there are definitions of it in Baker[4] and Baker[8]. A general definition of it is:

'Where two charges of the same explosive, of similar geometry, and with surroundings of similar geometry, are detonated in similar atmospheres, the radial distances from the centres of the explosive charges corresponding to specified effects of these detonations are proportional to the cube root of the blast energy released in each case.'

Thus

$$R = E_B^{0.333} \times Z_E \tag{3.3}$$

or

$$Z_E = R/E_B^{0.333} \tag{3.4}$$

where,

R — radial distance corresponding to a specified effect

E_B — blast energy released

Z_E — *scaled distance* expressed in terms of *energy* [dimensions $L/(ML^2T^{-2})^{0.333}$].

Field trials have demonstrated that Hopkinson's Law is applicable to explosions with energy levels ranging over six orders of magnitude — that is, a ratio of 10^6 to 1).

Hopkinson himself did not express his Law as presented in equations (3.3) and (3.4): he found it convenient to substitute the *mass* of the explosive for the *blast energy* it releases. This is feasible for dense chemical explosives (though not for nuclear explosives) because the blast energy (E_B) of a charge of such an explosive is the product of the *specific* blast energy of the material (E_{SB}) and its mass (M).

E_{SB} is taken for TNT to be $-4.2 \times 10^6 \, \text{J kg}^{-1}$ (see Table 2.22, page 125). Some authorities put this value somewhat higher but, since Hopkinson's Law involves only the cube root of E_{SB}, the resulting error is negligible.

There are a number of sources which give values of E_{SB} for different explosives and reactive substances. Some values are given in Table 2.22 and there are others in Baker[8] and in Phillips[9].

Substituting mass for energy gives the following expression of Hopkinson's Law:

$$R = M^{0.333} \times Z_M \tag{3.5}$$

or

$$Z_M = R/M^{0.333} \tag{3.6}$$

where $Z_M = scaled\ distance$ expressed in terms of *mass* [dimensions $L/(ML^2T^{-2})^{0.333}$]

'Scaled distance' is not an entirely satisfactory term for these parameters, as it implies that they are ratios of distances and therefore dimensionless, whereas that is not so. The term will, however, be used here as it is deeply embedded in the literature. Where the literature uses the term Z without subscript this denotes Z_M as that is its usual meaning, and this practice will be followed here.

Application of Hopkinson's Law

As already noted, among the effects to which Hopkinson's Law relates are *overpressure* and *impulse*.

A typical Hopkinson's Law plot is given in Figure 3.3 overleaf. In it the logarithm of side-on overpressure is plotted as ordinate, against the logarithm of scaled distance as abscissa, for a ground-burst charge of TNT. Such data have been obtained from extensive military field trials. There is a good deal of scatter in them, and a 'best fit' line is shown.

As noted in this formulation of Hopkinson's Law, the geometry of the surroundings must also be similar for the blast waves to be similar. In many process plant situations the explosion of dense explosives approximates to the *ground-burst* conditions represented in Figure 3.3. In these circumstances, the blast wave striking the earth is reflected and thus amplifies the incident wave. Consequently, a given value of overpressure at any distance will result from the explosion of a charge of about one half the size that would produce the same effect in a spherically symmetrical air burst (this multiplier may be reduced to

141

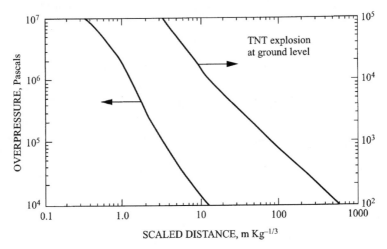

Figure 3.3 Hopkinson Plot: peak side-on overpressure versus scaled distance (for hemispheres of TNT detonated at ground level). (Source: Phillips, H. (ed), 1994, *Explosions in the Process Industries* (IChemE, UK).

about $1/1.8$ if a significant proportion of the blast energy released is dissipated in crater formation). This subject is discussed further in Baker[4], Baker[8] and Phillips[9].

If an explosive has a specific blast energy relative to TNT of X then the scaled distance at which the same effect may be produced for this explosive would be the scaled distance for TNT (whether based on mass or on energy) multiplied by $X^{0.333}$.

Where, however, the explosive differs in characteristics from TNT — for example, in detonation velocity, as does gunpowder which has a much lower value — Figure 3.3 would give only approximate results even if adjusted for differing specific blast energy. (See earlier note on values of specific blast energy for different explosive substances).

The attenuation of rarefied explosions

Where the differences are wide, as for example in comparing vapour cloud explosions, or blast waves from disintegrating pressure vessels, with TNT explosions, Figure 3.3 is at best a crude approximation. Rarefied explosions differ from dense explosions in the following ways:

(1) Their maximum peak overpressure is only a tiny fraction of that of dense explosions — for a vapour cloud explosion it is of the order of 1 bar and for pressure vessels it is likely to be less than 10 bar. Consequently they

have low *brisance* or shattering power and show little capacity for forming craters.

(2) They are far from being 'point sources', being, on the contrary, rather diffuse. Broadly speaking, for a given energy release, their effects will be smaller at the centre and greater in the far field.

(3) When they have the same impulse as a dense explosion this impulse will be characterized by a much lower overpressure and a much longer duration.

It would, however, be going beyond the scope of this book to discuss the attenuation of rarefied explosions in detail. The subject is referred in general terms in Chapter 4. It is discussed in detail elsewhere, for example, in Phillips[9].

3.2.4 Atmospheric resistance to moving objects

The effects of atmospheric drag are considered on two kinds of missile — those generated by an explosion and those generated by the disintegration of moving machinery.

Missiles from explosions

The generation of missiles by explosions was discussed in Chapter 2, Section 2.13 (page 121), and it was noted that they have velocities which range up to thousands of metres per second. The range of effect of the wind which arises from detonations was not considered there but, in the light of the above account of Hopkinson's Law, it can now be stated that its maximum range corresponds to a scaled distance Z_M of ca. 1.3.

The theory of the retardation by the atmosphere of missiles moving at such velocities lies in the field of fluid mechanics. The detailed study of this subject is outside the scope of this book, and it will be discussed only in a qualitative way. Students are referred, for further study, to any of the numerous available textbooks.

The initial deceleration of fast-moving missiles in the atmosphere is very rapid, and the missiles may consequently become very hot. Eventually, at low velocities, air resistance may become negligible.

Much depends upon the shape of the missile. Heavy missiles with an approximately spherical shape, and hence with a low surface-to-mass ratio, are least affected by atmospheric drag. Conversely, sheet materials which have a high surface-to-mass ratio are affected much more. Where the body is flat it may experience *lift*, which enhances its trajectory. Missiles may spin or tumble over in flight.

143

For relatively slow-moving missiles of low atmospheric drag, the horizontal range is approximated by:

$$R = [V^2 \sin(2\theta)]/g \qquad (3.7)$$

where,
R — range of missile;
v — projection velocity;
θ — angle to the horizontal at which missile is projected;
g — acceleration of gravity.

A maximum value of R occurs when θ is 45° ($\sin 2\theta = 1.0$). Conversely, if an incident is being investigated, the above equation can be rearranged to make an approximate estimate of the projection velocity of a missile for a known range:

$$V = [Rg/ \sin(2\theta)]^{0.5} \geq [Rg]^{0.5} \qquad (3.8)$$

Then V would have a minimum value at $\theta = 45°$.

Extensive studies of the ranges of missiles have been carried out by military researchers. The angle of projection is a very significant factor — thus, only a fraction of missiles achieve the maximum range, which can be several kilo-metres for large explosions. Missiles with a low angle of projection may bounce on hitting the ground (*ricochet*).

Primary missiles from dense explosions may be very small. Baker[4] suggests that they may have a mass as small as a gram. Pressurized receivers containing liquefied vapours or compressed gases usually generate relatively few, but correspondingly large, missiles. The initial velocities of such missiles are much lower than those of missiles arising from dense explosives, and their range may be up to several hundred metres. Baker[8] analyses such disintegrations and concludes that initial velocities may be around sonic velocity.

For a description of the fragmentation of a container of pressurized vapour see Chapter 5 under the heading 'Spanish campsite disaster' (page 237).

Missiles from moving machinery

The disintegration of any kind of moving machinery may generate missiles, but the greatest hazards from this source arise from the high-speed rotating machinery discussed in Chapter 2, Section 2.4 (page 36).

Missiles from rotating machinery differ from those arising from detonations mainly in that:

(1) they have sub-sonic initial velocities;
(2) their initial velocities are much more predictable.

Atmospheric drag on such missiles plays a less significant role than it does in the flight of missiles from detonations because they are moving relatively slowly. They come to rest through collision with static objects or through friction with the ground, or some combination of these.

3.2.5 Gas dispersion

For brevity in this subsection, the term 'gas' is used to mean either gas or vapour, according to the physical properties of the substance concerned.

The importance of understanding gas dispersion

It is important to understand how gas clouds disperse in order to be able to predict the distance to which such a cloud may remain flammable or the toxic concentration to which people, both on-site and off-site, may be subjected.

In Chapter 2, the principal realizations of hazards in the process industries were discussed. Some of these realizations took the form of the loss of containment of gases, or of liquids which could give rise to vapours. Where such loss of containment would lead to the emission of energy within a short range of the point at which the loss of containment occurred, these effects are discussed in Chapter 2. Such effects typically have been emissions of blast energy or of thermal energy consequent upon ignition. The behaviour of clouds of gas formed in this way, when these were either non-flammable or, if flammable, were not ignited at the point of release, were not mentioned. The mechanisms by which such clouds disperse and how, in dispersing, they transport harmful effects to more distant receptors will now be considered.

A fully comprehensive treatment of the atmosphere as a transmission path would include a discussion of the conveying of liquids in the form of droplets (aerosols) and of solids in the form of dust. In both cases the droplet/particle size is a major factor. In this book, gas dispersion is concerned with two phases — the atmosphere and an induced gas.

Fundamental studies

A quantitative understanding of the factors which determine the mechanisms of gas dispersion requires a knowledge of the principles of fluid mechanics. Fluid mechanics is defined in PDS[3] as follows:

Fluid mechanics — the study of gases and liquids at rest (fluid statics) and motion (fluid dynamics).

It also requires a knowledge of *mass transfer*, which is fundamental to an understanding of mixing. Mass transfer is defined as follows:

145

Mass transfer — a process in which one or more components of two discrete phases are transferred between the phases.

Since the process takes place in the open air, it requires an understanding of *meteorology*, which also depends on a knowledge of a highly specialized area of fluid mechanics.

It is impossible to treat gas dispersion *quantitatively* without a knowledge of fluid mechanics and mass transfer at an advanced level. Since readers are not expected to possess this knowledge, treatment remains at the *qualitative* level. Reference sources are provided which point the way to more advanced and quantitative study. A key reference is CCPS[10].

For the reasons given, responsibility for predicting the effects of the spillages of hazardous gases is usually entrusted to specialist safety professionals, who nowadays make extensive use of computer modelling.

Transport and attenuation

Clouds are generally dispersed by atmospheric agencies, particularly wind. This means that the *range* at which they are able to harm people or property may be increased. At the same time, because they *mix with*, and are thus *diluted by*, the air, their harmful effects are attenuated.

It is apparent that all gas clouds are hazardous when close to the point of discharge, but that at some distant point they have ceased to be hazardous on account of dilution. The degree of dilution required to render a cloud harmless depends upon the harmful property considered.

All gases, except for oxygen, are asphyxiants — that is, they may cause death by depriving people of oxygen. A dilution with approximately twice or three times their volume of air will remove this effect. With flammable clouds, depending upon their range of flammability, dilution with 10 to 40 times the volume of air will generally be sufficient to remove their flammable properties. Even so, such clouds may have a range of harm which can extend into the public domain. Toxics may need dilution with up to 10^5 times their volume of air before they cease to be harmful. Their range of harm may accordingly extend well into the public domain.

Buoyancy

The density of a gas relative to the atmosphere is the most significant factor influencing gas dispersion. Following the discussion of this topic in Section 2.6 (page 57), the term *buoyant* is used to describe a gas which, after spillage, has a density significantly less than that of the atmosphere, the term *neutrally buoyant* to describe a gas which, after spillage, has a density roughly equal to that of the atmosphere, and the term *negatively buoyant* for a gas which, after spillage, has a density significantly greater than that of the atmosphere.

It should be borne in mind that the density — and hence the buoyancy — of a gas depends not only on its intrinsic properties but also on its temperature, and that a change of temperature can alter its character from negative to positive buoyancy and *vice versa*.

As defined, only 10 gases are buoyant when at the same temperature as the atmosphere, and three of these would be encountered only in small or minute quantities. A list of these buoyant gases is given along with some neutrally, and some negatively buoyant gases, in Table 3.1.

Table 3.1 Buoyancy of some gases at ambient temperature

Gas	Formula	State	Molar mass (kg mol^{-1})	Relative density	Buoyancy category
Hydrogen	H_2	G	2	0.07	+
Deuterium	D_2	G	4	0.14	+
Helium	He	G	4	0.14	+
Tritium	T_2	G	6	0.21	+
Methane	CH_4	G	16	0.55	+
Ammonia	NH_3	V	17	0.59	+
Water	H_2O	V	18	0.62	+
Neon	Ne	G	20.2	0.70	+
Ethyne	C_2H_2	G	26	0.90	+
Hydrogen cyanide	HCN	V	27	0.94	+
Ethene	C_2H_4	G	28	0.97	0
Nitrogen	N_2	G	28	0.97	0
Carbon monoxide	CO	G	28	0.97	0
Air [dry]		G	28.8	1.00	0
Ethane	C_2H_6	V	30	1.04	0
Methanal	HCHO	V	30	1.04	0
Nitric oxide	NO	G	30	1.04	0
Oxygen	O_2	G	32	1.11	—
Fluorine	F_2	G	38	1.32	—
Chlorine	Cl_2	V	71	2.46	—
Phosgene	$COCl_2$	V	99	3.43	—

Notes
(1) The table is based upon the assumption that the gas is at ambient temperature.
(2) G = gas; V = vapour; + = positively buoyant; 0 = neutrally buoyant; − = negatively buoyant.
(3) The list of buoyant and neutrally buoyant gases and vapours is intended to be exhaustive, but the negatively buoyant gases listed are given only as examples. All gases and vapours not listed in this table are negatively buoyant under condition (1).
(4) Relative density of species = molar mass of species ÷ molar mass of air.

147

Stratification

There are three basic systems to be considered.

The first is one in which there is a spillage of negatively buoyant gas on to a surface. This forms a system with two layers, the upper one being air and the lower one the spilled gas. Such a system is said to be *stratified*. In such circumstances, and in the absence of other factors which may promote it, mixing takes place solely by *molecular diffusion* at the interface between the layers. This is a very slow process; the greater the difference in density between the layers, the slower it is. For this reason highly stratified systems are very stable.

The second system is one in which there is a spillage of a neutrally buoyant gas. Such a system will not easily stratify. There will be an indeterminate boundary between the layers and the area of the interface between them will tend to be greater than in the first system, and mixing and dilution more rapid.

The third system is one in which a buoyant gas is spilled. In this case the gas tends to rise vertically through the atmosphere in the way that flames do. The relative motion between the ascending gas and the atmosphere promotes rapid mixing. The more buoyant the gas, the more rapidly it rises and hence the more rapid is the mixing. In the open air the gas continues to rise until dilution has made it neutrally buoyant. At this point the mixing process slows down. However, the release of buoyant gases in buildings, where they may be prevented from rising freely, may present hazards for those in the upper parts of such buildings.

An everyday example of an initially buoyant emission which becomes neutrally buoyant is a chimney plume (see Figure 3.4). The gas leaving the chimney is originally buoyant because its temperature is higher than that of the atmosphere. It therefore rises vertically and, so long as it has not cooled below its dew point, it is invisible. Dilution by the atmosphere eventually makes the gas neutrally buoyant. This changes its direction of flow and causes it to move more or less horizontally with the wind. At the same time cooling below its dew

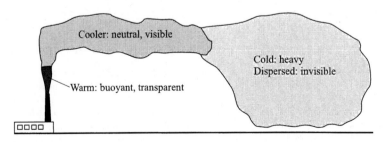

Figure 3.4 The chimney plume

point makes it visible. The increasing dilution of the plume is evidenced by its increasing cross-section. Eventually, because of evaporation of the water droplets in the plume, it becomes invisible again. Dilution and dispersion continue for long after the plume has ceased to be visible and eventually the plume 'grounds' — that is, its lower layers come into contact with the ground.

Factors which affect both neutrally buoyant and negatively buoyant gases are now discussed. The hazards of buoyant gases are much less serious than either of these and are not discussed further.

Essentially, the speed at which gas clouds disperse, and thus become non-hazardous by a sufficient dilution through mixing with the atmosphere, is determined by the degree of turbulence at the interface between the layers and within the layers themselves. Where the flow regime is *streamline* (see below) such turbulence does not exist and dispersion is very slow. Such conditions are not, however, encountered very frequently.

Regimes of flow

There are two quite distinct regimes of flow: *streamline* (or *laminar* or *viscous*) and *turbulent*.

Streamline flow is defined in PDS[3] as follows:

Streamline — a streamline is a line in a fluid such that the tangent to it at every point is the direction of the velocity of the fluid particle at that point at the instant under consideration. When the motion of the fluid is such that, at any instant, continuous streamlines can be drawn through the whole length of its course, the fluid is said to be in streamline flow.

It is characteristic of such flows that adjacent layers of fluid mix only very slowly. Turbulent flow is defined in PDS[3] as follows:

Turbulent flow — the type of fluid flow in which the motion at any point varies rapidly in direction and magnitude.

It is apparent that, by their nature, turbulent flows promote mixing.

These regimes were investigated by Osborne Reynolds at the turn of the century. His name has been applied to a dimensionless number which has wide application in fluid mechanics. This is the Reynolds number (*Re*) which is given by:

$$Re = \frac{Lv\rho}{\mu}$$

where L is a linear dimension which characterizes the geometry of the system, V a representative velocity of the flow, ρ is the density and μ the viscosity of the fluid.

When these variables are expressed in self-consistent units, the dimensionless number so obtained may be used as a criterion to distinguish streamline from turbulent flow. Thus, for flow in channels of circular cross-section (and where L is the diameter of the channel and V the mean linear velocity), the regime will be streamline when $Re \leq 2000$ and turbulent when $Re \geq 3000$. At intermediate values of Re the flow regime may fluctuate between the two regimes.

For systems of different geometry, different representative lengths and velocities are used and the critical values of the Reynolds number will differ from those quoted above. For two-phase systems the Reynolds numbers of the phases may differ and so may the regimes of flow.

The dispersion of gas clouds is greatly accelerated by turbulence and hence by conditions characterized by high Reynolds numbers. This applies chiefly, at least in the early stages of dilution, in the phase of the spilled gas, but also, to a lesser degree, in the phase of the ambient atmosphere.

The promotion of turbulence

There are three factors which principally influence turbulence, and hence the rate at which mixing proceeds, and dispersion models must account for all of these. They are the nature of the hazard source, the roughness of the ground and — more complicated and requiring more detailed discussion — meteorological factors.

The nature of the hazard source

This is sometimes referred to in the literature as the 'source term'. Spillages may lie on a spectrum from a slow leakage from a low-pressure container to a catastrophic failure of a high-pressure vessel. The former may, in some circumstances, give rise to streamline flow and hence to very slow mixing. The latter may be characterized initially by a gas velocity of the order of the sonic velocity in air — such emissions produce a high Reynolds number and hence a high rate of turbulence and mixing. Eventually, however, other mechanisms will predominate. Dispersion models must take account of the dynamics of mixing associated with the anticipated regimes of flow.

Roughness

This characterizes the nature of the ground surface over which the discharged gas flows, and includes all surface obstructions such as trees and buildings. Roughness promotes turbulence.

Meteorological factors

These include wind speed and direction, and atmospheric stability, which usually vary with the time of day and season of the year. Predictive techniques have to take account of this. Though wind speed and direction at night are generally stable, the speed of the wind and its direction under daytime conditions are both very variable, sometimes changing from minute to minute. Predictive techniques must therefore rely upon mean figures.

Wind speed and direction may be determined by recording anemometers and wind vanes. There is general agreement that these data are best collected on site rather than being accepted from the nearest weather station. The data on direction may be expressed as a *wind rose*, which is a diagram representing the number of days in any year in which the wind blows from any particular direction. The interpretation of data on wind direction and speed requires expert judgement.

Of equal significance is the atmospheric stability. To illustrate this, consider a dense gas under two widely different conditions.

The first case is one in which spillage takes place on a clear, cloudless, windless, winter's night in the temperate zone. Under such conditions, the ground radiates heat to outer space and it is much colder than the atmosphere above it. This condition is known as a *temperature inversion*. If the gas is spilled into a saucer-shaped depression under such conditions it possesses a high degree of stability. The cold ground cools the layers of gas closest to it and convection is totally suppressed.

The second case is one in which spillage takes place on a clear, cloudless, windless, summer's day in the temperate zone. Under such conditions the ground is receiving more heat from the sun than it radiates to outer space. In consequence it is hotter than the atmosphere above it. The ground heats the layers of gas closest to it and convection currents are established.

These convection currents transport dense gas from the lower layers to the interface between the layers. At the same time reverse convection currents transport cooler dense gas from the interface to the lower layers. If, on arriving at the interface, the dense gas has become buoyant, convection carries a gas which was originally negatively buoyant into the atmosphere. This can only occur when the dense layer is only slightly negatively buoyant or has become diluted to such an extent that it is approaching neutral buoyancy.

Pasquill stability classes

The difference between the two situations discussed above may be represented as differences in atmospheric stability expressed by the *lapse rate*. Lapse rate is defined in PDP[11] as follows:

Lapse rate — the rate of decrease of a quantity, usually temperature, with height in the atmosphere.

It may be expressed as $-d\theta/dH$, where θ is temperature and H is height. It is assigned a positive value when the temperature falls as the height increases. It has a theoretical value of 9.76 K per 1000 metres (ca. 1 K/100 m). This is known as the *dry adiabatic lapse rate* and is denoted by the symbol Γ_T. Moist, but unsaturated, air has the same value of Γ_T as dry air but the lapse rate for saturated air is only half that of dry air.

The actual lapse rate (Γ_A) at any given location at or near ground level (say about 1 metre above ground level) may vary from Γ_T by a factor of 100 or more — that is, from $\Gamma_A > 100\Gamma_T$ to $\Gamma_A < -100\Gamma_T$. Γ_A is generally positive in the daytime and is always negative at night.

Extreme values of Γ_A occur when the sky is clear. If the sky is cloudy, much smaller values of Γ_A, whether positive or negative, are to be expected. This is because, in the day time, clouds partly reflect radiation from the sun into outer space, while at night they partly reflect heat radiated from the ground back to the ground.

A number of stability classes have been identified by Pasquill[12], who represented meteorological conditions in the form of a grid with wind velocity and degree of cloud cover as parameters. Such a grid is shown in CCPS[10], page 78. Grid entries are known as Pasquill classes and are identified by the letters A to F, with some investigators adding a class G [see Marshall[13], p. 97].

Dispersion models

The scope of this book does not permit more than the barest outline of dispersion modelling. For more detailed information readers are referred to CCPS[10]. Such models must take account of all the factors outlined above. These include the nature of the hazard source, the buoyancy of the gas released, the degree to which it must be diluted to render it non-hazardous, coefficients of mass transfer and local meteorology.

Many dispersion models have been advanced over the last two decades and they have given widely divergent results. Their number has been greatly narrowed down by wind-tunnel experiments, by liquid-flow simulations and by field trials, which have tested their ability to predict dispersion behaviour. Field trials conducted in the USA and the UK prior to 1981 are discussed in

Britter and Griffiths[14]. The Thorney Island (UK) trials of 1982–84 are described in McQuaid[15].

Carter[2] gives a fairly up-to-date summary of the best models available, which can be used with confidence to predict the dispersion of a spilled gas at a particular site taking account of the factors discussed and the topography and layout of the site.

3.3 Water as a transmission path

3.3.1 Introduction

It is important to know how far water may convey harmful substances. An important class of such spills result from accidents involving ocean-going tankers, especially those carrying crude oil. Readers should refer to Fannelöp[16] for an account of the mathematical analysis of such phenomena as oil slicks. In the process industries, the number of incidents in which water has acted as a transmission path for the spillage of liquids and solids has been small compared with the number of cases in which the atmosphere has so acted for spillages of gases. This subject is therefore treated much less fully than gas dispersion. The similarities between water and the atmosphere are pointed out, and examples of the more important cases are quoted. The factors determining the direction in which water conveys materials that are spilled into it are also discussed.

3.3.2 Water and the atmosphere compared

There are many analogies between water transmission path systems and atmospheric transmission path systems. Both are governed by the same fundamental laws and thus they require a quantitative understanding of both fluid mechanics and mass transfer to be fully understood. As with the atmosphere therefore, the behaviour of water as a transmission path will be described only in qualitative terms.

As they obey the same fundamental laws, it has been possible to learn something of gas dispersion from liquid models. Table 3.2 shows similarities under typical conditions, while Table 3.3 shows differences (see overleaf).

3.3.3 The influence of velocity on water as a transmission path

Like the atmosphere, water may act as a transmission path over a wide range of velocities. At one extreme — as in a natural lake, a settlement lagoon or a canal — it may be static, or nearly so. At another — as in a river, a culvert, a

Table 3.2 Water and the atmosphere as transmission paths: similarities

Property	Similar characteristics
Flow regime	Similar flow properties at same Reynolds number
Roughness of solid boundaries	Enhances mixing in turbulent regime
Attenuation	Both attenuate with distance.
Buoyancy	Introduced second phase may be buoyant, neutrally buoyant or negatively buoyant.

Table 3.3 Water and the atmosphere as transmission paths: differences

Property	Water	Atmosphere
Miscibility of second phase	Sometimes (soluble)	Always
State of second phase	Liquid or solid	Gas
Chief determinant of direction of transmission path	Local topography	Wind rose

drain, a sewer or a water distribution system — it may be in turbulent flow with velocities up to, or even exceeding, $10\,\mathrm{m\,s}^{-1}$.

The attenuation of a harmful agent in water depends on the system: the concentration may vary inversely with the square of the distance as when it is spilled on the surface of a lake; it may attenuate approximately in a linear relationship with distance as when it is spilled on the surface of a canal; it may flow as a slug, with very little attenuation, where it is closely confined, as when it is incorporated in a water distribution system (see Figure 3.5).

3.3.4 Buoyant, insoluble liquids on static water

Such liquids slump under gravity like heavy gases spilled on the ground. Unlike such gases, they do not mix with the water but spread more or less indefinitely on its surface. If it is unconfined, the advancing front will be a circle; if it is confined, it may approximate to a line normal to the direction of flow. If the spilled liquid is volatile, then the vapour emitted will be carried with it.

Many liquid paraffins and aromatic hydrocarbons are both buoyant and insoluble. They are also volatile and flammable, so if ignition occurs the flame (with the possibility of explosion) may be transported over considerable distances (see Chapter 5, Manchester Ship Canal, page 231). If the spilled liquid is toxic, the toxicity may also be spread.

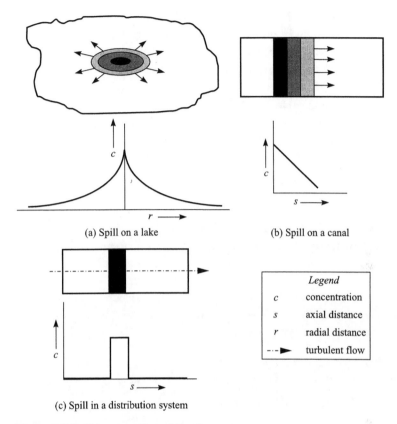

(a) Spill on a lake

(b) Spill on a canal

	Legend
c	concentration
s	axial distance
r	radial distance
$--\blacktriangleright$	turbulent flow

(c) Spill in a distribution system

Figure 3.5 Spills on to static and flowing water

3.3.5 Buoyant, insoluble liquids on flowing water

These also slump under gravity but the geometry of the pool they produce is different from the case above, with little tendency to spread upstream. Spreading is far more rapid than for fluids spilled on to static water. Flammable and toxic effects are likely to be similar. Where flammable fluids are spilled into drains or sewers there is a high risk of explosion. See Chapter 5, case histories of Cleveland (page 222) and Guadalajara (page 228).

3.3.6 Buoyant, soluble liquids on static water

These also slump under gravity and spread over the surface of the water. However, they also mix slowly with the water, mainly by molecular diffusion. Though this process is slow, it is much faster than the mixing of gases. Limits of flammability and vapour toxicity are governed by the partial pressure of the spilled liquid in the aqueous solution formed.

3.3.7 Buoyant, soluble liquids on flowing water

These tend to slump under gravity but mix rapidly with the water, mainly by eddy diffusion. Limits of flammability and vapour toxicity are also determined by the partial pressure of the spilled liquid in aqueous solution as above.

3.3.8 Non-buoyant soluble liquids in flowing water

Many aqueous solutions fall within this category. The hazard here is mainly that of toxicity by ingestion where the water is delivered by pipeline as potable water. For a case history see Chapter 5, 'Camelford' (page 219). For general information in this area see Keller and Wilson[17], which gives many case histories.

3.3.9 Non-buoyant, soluble solids in flowing water

If a solid is totally insoluble then no hazard will arise. There are, however, a number of substances which are commonly regarded as 'insoluble' but which are in fact of very low solubility. Some of these, because of their extreme toxicity, have to be treated as soluble. They may be hazardous if they are spilled into flowing water which is used as a source of drinking water. For a case history see Chapter 5, 'Basel' (page 214).

3.3.10 Soluble solids in the open air

Soluble solids spilled on to the ground in the open air may be dissolved by rain and washed into the ground.

3.4 The ground as a transmission path

The purpose of this short section is to draw attention to the fact that spillages on to bare earth may transmit their harm by passage through the ground. The ground is a medium by which, or through which, harm may be transmitted from a hazard source to a hazard receptor, and is thus a transmission path as defined in Section 3.1.1 (page 133). The ground may sometimes act as a transmission path in conjunction with water as rainfall, or through hosing down.

Spilled liquids, or water-soluble solids which have become aqueous solutions through rain or hosing down of spills will flow through the ground under gravity provided that it is *permeable*.

Permeability is a measure of the ease with which water can penetrate rocks. Its study is a branch of fluid mechanics and is discussed in Perry[18], Section 5 in connection with the design of filters. It is of great concern to civil engineers who study it, in combination with geology, to predict the movement of water in the ground.

Rocks differ greatly in their permeability, coarse sand being about 10^6 times as permeable as clay, while top-soil lies somewhere between these extremes. Typically, spilled liquids, or spilled solids dissolved in rain water, will flow downwards through the top-soil until they reach a layer of impermeable rock such as clay. They then flow under gravity along the top of the impermeable rock until it is intercepted by a stream or river (see Figure 3.6). The spilled substance, if a liquid, or its aqueous solution, is then carried along by the water-course.

In some cases materials may be adsorbed by clay, which is a very powerful adsorbent, with consequent attenuation of harmful properties. Where there is no intervening bed of clay or other impermeable rock the spillage may penetrate directly into an aquifer (a layer of rock from which water is abstracted for drinking purposes). This may give rise to toxic effects on the public.

3.5 Barriers

3.5.1 The nature of barriers

A barrier is interposed by process engineers and technologists to obstruct the transmission of harm by a transmission path. It is thus a device for attenuating the intensity of harm and may be expressed as a factor in the individual risk equation with a value between zero and 1.0. Barriers may have different forms, of which examples are given below. Two basic types, permanent and temporary, may be distinguished.

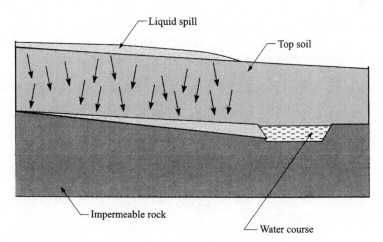

Figure 3.6 Liquid spillage on to the ground

157

3.5.2 Permanent barriers

These are barriers which, except during maintenance work, are permanently in place. In theory they are intended to provide total attenuation, eliminating individual risk. In practice, as the record shows, there is a small risk that they may fail and thus attenuation is not total. Such failures sometimes arise because of management errors such as when guards are removed from machinery for maintenance and the machinery is not switched off. Examples of such barriers are blast walls, blast-resistant buildings, bund walls around storages, machinery guards, and thermal insulation. Certain measures of personal protection, such as hard hats, may be regarded as permanent barriers.

3.5.3 Temporary barriers

These are actuated by the realization of hazards, or when there is warning of their imminent realization, either automatically or through human intervention. Examples are water curtains and spray systems. Certain measures of personal protection such as refuge rooms, respirators or air breathing apparatus may be regarded as temporary barriers.

References in Chapter 3

1. Marshall, V.C. and Ruhemann, S., 1997, An anatomy of hazard systems and its application to acute process hazards, *Trans IChemE, Part B, Proc Safe Env Prot*, 75 (B2): 65–72.
2. Carter, D. (ed), 1995, *Hazardous Substances on Spillage*, Major hazards monograph (A Report of the Major Hazards Assessment Panel Working Party on Source Terms) (IChemE, UK).
3. Uvarov, E.B. and Isaacs, A., 1986, *The Penguin Dictionary of Science*, 6th edn (Penguin, UK).
4. Baker, W.E., 1973, *Explosions in Air* (University of Texas Press, UK).
5. Jones, D.A. (ed), 1992, *Nomenclature for Hazard and Risk Assessment in the Process Industries* (IChemE, UK).
6. Hopkinson, B., 1915, *British Ordnance Board Minutes 13565*.
7. Sachs, R.G., 1944, *The dependence of blast on atmospheric pressure and temperature*, BRL Report 466 (Aberdeen Proving Ground, Maryland).
8. Baker, W.E., Cox, P.A., Westine, P.S., Kulesz, J.J. and Strehlow, R.A., 1983, *Explosion Hazards and Evaluation* (Elsevier, The Netherlands).
9. Phillips, H. (ed), 1994, *Explosions in the Process Industries*, Major hazards monograph (A Report of the Major Hazards Assessment Panel Overpressure Working Party) (IChemE, UK).
10. CCPS, 1987, *Guidelines for Vapor Cloud Dispersion Models* (Center for Chemical Process Safety of AIChE, USA).
11. Illingworth, V. (ed.) 1991, *The Penguin Dictionary of Physics*, 2nd edn (Penguin, UK).

12. Pasquill, F., 1961, The estimation of the dispersion of windborne material, *Met Mag*, 90: 33–49.

13. Marshall, V.C., 1987, *Major Chemical Hazards* (Ellis Horwood, UK).

14. Britter, R.E. and Griffiths, R.H., 1982, Dense gas dispersion, *J Hazardous Materials*, 6: 1.

15. McQuaid, J., 1985, Heavy gas dispersion trials at Thorney Island, *J Hazardous Materials*, 11: 1–33.

16. Fannelöp, T.K., 1994, *Fluid Mechanics for Industrial Safety and Environmental Protection*, Industrial safety series: 3 (Elsevier, The Netherlands).

17. Keller, A.Z. and Wilson, H.C., 1992, *Hazards to Drinking Water Supplies* (Springer Verlag, UK).

18. Perry, R.H., Green, D.W. and Maloney, J.O. (eds), 1997, *Perry's Chemical Engineers' Handbook*, 6th edn (McGraw-Hill, USA).

Harm to receptors

4

4.1 General principles

This chapter examines the harm to receptors resulting from emissions of energy or matter which arise from the realization of those hazards which are peculiar to, and most characteristic of, the process industries.

As regards safety activities, the aim is to concentrate on those which are in the sphere of process engineers and technologists. Those activities that are concerned with attenuating emissions to minimize harm to receptors fall within this sphere, so they are discussed at the appropriate places.

Although Chapter 6 refers to the duty of management to provide measures of first aid and to arrange for the prompt dispatch of injured people to hospital, these are not discussed in detail. For those wishing to undertake further reading in first aid treatment of process industry injuries, the appropriate sections in RSC[1] and Furr[2] are recommended. Though these relate to the treatment of injuries in the *laboratory*, there is very little difference between such treatment and the first-aid treatment of injuries sustained on the plant.

Acute and chronic harms

This chapter is concerned only with harms which arise from acute exposures of a duration of, say, an hour or less, and not with chronic exposures of days, weeks, months or more, which lead to occupational disease. The laws which govern occupational exposure may differ significantly from those which form the subject matter of this chapter.

Section 4.2 (page 162) identifies harms and links these qualitatively to the emissions which give rise to them. Section 4.3 (page 164) introduces concepts of *dose* whereby it is possible to quantify the absorption by a receptor of a harmful emission. Sections 4.5 to 4.9 (pages 177–194) examine in more detail the harm to people from the categories of emission with which the chapter is centrally concerned. Dose equations are set out and, where appropriate, tables of correspondences in which dose is related to severity of injury or damage for each category of emission are displayed. Attention is also drawn to barriers of attenuation which may be interposed to reduce the level of harm sustained by a receptor for each category of harm.

Section 4.10 (page 194) examines harm to equipment and buildings from emissions of pressure energy and Section 4.11 (page 197) examines harm to equipment and buildings from thermal energy. Section 4.12 (page 201) refers briefly to harm to the environment which may arise from emissions from process plant.

4.1.1 Terminology

We shall seek to develop a uniform and consistent terminology. The literature in this area has largely been created by specialists who have studied injury in individual categories such as mechanical and blast injuries, thermal burns and toxic injuries. Similarly, damage has been studied under such headings as mechanical damage to buildings and equipment through impact or blast, and damage by fire. There has been little attempt in the literature to provide a unified approach to the whole topic area.

Where the receptor is a living organism, the harm is described as *injury*: where it is an inanimate object, it is described as *damage*.

4.1.2 Harm and natural laws

Emissions and natural laws

The emissions with which this book is concerned are either of energy or of inanimate matter. They can be described in terms of the laws of physics and chemistry and may be subjected to dimensional analysis.

Injury and natural laws

In addition to the laws of physics and chemistry, the description of *injury* to living organisms requires an input from the laws of *biology*, or the *life sciences*, as these are alternatively known. These include such medical sciences as anatomy, physiology and toxicology. They are not readily amenable to dimensional analysis.

Damage and natural laws

In principle, if not always in practice, *damage* may be described in terms of the laws of physics and chemistry and thus may be subjected to dimensional analysis.

161

4.2 Injury and damage

4.2.1 Introduction

In this section emissions are related to the harm they produce. It is impossible within the scope of this book to list comprehensively all the different kinds of harm which may be inflicted upon receptors in the process industries. The aim is rather to provide examples of the most frequently sustained harms. Injury is dealt with first and then damage.

4.2.2 Types of harmful emission

Based upon the earlier analysis of hazard sources, the following types of harmful emission may be distinguished:

(1) mechanical energy;
(2) pressure energy;
(3) thermal energy;
(4) harmful substances.

These may give rise to various combinations of the injuries or damage which are listed in Section 4.2.3.

4.2.3 Types of injury

Mechanical injuries
Mechanical injuries may take any of the following forms:

(1) fractures of bones;
(2) dislocations of joints;
(3) cuts;
(4) lacerations;
(5) abrasions;
(6) penetration of organs;
(7) crushing of tissues;
(8) haemorrhages.

Releases of mechanical energy and of pressure energy can give rise to any of these, either directly or indirectly.

Thermal injuries
These may take any of the following forms:

(1) heat stroke;
(2) burns and scalds;

(3) hypothermia;
(4) cold contact burns.

Releases of radiative, convective, or conductive thermal energy may give rise to (1) and (2). The absorption of thermal energy *from* the receptor may give rise to (3) and (4). For the purpose of classification, these cases may be regarded as *negative* emissions of thermal energy.

Injuries from substances
Injuries may take the form of:

(1) asphyxiation;
(2) inhalation of toxics affecting the lungs, the bloodstream or the central nervous system;
(3) chemical burns.

Categories (1) and (2) may be brought about by releases of compressed gases or by spillages of volatile or flashing liquids. Category (3) may be brought about by spillages of corrosive chemicals.

4.2.4 Types of damage

Damage to equipment made of metals
These may take the form of:

(1) melting;
(2) loss of strength;
(3) distortion through stress beyond the elastic limit;
(4) loss of hardness;
(5) rupture of connections;
(6) bursting of vessels;
(7) loss of verticality in columns;
(8) loss of protective coatings.

Categories (3), (5) and (6) may arise through over-pressurization of vessels. All may arise, either directly or indirectly, through emissions of mechanical, pressure or thermal energy.

Damage to building materials
These may take the form of:

(1) collapse;
(2) spalling of surfaces;

(3) rupture of joints;

(4) loss of strength;

(5) distortion.

These may arise, either directly or indirectly, through emissions of mechanical, pressure or thermal energy.

4.3 Concepts of dose

4.3.1 Introduction

Quantifying absorption

The central theme of this section is that harm to a receptor arises from the absorption by the receptor of energy or matter emitted by a hazard source. The purpose of the section is to discuss how the energy or matter absorbed by a receptor may be quantified. This quantification will be termed *dose*. Unfortunately, however, the phenomenon of dose tends to be represented in the literature in different ways according to the nature of the emission under consideration. This chapter endeavours to define it in a more general way and offers a rational interpretation of the relationships between the various customary expressions of it.

The intensity of an emission may be characterized, where energy is involved, as power per unit cross-sectional area of path (also called *energy flux*). Where matter is involved, its intensity is commonly expressed by its concentration of harmful matter (a mass per unit volume).

Thus harm reaching a receptor is characterized by its exposure, over some interval of time, to a stream of energy or harmful matter, part of which is absorbed by the receptor. The portion absorbed is a function of a characteristic dimension of the receptor. It is assumed, for the moment, that this absorbed energy or matter is totally retained by the receptor. In practice it may be necessary to consider the concept of an *absorption fraction*, that is the fraction of the energy or matter which is actually retained by the receptor. (This fraction is a dimensionless ratio and so does not affect the dimensional analysis to which the various expressions of dose will be subjected).

A note on dimensional analysis

The meanings of the various expressions of dose can be most easily differentiated by the use of *dimensional analysis*. The subject of dimensional analysis is described in outline in PDM[3], PDP[4] and PDS[5]. There is an extended treatment of it in MEST[6]. In this case, the first stage is the main concern: the identification of the dimensions of the entities being analysed.

The SI units adopted rest upon seven dimensionally independent *base quantities*[7], though it is necessary for the present purpose to use only three of them, namely *mass* (M), *length* (L) and *time* (T). All other physical magnitudes are described as *derived quantities*, since they are made up of products of appropriate powers of the base magnitudes. Examples of important derived quantities are given in Table 4.1. Pure numbers have no dimensions (thus LL^{-1} is a *dimensionless ratio*).

The derived quantities from this table are used in the discussions below on indices of dose. On occasion, in order to make clearer the derivation of a dimensional formula, the dimensions of the derived quantities *area* and *energy* are represented by the symbols A and E, respectively.

Table 4.1 Examples of derived quantities

Description	Dimensions	Symbol
Area	L^2 (or A)	A
Volume	L^3	V
Velocity	LT^{-1}	v
Force	MLT^{-2}	F
Pressure	$ML^{-1}T^{-2}$	p
Energy	ML^2T^{-2} (or E)	E
Power	ML^2T^{-3}	P
Impulse	$ML^{-1}T^{-1}$	I
Concentration	ML^{-3}	C
Volumetric flow rate	L^3T^{-1}	Q

4.3.2 Definitions of dose

In common speech *dose* may be associated with a benefit as in 'a dose of medicine' or it may be associated with harm as in 'a dose of poison' or 'a dose of flu'. This book is concerned solely with doses which give rise to harm. The medical and pharmaceutical professions use *dose* in the meaning of a beneficial *mass* of substance (or its equivalent volume). Thus defined, dose has the dimension of mass, M.

Jones[8] does not define *dose* directly but says it is a synonym of *exposure*. It defines exposure, and hence, in its own terms, *dose*, as follows:

Exposure — The amount of a toxic substance to which an individual is exposed. This may represent the amount ingested, absorbed or inhaled or it may refer to the integral of concentration with time in the immediate

165

environment. Where ambiguity may arise the basis used to define the exposure should be specified.

In both parts this definition refers only to toxic *substances* — it does not refer to *energy*. The dimension of dose in the first part is clearly M and this corresponds with the medical usage of *dose*, whereas the quantity defined in the latter part has dimensions MTL^{-3}.

This definition is not entirely suitable for the purposes of this book. It gives two, dimensionally incompatible, meanings to *exposure*, and hence to *dose*, and it does not deal with the absorption of *energy*. The analysis given below suggests that there are at least 10 ways of expressing dose (see Table 4.2).

For the purposes of this book, *dose* is defined as follows:

Dose — the quantity of a harmful emission, which may be energy or a substance, which is absorbed by a receptor. It may thus have dimensions of energy (E) or of mass (M). The symbol D_E is used when it is energy, and D_M when it is matter.

However, dose as so defined is not a very useful concept, as the harmful effects produced will vary inversely with the size of the receptor. To avoid this, it is usually more convenient to use the concept of '*specific dose*':

Specific dose — a measure of dose related to a measure of the size of a receptor such as its mass or its surface area or some specified portion of these.

Specific dose is ascribed the symbols D_{ES} or D_{MS} according to whether it relates to energy or to matter. Specific dose may thus relate to mass or to surface area, so that D_{ES} may have the dimensions of energy per unit mass or energy per unit area and D_{MS} will be either a dimensionless ratio [mass absorbed per unit mass of receptor] or have dimensions ML^{-2} [mass absorbed per unit area of receptor].

It is also helpful to use the concept of a 'specific dose rate':

Specific dose rate — a measure of specific dose per unit time.

Specific dose rate is given the symbols D_{RES} and D_{RMS}. D_{RES} may have the dimensions $E M^{-1}T^{-1}$ or $E A^{-1}T^{-1}$ and D_{RMS} may have the dimensions T^{-1} or $ML^{-2}T^{-1}$.

4.3.3 Dimensional analysis of dose

A summary of the symbols and dimensions for dose and its derivatives is given in Table 4.2.

Table 4.2 Symbols and dimensions for dose and its derivatives

Quantity	Energy		Matter	
	Symbol	Dimensions	Symbol	Dimensions
Dose	D_E	$E\ (= ML^2T^{-2})$	D_M	M
Specific dose	$D_{ES} = D_E\,M_R^{-1}$	L^2T^{-2}	$D_{MS} = D_M\,M_R^{-1}$	1 or ML^{-2}
	or $D_E\,A_p^{-1}$	or MT^{-2}	or $D_M\,A_p^{-1}$	
Specific dose	$D_{RES} = D_E\,M_R^{-1}\theta^{-1}$	L^2T^{-3}	$D_{RMS} = D_M\,M_R^{-1}\theta^{-1}$	T^{-1}
rate	or $D_E\,A_p^{-1}\theta^{-1}$	or MT^{-3}	or $D_M\,A_p^{-1}\theta^{-1}$	or $ML^{-2}T^{-1}$

NB The symbols M_R and A_p represent respectively the mass and the projected area of the receptor. The symbol θ represents an appropriate interval of time.

4.3.4 The relationship of dose to emission

A model was set out in Chapter 1, in which a source may generate an *emission* of harmful energy or matter which, before it impacts a receptor, may have its intensity attenuated by transmission paths or barriers. Chapter 3 represents this generalized process in equation (3.2) (page 134), which is adapted for the present purpose as equation (4.1):

$$\phi_i = \phi_s(1 - \alpha_{TP})\,(1 - \alpha_B) \tag{4.1}$$

where ϕ_s represents the flux of energy or matter at the source of the emission and ϕ_i the flux incident on the receptor, while α_{TP}, α_B represent, respectively, the factors for attenuation due to transmission paths and barriers.

Following Marshall and Ruhemann[9], the incident dose can be related to the emission by one of the following equations:

$$\text{Energy}\quad D_E = \left\{\int_{t_0}^{t_1}\phi_{iE}\mathrm{d}t\right\} \times A_i = \left\{\int_{t_0}^{t_1}\phi_{sE}(1 - \alpha_{TP})(1 - \alpha_B)\mathrm{d}t\right\} \times A_i \tag{4.2}$$

or

$$\text{Matter}\quad D_M = \left\{\int_{t_0}^{t_1}\phi_{iM}\mathrm{d}t\right\} \times A_i = \left\{\int_{t_0}^{t_1}\phi_{sM}(1 - \alpha_{TP})(1 - \alpha_B)\mathrm{d}t\right\} \times A_i \tag{4.3}$$

where,

D_E, D_M are the incident doses of energy or matter, J or kg

t_0 is the time of arrival of the pulse, s

t_1 is the time when the intensity of the pulse becomes negligible, s

ϕ_{sE}, ϕ_{sM} are the fluxes of energy or matter emitted by the source, $\mathrm{W\,m^{-2}}$ or $\mathrm{kg\,s^{-1}\,m^{-2}}$

α_{TP} is the factor for attenuation due to transmission paths, number
α_B is the factor for attenuation due to barriers, number
A_i is the appropriate impact area of the receptor, m^2

It may be noted that in equations (4.2) and (4.3) the attenuation factors have been included under the integral signs. This is strictly necessary only if they are time-dependent, which may or may not be the case. However, this form of presentation has been chosen for the sake of clarity. The equations can of course be adapted to represent *specific* dose and so on.

4.3.5 The use of indices to represent dose

In the literature, dose is often expressed in terms which are dimensionally not compatible with any of those in Section 4.3.2 (page 165). These terms are actually *shorthand* expressions, and usually incorporate one or more unstated assumptions. Such forms will be termed *indices* of dose (D_I). The assumptions are examined below and it will be demonstrated that, when they are made explicit the resulting statement of dose is dimensionally compatible with the appropriate expression in Table 4.2.

4.3.6 Indices of dose for blast

It may be inferred from the somewhat simplified theoretical discussion in Section 4.3.2 that, for the purpose of correlating harmful effects, the most informative measure of blast dose would a *specific dose D_{ES}*, with the dimensions of energy per unit area (MT^{-2}). That this is not the general perception, is evident from the fact that this measure is not often found in the literature. It is apparent, rather, that investigators (perhaps the most authoritative source is Baker[10]) have been unable to identify a single parameter with which to correlate harm but have found it necessary to use different parameters, or indeed combinations of them, for dealing with different categories of harm. Of these parameters, the most commonly used are *over-pressure* and *impulse*. These quantities were defined in Chapter 3 (Section 3.2.3, page 139). They fall into the above-defined category of *indices*, and their significance and how they are related to *specific dose* must therefore be considered.

It should be noted that an index of *specific dose* may be transformed into an index of *dose* for the given medium by multiplying it by the projected area of the receptor — that is, the area of the receptor perpendicular to the direction of propagation of the wave front.

Indices of dose for blast: *overpressure*

As discussed in Chapter 3, the most common measure of blast is *peak (side-on) overpressure*. Many such observations have been obtained from extensive field trials of dense explosives. As an index of *specific dose* (of energy), this parameter has two defects — it is an *instantaneous* value of a quantity which varies throughout the duration of the pulse, and it has inappropriate dimensions (those of pressure, or force per unit area $(ML^{-1}T^{-2})$.

The first problem may be addressed by introducing a factor (this will depend on the shape of the wave but is typically between 0.4 and 0.6) to reduce the *peak* value to a *mean* value. The second requires multiplication by a factor having the dimension of *length* (L), to adjust the dimensions to those of *specific dose*, and it is suggested, intuitively, that an appropriate factor for this purpose would be the half-wavelength of the disturbance $(\lambda/2)$, that is approximately the length of the positive phase.

This length may be thought of as the *depth* of the positive phase of the blast wave — that is, the distance between its leading edge and its trailing edge—the edge at which point the overpressure has fallen to zero before entering its negative phase. It is equal to the product of the velocity (v_p) of propagation of the wave front and the duration (θ) of the positive phase.

Indices of dose for blast: *impulse*

Baker[10] cites evidence that, in addition to overpressure, a number of other effects of blast waves are significant in determining the harm caused to receptors of all kinds. Consequently, there is much variance in the injury or damage associated with any given level of overpressure. Of these other factors, the most important appears to be the *duration*, and investigators have therefore introduced the parameter *impulse* (defined in Chapter 3 as 'the integral of the pressure/time history of a blast wave') to account for the effects of the duration of the pulse as well as of its intensity (expressed by pressure).

Whereas the overpressure varies only, for a given type of explosive and geometry, with scaled distance (as defined in Chapter 3), the duration, and consequently the impulse, varies also with the explosive energy. For the purposes of this discussion, it is assumed that we are concerned with the impulse of blast waves where dynamic effects have attenuated to zero — that is, in the middle field and beyond. A single-valued correlation of impulse with scaled distance can be obtained by scaling the impulse by dividing it by the cube root of the explosive energy or mass, as shown in Figure 4.1 (data from Baker[10]).

Impulse has the dimensions of a product of pressure and time — that is $(ML^{-1}T^{-2}) \times (T)$ or $ML^{-1}T^{-1}$. In order to reconcile this dimensionally with

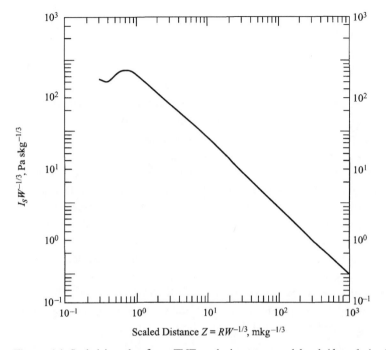

Figure 4.1 Scaled impulse for a TNT explosion at ground level (data derived from Baker et al.[10])

specific dose as defined above, it must be multiplied by a factor of dimensions LT^{-1} (equivalent to a linear velocity). Such a factor may be derived from the rate at which the pulse of overpressure displaces the atmosphere in front of the receptor — the velocity (v_p) of propagation of the wave front. Thus, for a sound wave in air, the *specific dose* (of energy) represented by an impulse of 1 pascal-second would be $330\,\mathrm{J\,m^{-2}}$ ($330\,\mathrm{m\,s^{-1}}$ is the sonic velocity in air).

For any given medium, the velocity of propagation is constant at a fixed temperature. Consequently, in that medium the *duration* of the positive phase is a linear function of the wavelength of the emission. This gives rise to the impression that the energy is a function of pressure and duration rather than of pressure and wavelength. It follows that impulse is a satisfactory index of specific dose *for a single medium*. On the other hand, if impulses with the same pressure and duration but arising from the propagation of blast waves in different media with different velocities of propagation (say, for example, air and hydrogen or air and water) are compared, they will correspond with different levels of energy because they will have different wavelengths.

170

Various expressions for the dose associated with blast waves are summarized in Table 4.3.

Table 4.3 Summary of expressions for dose in blast (based on unit area)

Measure	Dimensions	Referred to peak over-pressure Δp_{max}	Referred to impulse i
Dose $[D_E]$	ML^2T^{-2} ($\equiv E$)	$\Delta p_{max} \times \frac{1}{2}\lambda \times A_p$	$i \times v_p \times A_p$
Specific dose $[D_{ES}]$	MT^{-2} ($\equiv EA^{-1}$)	$\Delta p_{max} \times \frac{1}{2}\lambda$	$i \times v_p$
Specific dose rate $[D_{RES}]$	MT^{-3} ($\equiv EA^{-1}T^{-1}$)	$\Delta p_{max} \times \frac{1}{2}\lambda \times \theta^{-1}$	$i \times v_p \times \theta^{-1}$

Indices of dose for blast: calculations

When the mass of an explosive charge (as equivalent TNT) and its distance from a receptor are known, Hopkinson's Scaling Law (introduced in Section 3.2.3, page 139) can be used to calculate the *scaled distance* and hence to estimate point values of various parameters of the blast wave. Thus, the *peak over-pressure* can be deduced from the correlation presented in Figure 3.3 (page 142), and the *scaled impulse* from Figure 4.1. The absolute impulse may then be obtained by multiplying the scaled impulse by the cube root of the TNT equivalent of the mass of the explosive.

Alternatively, a plot of scaled duration can be used with the overpressure plot to estimate the impulse, approximating the integral as about one-half of the product of peak overpressure and duration.

4.3.7 Indices of dose for toxics

The first variant of the IChemE definition of *exposure* (see Section 4.3.2, page 165) is more or less consistent with our definition of *dose* (overlooking, for the time being, that a receptor may not completely absorb the emission to which it is exposed). The second defines a parameter which may be represented as $\int_{t_0}^{t_1} Cd\theta$, with dimensions (assuming that concentration is expressed as mass per unit volume) $MV^{-1}T$ or $ML^{-3}T$. These dimensions do not correspond with those of any of the forms of dose given in our taxonomy (see Table 4.2, page 167).

In terms of inhalation, which is the most common mechanism of absorption by animate receptors, the mass-based *specific dose rate* defined earlier may be viewed as being the product of a *concentration* C with a *specific respiration rate* $Q_{RS}(= Q_R M_R^{-1}$, where Q_R is the absolute rate), so that $D_{RMS} = C \times Q_{RS}$. The

171

mass-based *specific dose* will then be the time-integral of this quantity over the duration of exposure:

$$D_{MS} = \int_{t_0}^{t_1} (C \times Q_{RS}) d\theta \tag{4.4}$$

or, if Q_{RS} is invariant with time,

$$D_{MS} = Q_{RS} \times \int_{t_0}^{t_1} (C) d\theta \tag{4.5}$$

with dimensions $(M L^{-3}) \times (L^3 T^{-1} M^{-1}) \times T = M M^{-1}$, that is, *dimensionless*, as appropriate (see Table 4.2).

The IChemE two-part definition thus contains two variants which are dimensionally different, the first relating to *dose* and the second to *specific dose*. Equation (4.5) shows that the latter can be transformed to *specific dose* by multiplying by the *specific respiration rate*, Q_{RS} (provided this is constant). It seems therefore that this variant may be regarded as an *index* of *specific* dose (D_{IMS}) which implicitly assumes that all receptors have the same rate of respiration per unit mass, and which will be a reliable correlant for harm only if that condition is satisfied (this may of course be approximately true for a given species). That this relationship is not found to be exact in practice does not alter the dimensional argument.

Table 4.4 sets out the expressions for the various forms of dose in terms of the dose index D_{IMS}, together with their dimensions.

Table 4.4 Expressions for dose in toxics (based on unit mass)

Measure	In terms of dose index $D_{IMS} = \int_{t_0}^{t_1} C d\theta$	Dimensions
Dose D_M	$D_{IMS} \times Q_{RS} \times M_R$	$(ML^{-3}T) \times (L^3T^{-1}M^{-1}) \times M = M$
Specific dose D_{MS}	$D_{IMS} \times Q_{RS}$	$(ML^{-3}T) \times (L^3T^{-1}M^{-1}) = 1$
Specific dose rate D_{RMS}	$D_{IMS} \times Q_{RS} \times \theta^{-1}$	$(ML^{-3}T) \times (L^3T^{-1}M^{-1}) \times (T^{-1}) = T^{-1}$

4.4 Correspondence between dose and harm

4.4.1 Introduction

A qualitative account of the types of harm that result from the impact upon animate and inanimate receptors of various kinds of emissions arising from the realization of process hazards was given in Section 4.2. In Section 4.3, the quantification of such impacts, in terms of the concept of dose was discussed. The problem of correlating the harm sustained by a receptor with the dose causing it must now be addressed.

The sequence of events by which an emission is generated and then attenuated *en route* to a receptor is complicated enough, but at least it can be represented in terms of physical parameters. The correlation of harm with dose is much more difficult for three inter-related reasons (see Marshall and Ruhemann[9]).

Firstly, dose as defined in Section 4.3.2 (page 165) is not always easy to measure and data in these terms are often not available so that investigators commonly have recourse to *indices* of dose such as overpressure, concentration and so on which carry with them implicit constraints.

Secondly, the actual quantification of harm in animate receptors — and even in complex inanimate structures — is very problematic. Injuries to humans and animals, and damage to equipment and buildings, cannot generally be quantified on a continuous scale like temperature (though an approximation to this exists in relation to burn injuries — see Section 4.6.4, page 182).

Thirdly, the processes by which harm is caused are not amenable to simple mathematical modelling and are usually subject to a substantial element of chance. Consequently, it is usually found that there is not a single-valued relationship between a simple measure of dose and a corresponding measure of harm, and that it is necessary to resort to a *stochastic* correlation between a more complex representation of dose and a measure of the *probability* of harm being inflicted on a receptor at some specified level.

In recent years, investigators in the field of process safety have adopted procedures for dealing with such problems that have been elaborated in the context of research on the effectiveness of pesticides. In this section, these procedures are introduced in a general way, and subsequent sections illustrate their application in certain important instances.

4.4.2 The quantification of harm

In default of a continuous scale, it is customary to quantify harm by specifying a particular level of response (called a *quantal*) which definitely either *is* or *is not* displayed by a receptor — that is, a *binary* criterion. The most used quantal is fatality, both because of its obvious intrinsic importance and because it is virtually unambiguous. As readers may know, insurance companies commonly compensate clients for the loss of an organ or of a limb, and such an injury might also constitute a quantal. Various other quantals are also in use, however, and these are referred to as appropriate.

4.4.3 The concept of load

One might intuitively expect that it should be possible to correlate some measure of harm with a single measure of dose. However, investigators have been unable, in relation to some emissions, to obtain satisfactory correlations in this way. Rather, they have found it necessary to use a parameter having the form $(X^n \times \theta)$ as a correlant, where X is a dose rate such as energy flux ϕ or a dose index such as concentration C, θ is the duration of exposure and n is an empirically derived dimensionless exponent usually exceeding unity [some have used the equivalent form $(X \times \theta^{1/n})$.] They have called this quantity *load*[11,12]. In the context of a comprehensive treatment of the subject of *dose*, Marshall and Ruhemann[9] proposed the general term *quasi-dose* (*quasi:* Gk = 'as if')[9].

It must be emphasized that there is as yet no generally accepted theoretical basis for such relationships. However, bearing in mind the obvious complexity of the processes by which harm is caused, especially to living organisms (one must assume that physical, chemical and physiological mechanisms are involved), it is not too surprising. A possible interpretation of the above parameter emerges if it is rearranged as follows (an emission of energy is used as an example):

$$(D_{RES})^n \times \theta = (D_{ES}/\theta)^n \times \theta = (D_{ES}/\theta) \times \theta \times (D_{ES}/\theta)^{n-1}$$
$$= D_{ES} \times (D_{ES}/\theta)^{n-1} = D_{ES} \times (D_{RES})^{n-1}$$

Thus the correlating parameter in this case is represented as the product of the specific *dose rate* taken to a power $(n-1)$ with the specific *dose*, implying that, for such an emission, not only its *amount* striking the receptor per unit area but also the *rate* at which it does so affects the outcome.

It is to be noted that, in the case that the power n is unity, the *rate* factor disappears and only the specific *amount* remains.

4.4.4 The correlation of harm with dose

General statement
The dose-harm relationship may be represented by a symbolic statement of the form:

$$L_M \quad \text{or} \quad L_E \xrightarrow{T_{L \to H}} Q$$

where,
L_M, L_E are the *loads* of matter and energy impacting the receptor as defined above;

$T_{L \to H}$ is a notional *load-to-harm transform* (an operator);
Q is the *fraction* of the exposed (presumably uniform) population of receptors expected to sustain harm at a specified quantal level (or, to put it another way, the *probability* that an individual member of the population will respond with the specified quantal).

The transform $T_{L \to H}$ cannot generally be expressed as a mathematical function: it represents a statistical relationship which may take different forms according to the type of hazard system being considered and the nature of the available data.

Tables of correspondence

For particular agents, the transform $T_{L \to H}$ customarily takes the form of tables of correspondence, in which measures of incident dose or load and of harm are juxtaposed. The data in such tables may be derived from analysis of industrial incidents or from experiment on animal or on human subjects (the latter, of course, only for low levels of harm). Tables of correspondence are unavoidably crude, since they are not amenable to interpolation. Examples are given below in the Appendix *Toxicity Data*.

Probit analysis

If sufficient data are available (this implies observations or experiments on a large population) it may be possible to carry out a *probit analysis*. This technique is described, for example, in Finney[13]. In this method, a probabilistic relationship is developed between the logarithm of a measure of the incident dose or load and the fraction of a given population that will give a specified quantal response.

The relationship may be expressed as follows:

$Y = a + b \log$ (incident load)

where Y represents the probit and a, b, are coefficients characteristic of particular agents.

The logarithmic base is arbitrary, though the choice does, of course, affect the value of the coefficient b. Until recently, common logarithms (that is, to base 10) were more widely used, but the base e arises more naturally from mathematical analysis and has lately come to prevail.

The method is based upon the assumption of a log-normal distribution of response. A *probit* (the word is a contraction of '**prob**ability un**it**') is in effect a unit of standard deviation. It has become customary (for reasons — now obsolete — concerned with difficulties of calculation before the advent of

175

electronic computers) to adjust the definition so that a value of 5 is attributed to Y for a probability of 0.5. An illustrative plot of probit versus load is given in Figure 4.2.

Values of the coefficients a and b for a number of agents are quoted in the literature. Representative equations are quoted later in this chapter, and some are given in the Appendix *Toxicity Data*. Tables relating *probit* and percentage probability are given in standard textbooks on biological statistics[13]. Such percentage values have to be divided by 100 to give values of the quantal fraction Q defined earlier.

As discussed earlier, incident load may be expressed in the literature in terms of *dose* or of a *dose index* or in a more complex form. In Figure 4.2 it may have any of these forms.

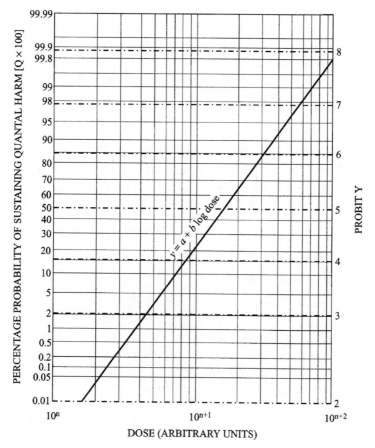

Figure 4.2 Indicative probit/dose relationship

Insufficiently critical use of the probit method has been deprecated, for example, by Marshall[14]. Of particular concern is the practice of expressing such correlations with a precision implying a wholly unrealistic level of accuracy, and a tendency to ignore the existence of threshold values of dose corresponding to nil response and to 100% response which apply to most practical situations. [Thus, for a toxic emission affecting a population of human receptors, there will be a lower dose level below which none is killed and an upper dose level above which all are killed.] These thresholds are not represented by the linear regression. Nevertheless, where adequate data exist it provides the most informative, and probably the most reliable, means for predicting response.

4.5 Harm to people from pressure energy releases

4.5.1 Injury to people

Direct or indirect injury
Injury to people from blast may be classified[15] as *direct* (primary) or *indirect* (secondary or tertiary). Primary injury is physical injury that arises directly from the blast itself. Secondary injury arises from causes such as the impact of missiles or buildings collapsing on people. Tertiary injury occurs when people are moved bodily by the blast wave so that they in effect become missiles and may be hurled against walls.

Both direct and indirect injury are greatly influenced by geometry. One such geometrical factor is *attitude* — that is, whether, for example, a person is standing up or lying down. Another geometrical factor is *orientation* — that is, the angle that a person presents to the wave front. A third geometrical factor is the relationship to the surroundings, that is whether a person is standing in the open, or whether they are close to an unyielding surface which may intensify the overpressure by reflection.

The dose from blast waves
Blast waves may arise from the releases of compressed gases and vapours discussed in Chapter 2, Section 2.5 (page 40), or from the explosive deflagrations and detonations discussed in Chapter 2, Sections 2.12 (page 115) and 2.13 (page 121).

The dose from a blast may be expressed as either (1) energy per unit *area* of the receptor or (2) energy per unit *mass* of the receptor. In the following discussion the former convention is used.

Examples have not been found in the literature of either usage (1) or usage (2) with reference to human receptors. Rather, dose is expressed in terms of shorthand *indices* of the kind discussed in Section 4.3, such as 'impulse' or 'peak overpressure'.

The determination of blast wave energy

For simplicity, blast waves in which the dynamic component has attenuated to zero are discussed.

The dimensions of overpressure are force per unit area. However, it is not pressure which determines energy but the product of pressure and volume, PV. Thus the volume associated with unit area needs to be known — that is, the *depth* of the wave front. This may be obtained from the positive phase duration and the velocity of propagation, which is the velocity of sound in air, v_s. Thus:

$$\text{Depth of wave front} = v_s \times \theta \tag{4.6}$$

$$\text{Incident energy per unit area} = \Delta p_m \times v_s \times \theta \tag{4.7}$$

If the mean overpressure, Δp_m, is taken as equal to ca. $0.5\,\Delta p_{max}$:

$$\text{Incident energy per unit area} = 0.5\,\Delta p_{max} \times v_s \times \theta = 0.5\,\Delta p_{max} \times 331 \times \theta \tag{4.8}$$

But there is a further factor. Thus equation (4.8) gives the energy which impacts the receptor rather than the amount which is absorbed by it and transformed into, say, kinetic energy. There must be a further factor, with a value between 0 and 1, representing the fraction of the incident energy absorbed by the receptor. This is called an *absorption coefficient* and is given the symbol Φ. Thus the full equation is:

$$\text{Energy absorbed by receptor per unit area} = 0.5\,\Delta p_{max} \times 331 \times \theta \times \Phi \tag{4.9}$$

In principle, Φ may be calculated using the laws of fluid mechanics which include the concept of a drag *coefficient*. This exercise has been done for the impacts of blast upon buildings. There are no data for Φ on human receptors, but one might guess it to be equal to 0.333.

A specimen calculation is given for imparted velocity based on $\Delta p_{max} = 0.1\,\text{bar}$ ($\equiv 10^4\,\text{Pa}$), $\theta = 10^{-2}\,\text{s}$, projected area $= 1\,\text{m}^2$, a body mass of 70 kg and an assumed value of 0.333 for Φ.

Energy absorbed by receptor $= 0.5 \times 10^4 \times 330 \times 10^{-2} \times 0.333 \times 1 \cong$ 5, 500 J

Propulsion velocity v is given by: kinetic energy $= 0.5 \, mv^2 \cong 5,500$ J, so $v \cong 12.5 \, \mathrm{m\,s^{-1}}$. (This is only a small fraction of the velocity of propagation of the incident blast wave).

If the receptor shortly afterwards struck an unyielding surface this would be approximately equivalent to a fall from a roof 8 metres high. However, these calculations are heavily influenced by the value chosen for Φ.

Dose and direct injury

When fatality is caused directly, it is almost always due to lung injury caused by the chest cavity being violently compressed. This is discussed in Glasstone and Dolan[16] and in Phillips[15].

The former reference gives a table relating injury to overpressure for long-duration impulses. This table shows that severe lung damage is likely at 1.7 bar and that fatality will occur at 4 to 6 bar. Somewhat higher overpressures would be required by the shorter-duration impulses associated with dense explosives. In the process industries, however, only overpressures from dense explosives are likely to cause fatalities arising directly from blast.

A probit equation for deaths from lung injury cited by Poblete et al.[17] is as follows:

$$Y = -77.1 + 6.91 \, \log_e \, \Delta p_{max} \qquad\qquad (4.10)$$

where $\Delta p_{max} =$ peak overpessure [Pa]

Note that dose is expressed here by an *index* and not by absorbed energy — that is, there are undisclosed assumptions in it relating to duration and fractional absorption. In fact, blast waves differ widely in their duration. Those arising from the detonation of dense explosives run from a few to a hundred milliseconds, whereas vapour cloud explosions may have a duration of perhaps a fifth of a second and nuclear explosions, according to Glasstone and Dolan[16], of about a second. Consequently, for a given positive overpressure, the dose of a blast wave, represented by impulse (measured simply as a product of intensity and duration), may vary by a factor of perhaps a hundred.

It is clear from observation that the degree of harm suffered from blast cannot be represented by a simple inverse relationship between overpressure and duration, but no value quoted for an exponent n in a *load* expression for blast has been found in the literature.

Phillips[15] reproduces a graph from Baker et al.[10] in which scaled impulse is plotted against scaled overpressure for contours of constant 'survivability' — that is, percentage probability of survival from lung damage resulting from direct exposures to blast. The original publication outlines a procedure for estimating 'survivability'.

Indirect injury

Most fatal and non-fatal injuries to people caused by explosions in the chemical and process industries have resulted from the indirect, rather than the direct, effects of a blast. However the question of indirect injury is very complicated as there are innumerable scenarios which could give rise to such injuries (most such injuries in any case are of a mechanical character). Phillips[15] provides graphs which may facilitate very approximate estimates of secondary and tertiary injury from blasts. The complexity of this field and the paucity of reliable data are, however, such that further discussion would not be justified.

4.5.2 Protection of people from pressure energy releases

The most important measures to be taken are those which protect people whose work requires them to spend an appreciable fraction of their working time in buildings in areas where there is a significant risk of the realization of hazard sources which can give rise to a blast. These measures are discussed in Section 4.11 (page 197) where buildings are considered as receptors. Hard hats afford a measure of protection for the head when pressure energy is released.

4.6 Harm to people from thermal energy releases

4.6.1 Harm from heat and cold

Temperature and the environment

Temperature is an environmental condition having certain bounds which, if exceeded, give rise to harm. These limits of temperature are not necessarily those of the general environment, as humans can create a micro-climate for themselves by means of clothing. This may be everyday clothing or it may be specialist clothing designed for extreme environments of climate or working conditions.

The body has an elaborate system of temperature regulation[18]. It generates heat continuously through the metabolism (combustion of food and muscular effort) and this has to be dissipated. The mean rate of dissipation for an adult is about 100 watts, but it can peak for short periods to perhaps 1000 watts. The temperature of the body is thus determined by the metabolism and by exchange of heat with the surroundings.

Core and skin temperature

Two principal temperatures characterize the thermal state of the human body. These are the *core* or *deep body* temperature, and the *skin* temperature. The core temperature is the internal temperature of the bodily organs. It is normally maintained at about 37°C. The skin temperature is self-evident.

The departure of either the core temperature or the skin temperature from a band of norms for each will lead to discomfort, pain, and in extreme cases, death. These bands are 35 to 39°C (mean 37°C) for the core and 20 to 40°C for the skin.

Chronic exposure which leads to core temperatures above 39°C is known as 'heat stroke'. Chronic exposure which leads to core temperatures below 35°C is termed 'hypothermia'. Chronic exposure leading to skin temperatures above 42°C constitutes a 'burn'. Chronic exposure leading to skin temperatures below 10°C constitutes 'frost bite'. Acute exposure to temperatures below − 40°C constitutes a 'cold contact burn'.

4.6.2 Industrial sources of thermal energy

These may be thermal radiation as, for example, from a fireball or a pool fire, or very hot solids, liquids, or gases. For contact with hot substances at any given temperature, the higher the thermal conductance of the material with which the skin is in contact, the greater is its hazard. In some instances injury may be caused through electro-magnetic induction from induction heaters or micro wave heaters.

Hot gases are a common source of injury. Above, say, 700°C, hot gases are incandescent and are described as 'flames'. However, severe injuries may be caused by hot gases even when they are non-incandescent. There are other sources of thermal gain, such as friction and the passage of electric current, which lie outside the scope of this discussion. However, electricity has a dose equation of similar form to the thermal energy dose equation.

The action of certain reactive chemicals upon the body produces injuries similar to those produced by the effect of high temperatures. This section is, however, immediately concerned only with injuries which arise purely from differences in temperature between the body and its surroundings. Those cases in which injury arises from chemical reaction with the body are discussed in Section 4.9 (page 192).

4.6.3 The nature of burns and scalds

In common speech a distinction is drawn between 'burns' and 'scalds', burns being associated with 'dry' heat and scalds with 'moist' heat. Burns are associated with materials with a temperature exceeding 60°C and with no upper limit of temperature. Scalds are associated with water or steam, with temperatures exceeding 50°C and with an upper limit of perhaps 110°C. The effects of scalds are the same as those of burns caused by dry substances at the same temperature.

181

4.6.4 Degrees of severity of burns

It has long been customary to consider burn injuries as lying on a scale of *degrees* which can be regarded as a measure of dose. Though this uni-dimensional scale does not command universal acceptance by those members of the medical profession who are concerned with the treatment of burns, an indicative scale of this sort is adequate for this text.

Four degrees of severity are distinguished, quantified by reference to the temperature difference between the skin and a contacting hot body (assumed to be a good conductor of heat). An initial skin temperature at the upper end ('threshhold') of the scale of comfort, namely 40°C, is assumed. Such comparisons may be found in standard general works of reference. After a dose equation for burns has been introduced, a table of correspondence between dose and severity will be provided.

In first-degree burns, the injury is produced by 30 seconds' contact with a hot body at 55°C (15°C above the threshhold). Such a burn resembles mild sunburn and there is virtually no destruction of tissue. It heals easily.

In second-degree burns, the injury is produced by 30 seconds' contact with a hot body at 60°C (20°C above the threshhold). This produces blistering and partial skin loss. It will probably heal without any need for skin grafting.

In third-degree burns, the injury is produced by 30 seconds' contact with a hot body at 65°C (25°C above the threshhold). The full thickness of the skin is destroyed and there is damage to underlying tissue. Skin grafting is essential to healing.

In fourth-degree burns, the injury is produced by 30 seconds' contact with a hot body at $\geq 70°C$ (30° above the threshhold). There is severe damage to underlying tissue and the injury is very difficult to repair.

4.6.5 The extent of injury

Complications from burns

The harm from burns is not confined to the surface of the body but may also involve the whole body system: for example, they may prove lethal by producing kidney failure. As they constitute an open wound they also may permit invasion by bacteria. There are many other possible complications.

Area affected and age of victim

The *area* affected by the burn, as well as its intensity, determines the risk of death or disabling injury. However, this is not by itself an absolute determining factor — for any individual at a given age, it is the *proportion* of the total area of the skin which is the dominant factor. [The total area of skin of an adult male is about $1.8\,\mathrm{m}^2$]. As well as severity and area covered, the age of the person is also highly significant. The best chances of recovery are for children and adolescents. After the age of 20, there is a steady decline in the prospects of recovery.

No one, at any age, will survive burns affecting the full thickness of the skin which involve 80% or more of the total body area. Young people will generally survive 60% body-area burns. However, the figures at age 60 are around 40% for a low probability of recovery and 20% for a high probability of recovery. People of age 80 or over are very unlikely to survive 20% body-area burns. There is further information on this in Brown[19] and in encyclopaedia entries on burns and scalds.

4.6.6 Dose and thermal energy

Influence of thermal conductance

The fact that there is a relationship, for a given degree of harm, between the rate at which heat enters the body and the duration of the exposure, is a matter of common experience. However, it is not possible to express this by a general dose equation which characterizes rate by the temperature difference between the skin and the ambient surroundings, because the thermal conductance of the immediate surroundings is highly significant. For example, whereas contact with a block of steel at 70°C for 30 seconds would produce a severe burn, contact for the same period with a block of foamed polystyrene at 70°C would do little harm.

In the case of hot fluids, their velocity relative to the receptor is a further determining factor because of the contribution to heat transfer of forced convection.

The Eisenberg dose equation

Eisenberg *et al.*[20] put forward the following equation to represent a dose for incident thermal radiation on bare skin:

$$L = \theta \times (\phi_R \times 10^{-3})^n \qquad (4.11)$$

where

θ — duration, s

ϕ_R — incident radiant energy flux, $\mathrm{W\,m}^{-2}$

L — 'thermal load, $\mathrm{s\,(kW\,m}^{-2})^n$

n — a dimensionless constant evaluated empirically at 1.33. [The constant is expressed as a decimal fraction, lest the use of the vulgar fraction 4/3 might be thought to imply a theoretical derivation].

It will be seen that the quantity 'thermal load' is the type of parameter defined in Section 4.4.3 (page 174). Equation (4.11) is thus an empirically determined formula for establishing a table of correspondences. Such a table, based on Eisenberg, is given in Table 4.5 below.

Table 4.5 Correspondence for thermal injury

$L (= \theta \times \phi_R^{1.33} \times 10^{-4})$ (s (kW m^{-2})$^{1.33}$)	Severity of burn
<700	First degree
ca 1200	Second degree
ca 2500	Third degree

Application to non-radiant heat
Further analysis suggests that, if the emissivity of human skin is 1.0 — that is, skin is a *black body* (confirmed by Hymes[21]), this equation also represents the thermal flux through the skin.

It is thus apparent that the equation is a general representation of dose rate associated with thermal gain, and not just for that arising from thermal radiation. Thus, whatever the source of heat and whatever the extent of attenuation by clothing, the same thermal flux will produce the same degree of harm (the subscript R can then be deleted). This may, however, over-simplify the situation if allowance has to be made for the transparency of skin to thermal radiation.

The Eisenberg probit
For fatal burns, Hymes attributes probit equation (4.12) to Eisenberg et al.[20]. He claims that it is a human probit based upon data from atomic bomb victims. It is quoted here as indicative, but is not vouched for as to its generality since, in the circumstances, few of the victims could have received effective medical treatment.

$$Y = -14.9 + 2.56\log_e [\theta \times (\phi_R \times 10^{-3})^{1.333}] = -14.9 + 2.56\log_e L \tag{4.12}$$

Literature references
Buettner[22-24] gives a detailed account of experiments on the effects of extreme heat and cold on the human skin while Hymes[21] gives a fuller discussion of the problems than can be given here.

4.6.7 Harm to people from loss of thermal energy

Harm from cold is a hazard situation which is exceptional in that harm is caused by heat *leaving* the receptor. It is thus an emission which is in the reverse direction to those discussed elsewhere in the book — *from* a receptor *to* a source — but which results in harm to the receptor.

Although it is not usual to speak of a *dose* of cold there seems no reason why loss of thermal energy from a receptor should be treated differently from other agents. In equation (4.12) ϕ (without subscript) may represent a rate of thermal energy loss per unit of receptor area $[\text{W m}^{-2}]$. This, when multiplied by the duration θ, gives the total quantity of energy lost per m^2. If this is multiplied by the area affected, it gives the total of energy lost $[\text{J}]$.

Acute and chronic conditions

The condition in which the core temperature is appreciably lower than $37°\text{C}$ has been extensively studied. It is known as *hypothermia*. There are degrees of hypothermia — a core temperature of less than $30°\text{C}$ is characterized as *severe hypothermia*. Data exist on ϕ for hypothermia but not apparently on the value of n in the dose equation.

Hypothermia is unlikely to occur in the chemical and process industries. A possible example might be if someone were to be trapped in a cold room; but, as it is usually produced by chronic exposure to cold conditions, it lies outside the scope of this book. The temperature of the skin lies between the core temperature and that of the environment. Skin temperature is much more variable than core temperature. Thus a person can have the very low skin temperature of $20°\text{C}$ without necessarily suffering from hypothermia.

Cold contact burns

A *cold contact burn* may arise from the hazards of cold materials as, for example, the flashing of liquefied vapours or the spillage of liquefied gases, both of which were discussed in Section 2.6 (page 57). Splashing of such liquids onto bare skin, or contact with metal cooled to such temperatures, may produce them. Contact with metal may cause the skin to freeze to it.

Though the phenomenon of the cold contact burn is real and is mentioned in all texts on the handling of low temperature materials, there is no explanation of why extreme cold should produce symptoms resembling those produced by extreme heat. It may simply be that, at very low temperatures, the nerves which are stimulated by heat also react to cold.

The symptoms of a cold contact burn resemble those of a first or second degree heat burn. Clearly, though, extreme cold cannot reproduce the chemical changes in tissue associated with high temperatures, which include charring.

Cold contact burns, if not promptly treated, can lead to the destruction of tissue. In this they resemble *frost bite* although this takes much longer to develop. The seriousness of cold contact burns is related, like that of hot contact burns, not only to their local severity, but also to the fraction of the body which is affected. For a case history involving cold contact burns, see Chapter 5, 'Spanish campsite disaster', page 237.

4.6.8 Protection of people from gain or loss of thermal energy

Protection from burns or scalds

Where people are regularly engaged in the handling of high-temperature materials, appropriate clothing of low thermal conductivity and low flammability is the most effective preventative measure. Where the hazard source presents a fairly low risk of fire it is not practical to expect people to wear heat insulating clothing regularly, but it is important that they wear clothing of *low flammability* — thus cotton overalls should not be worn.

4.7 Harm to people from asphyxiants

4.7.1 Introduction

This section, and Sections 4.8 and 4.9, discuss the harms which may arise to people from the inhalation of, or contact with, certain chemical substances, even at ordinary temperatures and pressures. The discussion will be confined to the harms that arise from *acute* exposure to such substances. The harms which may arise from *chronic* exposures to low concentrations of such substances, and which may lead to occupational disease, lie outside this book's remit. For this reason 'control' or 'threshold limits' which are intended to limit chronic exposure to chemicals in the workplace are not quoted.

The number of harmful substances is vast — indeed all chemical substances are harmful if inhaled or ingested at a sufficient concentration. It is therefore impossible to treat the subject comprehensively. Rather, the general principles and some important examples are discussed. Where the requisite data exist, these examples are treated from the standpoint of dose and probit analysis.

The substances discussed are divided into asphyxiants, toxics and corrosives and a separate section is devoted to each.

4.7.2 Definition of asphyxiation

Jones[8] gives the following definition:

Asphyxiation — endangering life by causing a deficiency of oxygen.

4.7.3 Types of asphyxiant

Solid and liquid asphyxiants
Any agent which physically impedes the flow of air to the lungs is an asphyxiant. Powders and liquids fall into this category when they cause death by choking or by drowning. This form of asphyxiation belongs in the category of general industrial accidents.

Gaseous asphyxiants
These are substances which asphyxiate by diluting the oxygen content of the air. As oxygen is the only gas which supports life, all other gases or vapours, when mixed with air, attenuate its ability to do so and are, to that extent, asphyxiants.

However, many such substances have other properties which cause harm and these are discussed under the heading of toxics. Only simple asphyxiants — that is, gases or vapours which can be breathed in concentrations up to, say, 10% in air, more or less indefinitely without harmful effects, but which are harmful in concentrations above about 40% — will be considered. Examples of such asphyxiants include the inert gases, hydrogen, the gaseous paraffins, Freons, and nitrogen, when it is present in excess of its normal concentration in air (about 78% by volume).

Dose related to harm
Table 4.6 relates the concentration of asphyxiant in air to the harm it produces. A probit for asphyxiation has not been encountered.

Table 4.6 Dose versus harm for simple asphyxiants

Concentrations (% by volume)		Duration (minutes)	Harm produced
Asphyxiant	Oxygen		
33	14		Deeper respiration
50	10.5		Giddiness, blue lips
60	8.5		Vomiting, ashen face
66	7	360	50% mortality
81	4	40	Coma, followed by death

Industrial sources of asphyxiants
Due to the high concentration of asphyxiant required, typically over 50%, asphyxiation seldom arises in the open air and is mainly a problem of confined

spaces. Asphyxiants may enter such spaces by leakage, but some cases of asphyxiation have been due to the presence of materials which have reacted with oxygen and produced an oxygen-deficient atmosphere.

Attenuation of harm

Entry into confined spaces must be closely regulated and governed by a permit-to-work system. All possible sources of in-leakage of asphyxiants must be sealed off. Personal protection is by the provision of breathing apparatus, either self-contained or hose-fed. Canister respirators, which operate by detoxifying air, are totally useless to protect against asphyxiation and wearing them would only serve to induce a false sense of security. Treatment is by removal to fresh air and the application of resuscitation.

4.8 Harm to people from toxics

4.8.1 Definition of toxic

Jones[8] gives the following definition:

> **Toxic** — a property of substances which, when introduced into or absorbed by a living organism, destroy life or injure health.

This definition would apply regardless of the administration route but, since administration by ingestion is of only minor importance in the acute situation, the discussion will be confined to inhalation and skin contact.

4.8.2 Sources of information on toxics

A significant monograph is Turner and Fairhurst[11], which discusses the methodologies used by the UK Health and Safety Executive to assess the toxic properties of those agents which they characterize as 'Major Accident Hazards'. On the basis of this work, the Health and Safety Executive has produced monographs on a number of agents including ammonia[25], chlorine[26], hydrogen fluoride[27] and hydrogen sulphide[28]. In addition, the IChemE has produced monographs on ammonia[29], chlorine[30] and phosgene[31].

The most important single source of data in the field is Sax[32]. A convenient shorter source reference is NIOSH[33]. There are extensive data on doses in NIOSH[34] but these may require expert interpretation. Marshall[35] discusses some important toxic agents in their industrial context.

Where monographs exist on individual toxics, these are cited at the appropriate point.

188

These data are presented — in some cases by direct quotation and in others by interpolation — for purposes of illustration and comparison only. Any reader wishing to make detailed use of them is strongly advised to consult the cited publications to ascertain their applicability to the problem at hand.

4.8.3 Toxicity and chemical composition

Toxic properties are intimately bound up with chemical composition. In this they differ from the classes of flammable, explosive or asphyxiating substances where in each class the same kind of harm may arise from substances which differ widely in chemical composition.

4.8.4 How dose is expressed

In calculating dose for each substance, the expression of the concentration in air has here been standardized as a molar ratio of parts per million. Concentration is sometimes expressed in the literature as milligrams per cubic metre and data expressed in this form have been converted, for the sake of uniformity.

Although, elsewhere in this book, time has been expressed in the SI unit of the second, in this section the duration of exposure is expressed in minutes because that is the universal practice in the literature of toxicology, probably because the second is too short an interval for significant effects to be observed.

4.8.5 Quantals

Three quantals are used. The first of these is death — though this seems unambiguous, animal experimenters qualify it by specifying a maximum time interval between the experiment and the occurrence of death. This quantal, as is usual for toxics inhaled from the atmosphere, is expressed as LC_{50} — that is, the harm which corresponds to death for 50% of an exposed population. (The equivalent dose is not an accurate figure and represents, at best, a mean value).

The second quantal is equivalent to the HSE's *Specified Level of Toxicity* (or SLOT) corresponding with a *dangerous toxic load* (or DTL)[11]. 'Serious harm syndrome' or SHS is substituted for the sake of brevity and in order to distinguish more clearly between a *dose* and the *effects* to which it gives rise. However, the HSE's *criteria* characterizing the syndrome are used, as follows:

Serious harm syndrome — a syndrome with the following characteristics:

- severe distress to almost everyone;
- a substantial fraction require medical attention;
- any highly susceptible people may be killed.

The third quantal is based on the criteria of the US IDLH (Immediately Dangerous to Life or Health), see NIOSH[36]. As with the HSE DTL, this term confuses *dose* with the *effects* to which it gives rise. This quantal is here termed 'Incipient Harm Syndrome' (or IHS).

IHS — a syndrome which arises from a borderline toxic exposure. It is an exposure from which one could escape within 30 minutes without escape-impairing symptoms or any irreversible health effects.

4.8.6 Data on toxics

Representative substances

Data are presented in the Appendix for a number of representative toxic substances of industrial importance, in the form of standardized data sheets arranged in alphabetical order of substance. Note that some items of data are missing. The term *load* is used, as defined in Section 4.4.3 (page 174). Some loads are related to *doses* and others to *indices* of dose. Where an exposure has been quoted as a concentration combined with a duration, the toxic *load* has been calculated, using the index n cited for the substance in question. Where no duration is quoted in the *load* column this implies a prolonged and indefinite duration. Where probits are quoted these are derived from observations on animals. They should be interpreted in the light of the discussion in Section 4.4 (page 175).

Smoke

There is general agreement that during fires in general, more people are killed by inhaling smoke than by burns. Though this statistic may be true for fires in general, the vast majority of which occur in confined spaces in domestic circumstances, it is not true for chemical and process plant where the predominant mode is the outdoor fire. It is nevertheless possible to have confined fires on a plant, especially in warehouses (see Chapter 5, 'Basel' and 'Bradford', pages 214 and 218).

Tuhtar[37] cites references which claim that between 20 and 40 different constituents are detectable in smoke from fires. A major constituent is carbon monoxide, which may administer a lethal dose. Smoke may also be an asphyxiant and can seriously limit visibility.

4.8.7 Comparison of toxicities

Rank order of quantals

For each agent studied in Section 4.8.6, the rank order of the doses corresponding to each of the quantals, IHS, US IDLH, OHS (British dangerous toxic load) and LC_{50} is the same.

Rank order of toxicity of substance

Table 4.7 gives the rank order of toxicity, as expressed by their LC_{50} dose, of the substances discussed in Section 4.8.6. For ease of comparison, all the doses which produce the LC_{50} effect are expressed as the concentration for a 30-minute exposure. Such values are either taken directly from the monographs referenced above or have been calculated by us from the data in these monographs. The substances are listed in order of increasing toxicity.

Table 4.7 Comparison of toxicities

Substance	Concentration (molar ppm) corresponding, for a 30-minute exposure, with LC_{50} quantal
Carbon monoxide	16,000
Ammonia	11,500
Hydrogen fluoride	2900
Hydrogen sulphide	840
Chlorine	400
Phosgene	19

4.8.8 Measures of attenuation

General precautions

The general precautions are those measures of sound engineering practice which take account of the realizations of hazards which are discussed in Chapter 2. Of especial importance is the general layout of the site which protects as many employees as possible by the attenuation of distance. This must also take account of the prevailing wind as a transmission path and avoids siting offices and so on downwind of the toxic hazards. In the case of water-soluble gases, water curtains actuated by toxic alarms may attenuate the harm at a point close to the source.

Respiratory protection

Management must provide suitable respiratory protection for those employees who may be exposed to toxic gases. In most situations it is known which of the toxic gases are likely to be encountered and the means of protection provided will be the most appropriate.

There are two basic approaches. The first aims at providing a total barrier and supplies air for respiration from a non-contaminated source; the second operates by detoxification of the air.

For high concentrations, only air-fed breathing apparatus, whether by cylinders or by hose from a remote source, is suitable. Such equipment aims at 100% attenuation, but this will be diminished by leaks or faults. In some cases, where the skin is attacked, it may be necessary to provide a suit which protects the whole body.

At moderate concentrations, canister or capsule respirators which aim to detoxify the air on its way to the wearer's lungs may be suitable. Such respirators operate by a variety of methods, including absorption with chemical reaction, such as providing alkaline agents to react with acid gases; adsorption with activated charcoal; and catalysis, whereby a toxic agent is converted into an absorbable form. Canister and capsule masks suffer from having a rather short duration of activity and sometimes giving little warning of exhaustion.

Protection of the public

In the far field, evacuation is sometimes advocated, though this is often impractical. The best solution is to provide a warning system and then for people to stay in their own homes but to cut off, as far as practicable, air entering from the outside. This means closing windows and shutting off fuelled heating appliances or air conditioning.

4.9 Harm to people from corrosives

This section covers those toxic substances which, in the form of liquids and solids, produce harmful effects by contact with the skin. Such agents are numerous and examples are quoted.

4.9.1 Definition of corrosive

Jones[8] gives the following definition:

Corrosive — in the context of toxic substances, a corrosive substance is one which may, on contact with living tissues, destroy them.

The term 'caustic', which comes from the Greek 'to burn', has the same meaning as corrosive. Some standard reference works use *caustic* as a synonym for *corrosive*. However, many people, because of the close association with alkalis which the term has acquired, identify it mistakenly with *alkaline*, rather than with *corrosive*, properties. To avoid confusion, the term 'caustic' is not used here.

4.9.2 Dose and corrosives

Some medical reference books provide data on the correspondence between dose and effects for some ingested (swallowed) toxics. This aspect has been excluded from consideration, so such data are not reproduced here.

For eye contact, one milligram or less is likely to cause serious harm. For skin contact, it seems reasonable to regard one gram as a dose which will produce significant local harmful effects. The general degree of harm will be proportional to the area affected. Thus where burns occur their effects are likely to be similar to those produced by a similar area of thermal burn and the relationships of area versus fractional mortality are likely to apply.

4.9.3 The nature of corrosives

General nature of injuries

Corrosives give rise to immediate injury which is painful and usually resembles the pain of thermal burns. In some cases there are powerful thermal effects arising from exothermal reactions between the agent and the tissues. Other features of thermal burns, such as reddening of the skin and the formation of blisters, are also observed. The exact nature of the attack depends upon the agent, but there seem to be two principal mechanisms — dehydration and oxidation.

Dehydrations

Any substance which reacts powerfully with water may give rise to dehydration injury. Such reactions may be highly exothermal, giving rise to temperatures in excess of 100°C. Examples are concentrated sulphuric acid, oleum and liquid SO_3. Concentrated solutions of potassium and sodium hydroxides also react powerfully with tissue to combine with the water it contains.

Oxidizing agents

Concentrated nitric acid and chromic acid react powerfully with tissue. The reaction is highly exothermal and may give rise to charring.

Other effects

Any agent which affects the pH level of the skin gives rise to discomfort and injury. Thus concentrated acetic acid, which is neither a dehydrating agent nor an oxidizing agent, will cause blisters.

Phenol is a solid at ordinary temperatures but is usually handled in a molten condition. Though it is not a dehydrating agent, an oxidizing agent nor is it highly acidic, it is, nevertheless, corrosive to the skin, which it readily penetrates. It is a systemic poison and death has ensued within 30 minutes of contact. Death has been known to follow a burn area of about $0.05\,\mathrm{m}^2$.

Hydrogen fluoride is an exceptionally serious hazard. It causes severe, slowly-healing burns. It readily penetrates the skin and diffuses rapidly through tissue. It may attack the bones and can give rise to gangrene.

4.9.4 Attenuation of harm

General precautions

The storage of corrosives requires, in the first place, suitable siting arrangements to segregate the hazard from people. This must include suitable catchment arrangements such as bunds to limit the flow of spilled materials. Secondly, ample water supplies from sprays are needed, so that victims may be sluiced down without delay.

Personal protection

This generally takes the form of gloves, aprons, and eye-shields, but in some cases whole-body protection is required. For some agents, such as hydrogen fluoride, suitable antidotes must be immediately available.

4.10 Harm to equipment and buildings from emissions of pressure energy

In this section the harm which may arise from the direct absorption of pressure energy associated with explosions both to equipment and to buildings is discussed.

4.10.1 General considerations

Accuracy

The subject area of damage from explosions is one of a low degree of accuracy. Thus formulae and data which include many places of decimals should be treated with caution and such precision regarded as having arisen fortuitously from calculations. Accuracies are seldom better than ±20%.

References

Important references are Baker *et al.*[10], Phillips[15] and Merrifield[38]. These references demonstrate the complexities of the relationship between blast energy and damage, and only a highly simplified version can be presented here. Marshall[35] contains case histories of damage to buildings with photographs and sketches.

Glasstone and Dolan[16] give much detail on the effects of blast from nuclear weapons on equipment and buildings. However, these latter may be only roughly comparable with the effects of blast from conventional explosives — for example, the duration of the positive phase in nuclear explosions is measured in seconds, as compared with milliseconds for conventional explosives, differing by a factor of about 10^3. On the other hand, blast from vapour cloud explosions is associated with a duration similar to that of nuclear explosions.

4.10.2 The significance of overpressure as an index

It has been pointed out, in an earlier section, that peak overpressure can only be an *index* of harm, as it does not have the dimensions of energy per unit area of cross-section of path. Though more reliable results have been claimed for the use of *impulse*, which is a product of overpressure and duration, this, similarly, does not have the dimensions of energy per unit cross-sectional area. No-one appears to have put forward a *load* expression for equal damage of the form of $(\Delta p^n_{max}) \times \theta$ where Δp_{max} is peak overpressure and θ is duration.

Overpressure will therefore be used as the index of damage. This also reflects that in most cases only overpressure data are available. It is relevant to point out that brittle structures appear to be more sensitive than ductile ones to the same level of overpressure for the same duration. Thus windows will suffer more damage than pipes in such circumstances.

4.10.3 Some representative values for equipment

The data in this area are very fragmentary. Phillips[15] reproduces a table from Stephens[39], in which the data are derived from nuclear testing, and damage is expressed in terms of quantals such as 'piping breaks' and 'unit overturns'.

According to this table, incipient damage (breakage of gauge glasses) sets in at 0.03 bar, whilst at the extreme end of the spectrum (1.5 bar), process plant is wrecked. Intermediately, a chemical reactor moves on its foundations at 0.25 bar and its frame deforms at 0.45 bar. The Flixborough vapour cloud explosion (see Chapter 5, page 227), in which overpressures of 0.7 to 1.0 bar were experienced, showed many examples of severe damage to process units and great distortion of piping.

4.10.4 Some representative values for buildings

Wartime data

Many data on damage to houses were assembled by the British authorities during the Second World War. These were based upon aerial bombing with conventional explosives, assumed to be TNT or equivalent. Overpressures were deduced from estimates of the calibre of the bomb by military intelligence followed by the application of Hopkinson's Scaling Law.

A set of damage quantals were established and these were related to the overpressure required to produce them (see Table 4.8).

Glasstone and Dolan[16], based on nuclear tests, cite 0.33 bar for total demolition of a brick-built house and 0.12 bar for C_b class damage. For further discussion of damage to housing from explosions, see Marshall[35].

Table 4.8 Housing damage and overpressure

	Damage category	Overpressure (bar)
A	Almost complete demolition	> 0.7
B	So severe as to require demolition	> 0.25 < 0.33
C_b	Severe but repairable	> 0.04 < 0.25

[The value of 0.04 corresponds to 90% window shatter.]

Damage to buildings in process plant

There are difficulties in relating damage to housing and damage to process buildings. In the past some kinds of industrial buildings have proved less robust than houses. Lessons have been learned from case studies which have led to codes for the construction of vulnerable structures such as control buildings. The principal features of these are discussed in Marshall[35]. In the main, such buildings are best constructed in reinforced concrete with a single storey. Doors are sited so as not to face the direction of likely blast. Windows are narrow and protected against glass being projected into the room. In-fill panels are of reinforced concrete which is ductile, whereas brick in-filling is not.

4.10.5 Attenuation of harm from explosions in process plant

Off-site
The only practicable approach is by attenuation through distance. This is accomplished through land use planning, which requires co-operation between management and the public authorities.

On-site
Again, the best means of attenuation is by distance. Buildings which cannot, for operational reasons, be sited completely out of the range of likely blast must be built to approved codes, so as to render them sufficiently resistant. In some cases the provision of blast walls as barriers may be appropriate.

Buildings in hazardous areas should be designed to accommodate only those functions which are essential for a building in such a location. Personnel housed in them should be restricted to those whose presence there is essential.

4.11 Harm to equipment, materials and buildings from emissions of thermal energy

This section examines first the general nature of the harmful effects of thermal energy on equipment, on materials in process, and on buildings. Some special aspects of fire in relation to buildings and structures are then considered.

Chemical and process plant and materials in process are composed of many different substances. There are 10s of 1000s of substances which form the raw materials, materials in process, finished products and waste materials of the industries. They may be handled in equipment made of both metals and non-metals. The buildings which house equipment and serve the industries are made in the main of reinforced concrete and brick with glass and a certain amount of wood. The subject is highly complex and it is only possible to draw attention to some salient points. Marchant[40] gives a detailed discussion of the effects of fires.

4.11.1 The harms from thermal radiation and convection

Of the three mechanisms of heat transfer, conduction is the least important in this context. Thermal radiation and convection, especially through flames, may cause direct harm by inducing chemical and physical changes in materials in process and materials of construction. If they cause materials to catch fire, they may also cause indirect harm by the effects of the water, or other coolant, applied to combat the fire, and by the effects of smoke (see Section 4.8.6, page 190).

The most obvious chemical effect is combustion, but lower temperatures may still produce serious harm. Raising the temperature of process materials may render them useless by altering their chemical composition. This applies with particular force to fine organic chemicals such as pharmaceuticals.

In the case of materials of construction, raising their temperature will usually weaken them so that, for example, structures may collapse and pressure vessels may no longer be able to withstand the pressures for which they are designed. Raising temperatures may alter the properties of metals by changing their crystalline structure so that, even after they have cooled off, they have suffered permanent harm and are no longer suitable for their original purpose.

Non-metallic materials such as brickwork or concrete may lose their physical nature. They first weaken and then disintegrate. Thus concrete, which varies greatly in composition, loses half its strength at 300–400°C, and structural steel loses half its strength at about 650°C.

Differential thermal expansion may play a role, especially with brick and window glass. Both, and especially the latter, unless specially treated, are shattered by it. Georgian wired glass retains its geometry after shatter but it is not recommended for explosion situations.

Some materials, such as plastics, may soften or melt. Electrical and instrument cables will fail at around 120° to 140°C and can only withstand a prolonged incident flux of $2\,kW\,m^{-2}$ (see Mecklenburgh[41]). The spread of fire in ordinary buildings, and the attenuation of the risk of harm to people from such fires, are extensively treated in standard works on fire prevention and precautions.

4.11.2 Fires in storage

Due to the large inventories involved (which usually much exceed the inventory of materials in process), fires in storage facilities can be both intense and prolonged. Such fires may result in financial loss through destruction of stocks and buildings and interruption of production. They may cause serious alarm in the neighbourhood and lead to environmental pollution. Such facilities may be classified into two main categories — tank-farms and warehouses.

Tank farms

Tank farms typically comprise a fairly limited number of relatively large storages each dedicated to storing a particular material or class of materials in liquid form.

The problems of the effects of thermal energy upon tanks and their loading and unloading facilities have been the subject of many studies by the chemical and petroleum industries. They represent a classic case of the potential of hazard receptors to become secondary sources, known sometimes as the 'domino effect'. Even liquids of high flash point, on receipt of sufficiently intense thermal energy, may become flammable. An example of a serious tank-farm incident is described in a HSE report on 'Milford Haven'[42].

Attenuation of harm on tank-farms

The hazards may be reduced by inventory limitation — that is, by a critical analysis of how much material it is necessary to store, consistent with operational efficiency.

Hazard is attenuated by geometry and this is treated by imposing safety distances. Mecklenburg[41] gives indicative distances. Bunding — the provision of barriers to the spreading of spilled liquid — is much used. Tanks may have their radiant emissivity reduced by providing reflective surfaces.

Attenuating the spread of actual fire may be secured by (1) the provision of built-in permanent fire-fighting equipment and (2) the intervention of fire-fighters. Built-in equipment includes water sprays and foam systems. These latter provide a barrier to the receipt by a flammable liquid of thermal radiation from a fire above it which vaporizes the liquid beneath, as well as providing cooling. They are particularly indicated for hydrocarbon fires. Fire-fighting includes the cooling of receptors to prevent them from becoming sources.

Risk attenuation is secured by a regime of ignition source suppression and by the provision of alarm systems. A useful reference work on this subject is by Cox et al.[43].

Warehouse fires

The most significant examples of chemical warehouses are those which serve multi-product batch-operated plants. These may store 100s of different chemicals, usually in sacks small enough to be handled manually, or in drums. There have been a number of serious fires in chemical warehouses. Two of these are cited as examples in Chapter 5 ('Basel', page 214, and 'Bradford', page 218).

Certain features of warehouses may lead to a rapid spread of fire. The materials are usually stacked on pallets or on racks, perhaps up to six or seven metres high. This arrangement favours vertical fire spread by convection. Incompletely burned combustion products tend to accumulate under the roof and this can promote 'flash-over', with lateral spread of the fire. For an example, see King[44].

Both of the case histories cited were also significant sources of environmental pollution. This is a likely consequence if steps have not been taken to impound the run-off of fire-fighting water. The smoke from such fires, which contains a great variety of combustion products, may be especially harmful.

Attenuation of harm in warehouses

As with tank farms, the hazard may be attenuated by minimizing inventories. An important method of hazard attenuation is by the use of barriers to compartmentalize warehouses and thus restrict the lateral spread of fire. Barriers may also segregate incompatible materials such as oxidizing and reducing agents. Bagging and filling operations should be segregated from storage.

Risk may be attenuated by avoiding ignition sources, and automatically operated roof vents reduce the risk of lateral spread.

The BLEVE scenario

A particular type of realization which usually entails the total destruction of a pressure vessel and probably serious secondary harms is the boiling liquid expanding vapour-cloud explosion or BLEVE. This phenomenon is described in Chapter 2 (page 51) and it is illustrated in two case histories in Chapter 5 ('Feyzin', page 225, and 'Mexico City', page 232).

4.11.3 Fire and buildings

Thermal resistance criteria

This section deals with the effects on buildings from the impact of external thermal energy. Internal effects are covered by standard works on the subject as noted in Section 4.11.2.

There is no generalized attempt in the literature to correlate a quantal level of harm Q with a *load* such as $\phi^n \times \theta$ in the manner used above for other harmful agents (where ϕ is an intensity or flux, n an empirically determined exponent and θ the duration of exposure). Instead buildings have to conform to a requirement that they can withstand a standard radiant flux for one hour. The flux specified for one hour in the UK, for a glazed building with exposed wood, is about $14 \, \mathrm{kW \, m^{-2}}$ (see Mecklenburgh[41]).

Structural considerations

Major inhabited buildings in the process industries are likely to be steel-framed. Where there is a significant risk of exposure to fire, the steelwork in such buildings may be encased in concrete. Though concrete loses its strength at a relatively low temperature, it is a good thermal insulator and considerably extends the time before the steel it encases suffers a significant loss of strength.

Attenuation of harm to buildings

The most significant measure to be taken is attenuation by geometry such as through distance. This may be planned by appropriate lay-out of the plant, though it is possible to nullify the planning by the introduction of temporary hazards, for example, by permitting trucks laden with flammables to park nearby or by tolerating the presence of drum parks in the vicinity.

The level of incident thermal energy may be reduced by means of permanently installed sprays on vulnerable sides of the building, or by arranging for fire-fighters to train jets on to heated walls.

4.12 Harm to the environment from acute emissions

The phenomenon may be regarded as one in which an emission creates off-site secondary hazards which have the potential to harm people by toxic effects. This may occur through direct contact, in which case the secondary hazards created are passive hazards, or the effects may occur through a transmission path when polluted food or drink is ingested. In such cases, the transmission path could be animal or vegetable in character. This section is devoted to the effects of acute emissions only.

4.12.1 Transmission paths

Harm from primary sources, leading to environmental pollutions through the creation of secondary hazards, may be transmitted by the atmosphere or through water. The atmosphere may act as a transmission path for droplets or suspended solid particles, including smoke. Examples are given in Chapter 5 under 'Basel', 'Bradford', and 'Seveso' (pages 214, 218 and 235 respectively). Water courses may carry harmful materials, either in suspension or in solution, which may be toxic to aquatic life. The cases of 'Basel' and 'Bradford' in Chapter 5 are examples of this.

4.12.2 Persistence

An important factor is persistence. Toxic gases are generally of low persistence under any other than exceptional atmospheric conditions. Buoyant gases are clearly non-persistent. Generally, the higher the density of the gas the more persistent it is likely to be.

However, solids and liquids are potentially much more persistent than gases. An example is mustard gas. In spite of its name this is in fact a liquid and when used in the First World War as a blister agent, it could persist on the ground for weeks, especially in winter. This material has, however, little commercial significance. Dioxin, released at Seveso, is an example of a highly persistent agent.

4.12.3 Secondary transmission paths

These are transmission paths which transmit harm from secondary hazards. If the secondary hazard is edible then harmful substances may enter the food chain and harm humans. Thus meat, milk, fish and vegetables may be transmission paths.

4.12.4 Attenuation of harm to the environment

To attenuate hazards having the potential to give rise to pollution, it is necessary to examine hazard sources for such potential and, where possible, to substitute less hazardous materials. However some substances such as insecticides and herbicides are manufactured for their biocidal properties and this course may not be possible. Inventory limitation is probably desirable, and special measures should be taken to trap materials which may be released in the event of process malfunction.

Precautions must also be taken to impound the run-off of water used for fire-fighting where biocidal materials may be exposed to fire. Cases of river pollution from this cause are given in Chapter 5 under 'Basel' (page 214) and 'Bradford' (page 218).

In the event of a release having off-site effects, and where toxic effects through the food chain are anticipated, the harm may be attenuated by precautionary slaughtering of animals and/or by the temporary sterilization of agricultural land. Vegetables may have to be washed. 'Seveso', referred to in Section 4.12.2 (a case histroy is given in Chapter 5), is an important case where such measures were taken. Emergency planning may have to include the preparation of measures for decontamination.

References in Chapter 4

1. Luxon, S.G. (ed), 1992, *Hazards in the Chemical Laboratory*, 5th edn (Royal Society of Chemistry, UK).
2. Furr, A.K. (ed), 1990, *CRC Handbook of Laboratory Safety* (Bocu Raton Co, Wolfe).
3. Daintith, J. and Nelson, R.D., 1989, *The Penguin Dictionary of Mathematics*, (PDM) (Penguin, UK).
4. Illingworth, V. (ed), 1991, *The Penguin Dictionary of Physics*, (PDP) 2nd edn (Penguin, UK).

5. Uvarov, E.B. and Isaacs, A., 1986, *The Penguin Dictionary of Science*, (PDS) 6th edn (Penguin, UK).
6. MEST, 1997, *McGraw-Hill Encyclopedia of Science and Technology*, 8th edn, vol 5 (McGraw-Hill, USA).
7. BSI, 1993, *BS 5555 The Use of SI Units* (British Standards Institution, UK).
8. Jones, D. (ed), 1992, *Nomenclature for Hazard and Risk Assessment in the Process Industries*, 2nd edn (IChemE, UK).
9. Marshall, V.C. and Ruhemann, S., 1997, An anatomy of hazard systems and its application to acute process hazards, *Trans IChemE, Part B, Proc Safe Env Prot* 75(B2): 65–72.
10. Baker W.E., Cox P.H., Westine, P.S., Kulesz, P.S. and Strehlow, R.A., 1983, *Explosion Hazards and Evaluation* (Elsevier, The Netherlands).
11. Turner, R.M. and Fairhurst, S., 1989, *Assessment of the toxicity of major hazard substances*. Health & Safety Executive Specialist Inspector Reports No 21 (HMSO, UK).
12. Lees, F.P., 1994, The assessment of major hazards, *Trans IChemE, Part B, Proc Safe Env Prot*, 72(B3): 127–134.
13. Finney, D., 1971, *Probit Analysis*, 3rd edn (Cambridge University Press, UK).
14. Marshall, V.C., 1989, The prediction of human mortality from chemical accidents with special reference to the lethal toxicity of chlorine, *J Hazardous Materials*, 22: 13.
15. Phillips, H. (ed), 1994, *Explosions in the Process Industries*, Major hazards monograph (A Report of the Major Hazards Assessment Panel Overpressure Working Party) 2nd edn (IChemE, UK).
16. Glasstone, S. and Dolan, P.J., 1980, *The Effects of Nuclear Weapons* (Castle House, UK).
17. Poblete, B.R., Lees, F.P. and Simpson, G.B., 1984, The assessment of major hazards — estimation of injury and damage round a hazard source, *J Hazardous Materials*, 9: 355–371.
18. Moran, J.M. and Morgan, M.D., 1994, *Meteorology*, 4th edn (Macmillan, UK).
19. Brown, R.F., 1978, Injury by burning, in J.K. Mason (ed), *The Pathology of Violent Injury*, (Arnold, UK) pp. 386, 388, 390.
20. Eisenberg, N.A., Lynch, C.J. and Breeding, R.J., 1975, *Vulnerability Model* (US Coastguard Report CG-D-136-75, US Dept of Transportation).
21. Hymes, I., Boydell, W. and Prescott, B.L., 1994, *Report HSE/AEA/R275/Issue 2/94* (unpublished).
22. Buettner, K.J., 1951, Effects of extreme heat and cold on the human skin I, *J Appl Physiol*, 3: 691–702.
23. Buettner, K.J., 1951, Effects of extreme heat and cold on the human skin II, *J Appl Physiol*, 3: 703–713.
24. Buettner, K.J., 1952, Effects of extreme heat and cold on the human skin III, *J Appl Physiol*, 5: 207–270.

25. Payne, M.P., Delic, J. and Turner, R.M., 1990, *Toxicology of Substances in Relation to Major Hazards: Ammonia* (HMSO, UK).

26. Turner, R.M. and Fairhurst, S., 1990, *Toxicology of Substances in Relation to Major Hazards: Chlorine* (HMSO, UK).

27. Meldrum, M., 1993, *Toxicology of Substances in Relation to Major Hazards: Hydrogen Fluoride* (HMSO, UK).

28. Turner, R.M. and Fairhurst, S., 1990, *Toxicology of Substances in Relation to Major Hazards: Hydrogen Sulphide* (HMSO, UK).

29. IChemE, 1988, *Ammonia Toxicity Monograph*, Report of the Major Hazards Assessment Panel Toxicity Working Party (IChemE, UK).

30. IChemE, 1989, *Chlorine Toxicity Monograph*, 2nd edn, Report of the Major Hazards Assessment Panel Toxicity Working Party (IChemE, UK).

31. IChemE, 1993, *Phosgene Toxicity Monograph*, Report of the Major Hazards Assessment Panel Toxicity Working Party (IChemE, UK).

32. Lewis, R.J. and Sax, N.I., 1996, *Sax's Dangerous Properties of Industrial Materials*, 9th edn (Van Nostrand Reinhold, USA).

33. NIOSH (National Institute for Occupational Safety and Health), 1997, *NIOSH Pocket Guide to Chemical Hazards* (NIOSH Publications, USA).

34. NIOSH (National Institute for Occupational Safety and Health), 1982, *NIOSH Registry of Toxic Effects of Chemical Substances* (US Dept of Health, Education and Welfare, USA).

35. Marshall, V.C., 1987, *Major Chemical Hazards* (Ellis Harwood, UK).

36. NIOSH, 1987, *NIOSH Respirator Decision Logic*, US Department of Health and Human Services, Public Health Service, Centers for Disease Control, DHHS (NIOSH) Publication No 89-115.

37. Tuhtar, D., 1989, *Fire and Explosion Protection* (Ellis Horwood, UK).

38. Merrifield, R., 1993, *Simplified Calculations of Blast Induced Injuries and Damage*. Specialist Inspector Reports No 37 (Health and Safety Executive, UK).

39. Stephens, M.M., 1970, *Minimising Damage to Refineries* (US Department of the Interim, Office of Oil and Gas) February.

40. Marchant, E.W., 1972, *A Complete Guide to Fire and Buildings* (Medical & Technical Publishing Co, UK).

41. Mecklenburgh, J.C., 1985, *Process Plant Layout*, 2nd edn (Godwin in association with IChemE, UK).

42. HSE, 1997, *The explosion and fires at the Texaco refinery, Milford Haven, on 24 July 1994* (Health and Safety Executive, UK).

43. Cox, A.W., Lees, F.P. and Ang, M.L., 1990, *Classification of Hazardous Locations* (IChemE, UK).

44. King, R. and Hirst, R., 1998, *King's Safety in the Process Industries*, 2nd edn (Arnold, UK).

45. Zwart, R. and Woutersen, K.A., 1988, Acute inhalation toxicity of chlorine in rats and mice: time-concentration-mortality relationships and effects on respiration, *J Hazardous Materials*, 19: 195–208.

Appendix to Chapter 4
– toxicity data sheets

Nomenclature

In the following data sheets, c represents volumetric concentration (ppm), θ represents duration of exposure (min) and n represents an empirical exponent (dimensionless).

Toxicity data sheet 1

1	Name of substance	**Ammonia**	
2	Chemical formula	NH_3	
3	Molar mass ($kg\,kmol^{-1}$)	17	
4	State of matter as usually handled	Liquefied vapour	
5	Colour and smell	Colourless, pungent odour	
6	Organ or part of system attacked	Lungs, eyes	
7	Effect produced	Irritation, oedema of lungs	
8	Value of n in load expression $c^n \times \theta$	2 (reference 1)	
9	Probit equation	$Y = -35.9 + 1.85\log_e{(c^2\theta)}$ (reference 3)	
10	**Table of correspondences**		
	Load	**Harm**	
	5 ppm (ref 3)	Odour threshold	
	$2.7 \times 10^6\,ppm^2 \times min$ (ref 2)	IHS	
	$3.76 \times 10^8\,ppm^2 \times min$ (ref 1)	SHS	
	$4 \times 10^9\,ppm^2 \times min$ (ref 1)	LC_{50}	
11	References: (1) Payne et al.[25], (2) NIOSH[33], (3) IChemE[29].		

Toxicity data sheet 2

1	Name of substance	**Carbon monoxide**[a]	
2	Chemical formula	CO	
3	Molar mass ($kg\,kmol^{-1}$)	28	
4	State of matter as usually handled	Gas	
5	Colour and smell	Colourless, odourless	
6	Organ or part of system attacked	Blood	
7	Effect produced	Combines with haemoglobin	
8	Value of n in load expression $c^n \times \theta$	One	
9	Probit equation	None found	
10	**Table of correspondences**		
	Load		**Harm**
	3.6×10^4 ppm $\times$ min (ref 1)		IHS
	Not known[b]		SHS
	Not known[b]		LC_{50}
11	References: (1) NIOSH[33]		

Notes

(a) As a byproduct from burning carbonaceous fuels, carbon monoxide probably kills more people, worldwide, than any other toxic agent. It is insidious because it has neither taste nor smell. Its declining significance as a cause of death in the process industries in recent decades is associated with the decline of coal-based technology. Nevertheless it remains an important toxic agent for the process industries.

(b) There is a considerable amount of published information concerning the toxicity of carbon monoxide, for example in Sax[32] but it is not presented in these terms.

Toxicity data sheet 3

1	Name of substance	**Chlorine**
2	Chemical formula	Cl_2
3	Molar mass ($kg\,kmol^{-1}$)	71
4	State of matter as usually handled	Liquefied vapour
5	Colour and smell	Green, pungent smell
6	Organ or part of system attacked	Eyes, lungs
7	Effect produced	Irritation and oedema of lungs
8	Value of n in load expression $c^n \times \theta$	2 (reference 1) (uncertain)
9	Probit equation[a]	$Y = -26.84 + 2.89 \log_e c$ $+2.78 \log_e \theta$ (ref 1)
10	**Table of correspondences**	
	Load	**Harm**
	0.2 to 3.5 ppm (ref 1)	Odour threshold
	15 ppm (ref 1)	Onset of irritation
	$1.08 \times 10^5\,ppm^2 \times min$ (ref 2)	SHS
	$4.8 \times 10^6\,ppm^2 \times min$ (ref 1)	LC_{50}
11	References: (1) IChemE[30], (2) Turner and Fairhurst[26]	

Note

(a) It appears that it is not possible to express the probit equation for chlorine in the simple form $Y = a + b \log_e (c^n \times \theta)$. This is discussed fully in Zwart and Woutersen[45]. The probit quoted above for rats is in a more complex form. Reference 1 provides also a probit equation in similar form for mice: $Y = -33.74 + 4.05 \log_e c + 2.72 \log_e \theta$.

Toxicity data sheet 4

1	Name of substance	**Hydrogen fluoride**
2	Chemical formula	HF
3	Molar mass ($kg\,kmol^{-1}$)	20
4	State of matter as usually handled	Volatile liquid or gas
5	Colour and smell	Fumes in moist air, pungent, irritating odour
6	Organ or part of system attacked	Eyes, upper respiratory tract, lungs, skin
7	Effect produced	Inflammation of skin, damage to eyes, inflammation, congestion and oedema of lungs (ref 1)
8	Value of n in load expression $c^n \times \theta$	1 (ref 1)
9	Probit equation	None found
10	**Table of correspondences**	
	Load	**Harm**
	900 ppm × min (ref 2) 12,000 ppm × min (ref 1) ca. 90,000 ppm × min (ref 1)	IHS SHS LC_{50}
11	References: (1) Meldrum[27] and (2) NIOSH[33]	

Toxicity data sheet 5

1	Name of substance	**Hydrogen sulphide**
2	Chemical formula	H_2S
3	Molar mass ($kg\,kmol^{-1}$)	34
4	State of matter as usually handled	Gas
5	Colour and smell	Colourless, smells of rotten eggs
6	Organ or part of system attacked	Eyes, respiratory tract, cells
7	Effect produced	Irritation of eyes and respiratory tract, inhibition of oxygen exchange at cellular level (ref 1)
8	Value of n in load expression $c^n \times \theta$	4 (ref 2)
9	Probit equation	None found
10	**Table of correspondences**	
	Load	Harm
	$< 0.1\,ppm^a$ (ref 2)	Odour threshold
	$3 \times 10^9\,ppm^4 \times min$ (ref 1)	IHS
	$2 \times 10^{12}\,ppm^4 \times min$ (ref 2)	SHS
	$1.5 \times 10^{13}\,ppm^4 \times min$	$LC_{50}^{\,b}$
11	References: (1) NIOSH[33] , (2) Turner and Fairhurst[28]	

Notes
(a) At concentrations above 150 ppm olfactory fatigue sets in and the smell is no longer noticeable. Thus at IHS and SHS levels odour does not give a warning.
(b) The LC_{50} index has been estimated from data in Furr[2].

Toxicity data sheet 6

1	Name of substance	**Phosgene**
2	Chemical formula	$COCl_2$
3	Molar mass ($kg\,kmol^{-1}$)	99
4	State of matter as usually handled	Liquefied vapour, gas
5	Colour and smell	Colourless, smells of moist hay, pungent at high concentrations
6	Organ or part of system attacked	Eyes, respiratory tract, lungs
7	Effect produced	Irritation, oedema (sometimes delayed for hours)
8	Value of n in load expression $c^n \times \theta$	1 (ref 1)
9	Probit equation	$Y = -27.2 + 5.1\log_e{(c\theta)}$ (ref 1)
10	**Table of correspondences**	
	Load	**Harm**
	0.5 ppm (ref 1)	Odour threshold
	60 ppm × min (ref 2)	IHS
	Not known	SHS
	570 ppm × min (ref 1)	LC_{50}
11	References: (1) IChemE[31], (2) NIOSH[33]	

Significant case histories

5

The preceding chapters of this book have been designed to facilitate the appreciation of process hazards and their consequences by outlining them in a rationally structured way. Although such an approach is necessary, it may also appear somewhat abstractly didactic, needing to be complemented by some account of 'real-life' events. To this end, a modest collection of case histories has been assembled in this chapter to illustrate particular phenomena described in the text.

The chapter is not in any sense intended as a rival or substitute for the more encyclopaedic collections of, for example, Lees[1], Kletz[2] or the IChemE Accident Database[3], all of which are strongly recommended for reference. Nor does it contain the extensive (and sometimes controversial) analyses of more limited numbers of cases to be found in works such as Marshall[4] or King[5]. It is hoped, however, that it will help bring the text to life and demonstrate the reality of the phenomena described.

Readers are warned that the realizations of hazards are typically complex, and often proceed extremely rapidly, and that they may well have a very traumatic impact on witnesses, leading to conflicts of factual evidence. Moreover, even where experts agree on the known facts, their interpretations sometimes differ. For each case, one or more of the most authoritative and/or informative references available are included.

Readers may obtain brief details of many other incidents referred to by their location and date from the Major Hazard Incident Data Service published by the UK Atomic Energy Authority[6].

There was in the past a widespread view that, because of the bewildering variety of hazards and modes of realization presented by the process industries, it was only possible to teach the subject of process safety by the study of such case histories. Much has indeed been learned in this way though, as Kletz points out[7], such lessons are sometimes either not learned or, if learned, soon forgotten. In order to make effective use of such data, information about accidents occurring in particular situations must be extrapolated to other sets of circumstances. Even more importantly, perhaps, scenarios need to be foreseen which have not yet occurred, or of which there is no record. Accordingly, the study of case histories is viewed as a secondary, though essential, complement to the more generalized account of this text.

5.1 Abbeystead (UK)

See Section 2.11.2 (page 110).

This disaster occurred on 23 May 1984, at 1930 hours in a subterranean valve-house of the local Water Authority by the River Wyre in Lancashire, England, during an inspection visit by a party consisting of 36 local residents and eight employees.

The purpose of the visit was to reassure the residents that a 12 km tunnel which had been constructed to draw water from the River Lune was not contributing to the flooding of the Wyre. When a methane/air mixture exploded, 13 of the visitors and three of the employees were killed and all the remaining members of the party were injured, either by burns or by the collapse of the roof.

The pumps had been started up for demonstration purposes, after being idle for 17 days. The tunnel was initially full, of air rather than water as the result of an inappropriate draining operation. The pumps consequently transmitted a slug of air which — as was subsequently established[8] — was contaminated with methane which had escaped from solution in ground water and had leaked into the tunnel. After 18 minutes there was a flash of light, followed immediately by an explosion.

Later simulation showed that a concentration of methane close to the lower flammable limit could accumulate in the valve house if — as was the case — the tunnel was ventilated through it and not independently.

This incident demonstrated the propensity of ground water, when exposed under pressure to geologically-derived methane, to dissolve it to a degree such that a combustible atmosphere can be generated when the pressure is relaxed. This phenomenon was not then known in the water supply industry, and was certainly not foreseen by the designers of the Abbeystead system or by its operators. The incident also showed the importance of ventilating air from tunnels by routes not involving its passage through spaces that may be occupied by people.

A slightly more detailed account of this incident is given by Marshall[4].

Further reading
Health and Safety Executive (HSE)[8] and Marshall[4].

5.2 Anglesey (UK)

See Section 2.11.3 (page 111).

This plant manufactured aluminium powder using a jet of air to break up molten metal from furnaces into droplets and allowing them to freeze and fall into collectors. On 16 July 1983, a series of explosions injured two of three workers present and caused £1 million of damage to the plant.

The exact cause of the disaster has not been ascertained. Analysis of the damage suggests that an initial dust explosion occurred in the one of two parallel collecting systems that was currently working; that this was followed by two secondary explosions — one centred in the other collection system and one in the screen house — involving previously accumulated dust disturbed by the blast wave; and that a fourth may have occurred in the open space between the two lines. The original ignition source is supposed to have been a spark caused by the displacement of a component, but the subsequent explosions would have been ignited by flames from the earlier ones. One report (MHIDAS AN 1405[6]) — although not very well substantiated — is that the initial explosion 'sent a fireball 100s of feet in the air'. The same report stated that 'all buildings within 200 yards (were) wrecked' and that 'debris blocked (the) main London-Holyhead rail line'.

It may well be thought that such a process, involving fine particles of hot metallic aluminium suspended in a current of air, was too inherently hazardous to be tolerated. The HSE considered, however, that the process, though hazardous, was acceptable on account of the propensity of this metal to form, in contact with atmospheric oxygen, a protective layer of oxide. Thus they concluded that overall the plant was safely designed and constructed, but recommended that:

- the relief panels on line 1 should be made to release more quickly;
- a somewhat greater relief area should be fitted to the collectors of line 2;
- the plant layout should be more generous to allow for the possibility of flame and burning dust being 'ejected over considerable distances';
- more care should be taken to prevent accumulation of dust;
- the cladding panels fitted to the walls and roofs should be restrained to prevent them from becoming missiles in the event of an explosion.

Further reading
MHIDAS AN 1405[6], Barton and Seaton[9], Eckhoff[10] and Lunn[11].

5.3 Basel (Switzerland)

See Sections 3.3.9 (page 156), 4.11.2 (page 199), 4.12.1 (page 201) and 4.12.4 (page 202).

A large fire occurred in a warehouse belonging to the Swiss chemical company Sandoz at Basel on 1 November 1986. The warehouse, though originally built for storing machinery, was approved for agro-products and chemicals of flash point exceeding 21°C, and had recently been inspected.

The fire generated a heavy smoke containing offensive materials such as phosphoric esters and mercaptans, and the local population was warned to take refuge indoors and close their windows until the 'all clear' was sounded after seven hours. Although many people sustained minor, short-term effects such as headaches and nausea, no serious or long-term damage to the health of the local population was detected.

Much more serious consequences resulted from the fire-fighters having to resort to water to prevent the fire from spreading because the use of foam had failed. In the absence of adequate provision for retention, $10,000 \, m^3$ of fire water drained into the River Rhine, carrying with it about 30 tonnes of chemicals from the warehouse, including about 150 kg of highly toxic mercury compounds. Severe ecological damage was caused to the river over a distance of about 250 km, including the death of large numbers of fish and eels. The damage, although serious, seems to have been short term, and the river life recovered quickly. However, during the days following the fire there were many reports of unusual local pollution downstream, suggesting that some unscrupulous operators had exploited the crisis to dump their own offensive wastes into the river.

The disaster caused much political disturbance in Switzerland, where complacency about the supposedly high level of hygiene had prevailed, and also in Germany, through which the Rhine flows for most of its length. Severe criticism was provoked by the company's long delay in warning the monitoring stations downstream.

Measures taken subsequently to avoid recurrence included:

- reducing the output of insecticides at the Schweitzerhalle Works;
- reducing the stocks of agro-chemicals in the warehouse;
- eliminating all processes involving the use of phosgene;
- discontinuing worldwide manufacture and sale of all products containing mercury;
- reviewing the product range in respect of both economic and hazard criteria;
- strengthening safety regulations for storing toxic and flammable substances;
- installing two catch basins of capacities 5000 and $2500 \, m^3$ for fire-water retention;
- negotiating and settling many compensation claims.

214

The shock resulting from this fire-turned-ecological-disaster has forced Sandoz to revise its technological policies, and especially the conduct of its relations with the public.

Further reading
See Anon[12], Beck[13], Crossman[14], Layman[15] and Williams[16].

5.4 Bhopal (India)

See Sections 2.7.6 (page 78), 2.8.1 (page 80), 2.8.4 (page 90) and 6.2.2 (page 258).

This plant produced the insecticide Sevin (1-naphthyl-N-methyl-carbamate) via methyl isocyanate (MIC). On 3 December 1984 it gave rise to the worst disaster in the history of the chemical industry. About 3000 people in the area surrounding the plant were killed and 200,000 injured (10,000 permanently), although the figures are disputed. If there were any casualties on the plant, their number appears to have been swept up in the enormous toll of the local population.

It is generally agreed that the escape through a relief valve of 30–35 tonnes of MIC vapour (with decomposition products) arose from the over-pressurization of a storage tank holding 41 tonnes of MIC, as the result of a runaway polymerization reaction caused by the improper ingress of over two tonnes of water to the tank. There is argument as to whether the entry of water resulted from a faulty pipe-washing procedure or from a deliberate act of sabotage by a disgruntled employee. The reaction appears to have been promoted by the presence of small quantities of various contaminants.

MIC (CH_3NCO) is a highly volatile liquid at room temperature; it is highly and acutely toxic, affecting the lungs, eyes, stomach, liver and skin. With a molar mass of $0.057\,kg\,m^{-3}$, its vapour is twice as dense as air at the same temperature.

With so much at stake and so many interests involved (the plant's local owners, their American parent company, the Indian Government and the local authorities, as well as the representatives of the victims and their families), the investigations were very controversial and there are suspicions of obfuscation from various quarters.

The major factors to emerge are as follows:

- The plant had been having a difficult time commercially and was somewhat rundown, with generally low staffing levels relative to the technology in use, low management standards and poor general morale. This may explain, though it does not excuse, some of the operational deficiencies.

215

- Crucially, the plant carried a very large inventory (up to 120 t capacity) of the highly toxic MIC — much larger than necessary. Similar processes are conducted with MIC being produced on a 'just-in-time' basis.
- While the 'sabotage scenario' is perhaps the more probable, it does not excuse the management, which should have been aware of such hazards and had measures in place to prevent their realization.
- One protective system (refrigeration of the storage tanks) had been decommissioned some time before, apparently for the sake of economy; a second (a caustic soda scrubber) may have been out of commission but was in any case probably inadequate to handle an escape of this magnitude; a third (a flare stack) was in a failed state, presumably awaiting repair.
- There was a very serious failure on the part of both the company and the local authorities, engendered either by complacency about the hazard (ignorance has been pleaded but this is very dubious) or by sheer incompetence, to warn the population and advise them on measures of self-protection (the simple precaution of breathing through a water-moistened cloth would have saved many lives).
- There was a very large and overcrowded residential population very close to the plant living in primitive housing with inadequate local medical services. From the standpoint of a highly developed country this may seem quite inexcusable, but such conditions are a universal concomitant of a situation of rapid industrial development in a poor country and are very difficult to control.
- The Indian Government restricted the company's investigators' access to documentation and witnesses on the grounds that criminal proceedings were under way. This hindered their investigations and may have brought about a distortion of the findings.

There were many complex technical issues involved, but underlying the episode were grave ethical questions surrounding the conduct of a very hazardous process by a foreign company in a relatively underdeveloped country. For example, the compensation eventually accepted was very low by Western standards — it would seem that political pressure was put on the Indian Government — although there is room for argument as to whether compensation levels should be the same everywhere or whether they should reflect the economic conditions of the country concerned.

Further reading
Marshall[4], Ayres and Rohatgi[17], Kalelkar[18] and Shrivastava[19].

5.5 Bolsover (UK)

See Section 2.7.6 (page 78).

A runaway reaction occurred on 24 April 1968 in a batch reactor making 2,4,5-tri-chlorophenol (TCP) by the reaction of tetrachlorobenzene with caustic soda in ethylene glycol solution. This brought about a release of combustible gases which, on mixing with atmospheric oxygen, was ignited — apparently by an electric lamp — and underwent an internal explosion.

One person (the shift chemist) was killed by falling masonry. About 90 workers subsequently experienced more or less severe symptoms of chloracne, which was attributed to the small amount of *dioxin* (2,3,7,8-tetrachlorodibenzo-p-dioxin) (TCDD) which appears to be associated with this process and was present in the escaping gases. The health of this group of workers was monitored over a number of years, but on balance there seems to be no strong evidence of any abnormal health problems among them.

The plant was repaired and resumed production, but was eventually closed down in the wake of the Seveso disaster (q.v.).

Further reading
Gough[20], Hay[21] and May[22].

5.6 Boston (USA)

See Section 6.2.2 (page 257).

On 13 February 1919, a storage tank on the Boston dockside, containing about 12,500 tonnes of molasses, burst, disintegrating into seven pieces and discharging its contents over the surrounding area. It is reported that 21 (the number is sometimes given as 12) people and a large number of horses were killed (presumably by drowning) and 40 people injured; a number of houses were destroyed; and a column supporting an elevated railway was sheared off, causing the partial collapse of the railway.

A major trial followed, during which the defence tried unsuccessfully to claim that the disaster was caused by a bomb placed by anarchist terrorists. It emerged, however, that the tank had been hydraulically under-designed according to current standards (the safety factor normally applied to the dimensions of vital members to allow for failure mechanisms not then fully understood had been halved). Secondary factors in the number of casualties were the absence of a bund (which would have had to be very substantial, and for which there was no space on the site) and the congested nature of the site in the docks area. Consequently, damages of $300,000 (equivalent to over $3 million today) were awarded to 119 individual plaintiffs, and larger sums to the City Council and the elevated railway company.

This incident is a classic demonstration of the fact that the most apparently innocuous substances can pose very serious hazards in certain circumstances.

Further reading
Brown[23], Anon[24] and Marshall[25] (of which the present account is a précis).

5.7 Bradford (UK)

See Sections 4.11.2 (page 199), 4.12.1 (page 201), 4.12.4 (page 202) and 6.2.4 (page 263).

This plant manufactured some 2000 different products, mainly polymers. It was located in an area of Bradford, Yorkshire which, though formerly highly industrialized, had become largely residential. On 21 July 1992 it sustained a series of warehouse explosions which resulted in a serious fire. The fire generated a dense black pall of smoke, which interfered with traffic on nearby motorways and spread eastward for several kilometres. It lasted some three hours, though it was only 18 days later that the danger of re-ignition was considered to have passed, allowing the fire brigade to be withdrawn.

There were no fatalities, but 33 people (including three members of the public) required hospital treatment, and a police officer who had stood in the path of the smoke cloud to direct traffic was off duty for four months. Residents in adjacent properties were evacuated, and about 2000 people were confined to their houses for some hours. Fire-water run-off caused serious pollution of the River Calder, killing some 10,000 fish. The raw materials warehousing was destroyed, a finished goods warehouse was seriously damaged, a road tanker carrying butyl acetate was burned out and many plastic drums were burned. Other storages more remote from the fire were unaffected, as were the production facilities. The company suffered property losses of £4.5 million and further indirect losses.

The incident was investigated by the Health and Safety Executive. It concluded that the fire had been initiated by the thermal decomposition, due to heating by a nearby steam pipe, of part of a quantity of 1.9 tonnes of azodiisobutyronitrile (AZDN), a thermally unstable reducing agent, which was stored in kegs in 'oxystore 2'. The consequent rupture of some of the kegs led to the release of AZDN powder, which then reacted with some adjacently stored sodium persulphate, an oxidizing agent The presence of AZDN in this store resulted from its erroneous classification as an 'oxidizing agent' (it is also flammable in air). It was found that other materials had also been wrongly classified for storage purposes, and eventually it emerged that the 'Logistics' department, which was responsible for the movement and storage of raw materials, intermediates and products throughout the plant, was devoid of staff qualified either in chemistry or in safety.

The HSE detected a series of defects in the company's management of safety and made a total of 14 recommendations concerning mainly:

- segregation of incompatible materials in storage;
- training of all those involved in the running of warehouses;
- full incorporation of all non-production areas (especially storage) in the ambit of the company's safety policy;
- updating of safety policy and practice in line with management systems and monitoring of safety procedures;
- prompt invocation and hazard briefing of the emergency services (there had been a delay of nearly an hour in summoning the municipal Fire Brigade);
- the use of the siren for warning the public (and provision of back-up power for it);
- provision for minimizing environmental pollution caused by major incidents and, in particular, prevention of fire-water run-off;
- lay-out of sites to avoid congestion.

The company claim to have implemented all the recommendations. They were subsequently prosecuted by the HSE and fined £100,000 for breaches of the Health and Safety at Work Act, with costs. They were also prosecuted by the National Rivers Authority for 'unauthorised releases into controlled waters' and, though they received an absolute discharge, were ordered to pay the prosecution's costs and £5000 compensation for restocking.

The incident prompted one of the authors to write an article pointing to some wider lessons for the safety management of this type of installation[26]. More recently, a useful survey of warehouse incidents has been published by Fowler[28], while Gladwell[29] has published an account of a number of incidents involving AZDN.

Further reading
Marshall[26,27], Fowler[28], Gladwell[29], HSE[30].

5.8 Camelford (UK)

See Section 3.3.8 (page 156).

On 6 July 1988, a delivery of aluminium sulphate solution at the Lowermoor Treatment Plant of the South West Water Authority was accidentally admitted to the tank in which the treated water was held for final pH adjustment prior to release, instead of to the appropriate storage tank. The effects of the contamination were felt almost immediately, but the problem was only acknowledged by the Authority after a delay of six days, and the cause was not identified until, after two weeks, the persistent complaints from the public forced the local health authorities to institute an inquiry.

It emerged that the site was not staffed, and was being controlled by telemetry from the regional headquarters in Exeter. The driver, who was on relief duty and visiting this site for the first time, was not met there, as he had been led to expect, by an Authority employee but had, been provided with a key to unlock the site gate and — ostensibly — the inlet pipe to the appropriate tank. He had discharged his load, left an unsigned delivery note and departed.

The situation was confused by the coincidence of a relatively minor error in the lime dosing of the treated water, which appeared to account for the high acidity of the water as delivered to the mains so that, when this was corrected, the Authority assumed that the problem had been eliminated.

Aluminium sulphate dissociates in solution, producing sulphuric acid. Although there was doubt (not satisfactorily resolved by the Authority) as to the degree of contamination, it appears that the injuries inflicted (mouth ulceration, skin blistering and so on) were consistent with a pH as low as 2, corresponding with a concentration of about $15 \, \mathrm{mg} \, \mathrm{l}^{-1}$. The acidity also caused copper from domestic piping to be dissolved in the water, leading to a copper content in the water exceeding $20 \, \mathrm{mg} \, \mathrm{l}^{-1}$ and causing colouration of people's hair. These effects were, fortunately, temporary; but there is continuing concern over the possible longer-term effects of the ingestion of aluminium salts on the human brain.

This incident was disturbing, not only for the fact that such errors could occur, but because the consequences were probably aggravated by delays, misinformation and general obfuscation on the part of the Water Authority. It is reported that institutional changes have been made subsequently which should prevent a recurrence of such behaviour.

Further reading
Keller and Wilson[31].

5.9 Castleford (UK)

See Section 2.11.4 (page 113).

On 21 September 1992, a serious fire occurred at the chemical works of Hickson and Welch Ltd, Castleford, Yorkshire, England. Altogether, five people were killed, two suffered reportable injuries, 181 people suffered toxic effects in varying degrees and there was substantial damage to plant and buildings.

The firm, part of an international group, manufactured at this site a wide range of organic chemicals, in particular nitrotoluenes. A stage in the — otherwise continuous — production of isomers of mono-nitrotoluene (MNT) involved the batch distillation of a residual material called 'whizzer oil' to effect a final recovery of MNT.

Over a period of time prior to the incident, concern had been growing over the accumulation of a tarry residue in the base drum of the still used for this purpose, which had not been cleaned since it was brought into service in 1961.

Eventually, it was decided to clear the drum by raking the sludge out through a manhole after first softening it by heating using the internal steam coil. After this operation had been proceeding for three hours, a jet of flame erupted from the manhole. This flame cut through the office/control building which was about 23 metres away across a roadway, killing two employees and severely injuring three others, two of whom died subsequently, and then struck a large office building immediately behind, where it shattered windows and started a fire. Of the 63 employees in this building all escaped except one young woman who was overcome by smoke in a second-floor toilet and died later in hospital.

The incident was investigated by the HSE. Their report[40] noted that the sludge in the still base was rich in mono- and di-nitrotolenes and nitrocresols, which are heat-sensitive redox molecules, and attributed the fire to runaway reaction arising from overheating, which stemmed partly from the fact that the thermometer probe used to monitor the temperature was in the vapour space above the sludge.

The report noted that the expertise available at higher levels in the company had not been applied to the cleaning operation. Its hazards were not properly assessed and appropriate precautions had not been taken. In the wake of staffing changes the supervisory personnel were not adequately briefed on the nature of the materials involved. Smoke barriers had been compromised by building alterations and the roll-call system for emergencies was defective (there had been a fatal delay in locating the fifth victim). The lessons drawn in the report are summarized:

- still residues should be analysed, monitored and removed regularly;
- proposals to carry out non-routine operations should be authorized only after very careful scrutiny;
- all operations, including maintenance and those occurring only occasionally, should be subject to safe systems of work which are regularly monitored and reviewed;

221

- careful attention should be paid to the safety of control systems on process plant, especially where they are to be used for non-routine operations;
- workloads of managers should be regulated so that they are able to pay proper attention to their health and safety responsibilities;
- supervisory staff returning to an area where they have worked previously must be retrained;
- attention must be given to the design and location of control and office buildings associated with hazardous plant so that risks to employees are minimized;
- alterations to buildings must be properly scrutinized for their possible effect on fire safety;
- emergency roll-call systems should provide for rapid communication of information to fire officers and should be checked and practised regularly to ensure their effectiveness at all times.

The company was subsequently prosecuted for offences under the Health and Safety at Work Act. They pleaded guilty and were fined £250,000 with £150,000 costs. The judge, Mr Justice Holland, concluded: 'There was no safe system of work, none such was maintained, notwithstanding hazards that were to be perceived, the hazards that were there as a potential. This was not a casual breach of an employer's duty . . . but a plain gap in the employer's management which should never have occurred . . .'.

Further reading
HSE[32] and Kletz[33].

5.10 Cleveland (USA)

See Sections 2.2.10 (page 34), 2.5.7 (page 56) and 2.10.9 (page 109).
Cleveland was the site of the first-ever 'peak-shaving' plant for a public natural gas supply. The consumption of gas fluctuates through the day, and pipeline capacity to bring gas some 250 km to the city at a rate corresponding with the maximum demand would have been very expensive. The solution adopted was to install a plant which could receive gas continuously at the average demand rate, liquefying the excess during periods of low demand and storing it in tanks, to be re-gasified and added to the supply when the demand rose. In this way, the pipeline capacity could be limited to that equivalent to the average demand. It was claimed the cost of the plant was only one third of that of the additional pipe capacity which would otherwise have been needed. The refrigeration plant was of the cascade type, using ethene, ammonia and water. The liquefied gas,

which was 85% methane, was stored at about its normal bubble point (−157°C).

On 20 July 1944, the failure of one of the tanks led to the loss, initially, of 1900 tonnes of liquefied natural gas (LNG) and subsequently, when another tank collapsed as a result of flame engulfment of its legs, of a further 1000 tonnes. Some of this liquid was vaporized on the site and quickly ignited to generate a large pool fire. Much of it, however, flowed over the boundary and into the neighbouring streets, where it quickly entered storm sewers. It thus came into contact with the much warmer sewer waters and became widely distributed, causing many physical explosions as it boiled including, possibly, so-called *rapid phase transitions* of the kind described in Section 2.5.7 (page 56). The vapours then mixed with air and, coming into contact with the innumerable ignition sources present in a city, initiated many fires which coalesced into a major conflagration. There was evidence of many minor confined explosions, but none of a vapour-cloud explosion.

Estimates of fatalities ranged from 109 to 128, and of non-fatal casualties from 200 to 400. A large part of the plant and many buildings were destroyed and property damage was estimated (in 1944 values) at $6,800,000.

The cause of the disaster could not be established with certainty, but the investigations pointed to the conclusion that the 3.5%-nickel steel of which the tank was constructed was only marginally suitable for the duty in respect of low-temperature embrittlement, and that the tank failed because of a minor ground shock from either a passing locomotive or a steam hammer.

The official enquiry report made a number of recommendations:

- installations carrying large inventories of flammable liquids should be isolated;
- activities not directly related to their operation should be prohibited on site;
- the spacing of plant units should be designed to avert secondary realizations;
- more provision should be made for capturing escaping liquid from failed tanks.

Further reading
Marshall[4], Davis[34] and Elliot et al.[35].

5.11 Crescent City (USA)

See Section 2.4.2 (page 37).

In the morning of 21 June 1970, a freight train consisting of four diesel-electric locomotives, 108 cars and a guard's van became derailed at Crescent City. The train included a string of 12 LPG tank cars (numbers 26 to 37), each carrying on average 63.6 tonnes of propane. The derailment was initiated by the mechanical failure of a journal bearing on the 20th car, which was carrying 75.9 t of glass sand. It emerged that this was an increasingly common type of failure despite many efforts to prevent it, though no specific reason was identified for this particular occurrence.

The initial derailment caused the following 15 cars (including 10 of the LPG tank cars) to derail and pile up across the track, three of them impacting nearby buildings and inflicting serious damage. The leading LPG car (no. 26) came to rest across the track, and consequently the following one rammed its top, causing major fractures to its shell. About half of the contents of this car were released very violently and were almost immediately ignited (probably by a spark struck between colliding metal surfaces), generating a fireball 100s of feet in diameter, the radiation from which destroyed nearby properties. The remainder of the contents of this tank then formed the base of a pool fire which, in due course, brought about a BLEVE in car no. 27, generating a huge missile and another fireball.

Half an hour after the derailment, a police sergeant arrived at the scene and, observing the involvement of tank cars and learning the nature of their contents, ordered an evacuation of the public and instructed the fire-fighters to retreat to a safe distance. A cyclic succession of events followed in which heat from the burning propane escaping from one tank brought about a similar process in the next — several more tanks 'BLEVED' in this way, some of them ejecting very large missiles to distances of up to 480 m, and several generating fireballs.

Several fire brigades were called to the scene, but their efforts were limited by shortages of water due to the inoperability of pumps resulting from a well-intentioned but probably mistaken decision to cut off the electricity supply to the area when some transmission lines were cut. Eventually it was decided to allow the fires to burn themselves out.

Largely because of the above-mentioned precautions, no fatalities resulted from this incident, though 66 people received hospital treatment, mostly for burns, of which some were very serious (among the victims was the Fire Chief). Total property damage was estimated at $3 million (in 1970 values).

It is claimed that lessons were learned from this disaster which enabled the transportation of LPGs to be carried out more safely, but what these were is not clear from the accounts.

Further reading

Lees[1] and Lewis[36] (a very detailed account).

5.12 Feyzin (France)

See Sections 2.2.10 (page 34), 2.5.4 (pages 45, 52), 2.6.6 (page 63), 2.10.7 (page 106), 2.10.9 (page 109) and 4.11.3 (page 200).

The incident occurred on 4 January 1966. It started in the LPG storage area of an oil refinery. A detailed description is given in Marshall[4]. An operator tried (as part of daily routine) to run off settled water from a 1200-m³ sphere containing liquid propane. Initially there was no flow — the draw-off system was blocked, apparently with propane hydrate (the ambient temperature was about 0°C). He opened both cocks fully: liquid gushed out, injuring the operator (by 'cold burn'), who could not close the valves as the only key had been dropped and was irretrievable.

The spilled propane flashed and, with little wind, the vapour cloud drifted in all directions, reaching a nearby service road (the motorway at 160 m had been closed off in response to the alarm), where it was ignited 35 mins later, apparently as the result of an electrical fault on a stationary car. This started a flash fire (killing the driver, who had left the car).

This fire quickly burned back to the source, where it ignited a jet flame at the pipe-end. The liquid that had accumulated in the bund (which contained seven other LPG spheres) then formed the base of a pool fire, which quickly enveloped the sphere.

The pressure in the vessel was initially ca. 7 barg, but the heating of the contents caused it to increase, blowing the relief valve (set at 18 barg) and igniting another jet flame 30–40 m high at the top of the vessel. Two hours after the start, when the wall temperature reached 600–700°C, the metal was weakened and failed by 'petal fracture', and the sphere suffered a BLEVE as described in Section 2.5.4 (page 51). The sudden release of approximately 340 m³ of liquid propane under pressure led to extremely rapid flashing, producing a violent pressure wave (physical explosion), and the ignition of the vapour cloud resulted in a fireball reported as being about 700 m high.

18 people were killed (of whom 11 were firemen and one the driver of the car believed to be the original ignition source), 81 injured (40 seriously) at distances of up to 300 m. The thermal radiation from the pool fire, plus missiles from the rupture of the original sphere, led to BLEVEs of 4 further spheres and a general conflagration causing the destruction of two horizontal LPG pressure vessels and several petrol and crude-oil tanks. About 5100 m³ of LPG and 3800 m³ of aviation kerosene were destroyed in tanks, plus an unknown quantity from broken pipework. It took 48 hours to bring the fires under control. There was extensive, though not severe, structural damage in the village 500 metres away. The significant issues identified are summarized below.

The operator wrongly opened the outer valve first, so the cooling effect of throttling occurred there, contrary to the procedure laid down. However, the consequences would have been much less serious if the draw-off system had not been arranged to discharge under the vessel — some steam-tracing was provided, but not enough. It is now usual to provide for isolating a small quantity of propane containing the water to be drained off before opening to atmosphere, and to operate the valves by remote control.

The escaped liquid was allowed to accumulate beneath the vessel: it should be directed away, by sloping ground and appropriate piping, to a place where it could be allowed to burn harmlessly.

It took 10 minutes to raise the alarm (the men walked 0.8 km, fearing to use the local telephone or start their truck). It should have been possible to prevent the 'fatal' car from entering the service road.

The fire-fighting strategy was to employ the limited supply of water to keep the adjacent storage vessels cool while allowing the contents of the affected tank to 'burn out'. This failed to take account of the BLEVE scenario, which then ensued. As it was, the resulting pressure wave and fireball destroyed the adjacent vessels anyway.

It would have been better to: (a) transfer the contents of the leaking tank to others (capacity was available); (b) reduce the pressure if possible (if the wall was weakened by high temperature, it might fail before the relief valve opened); (c) cool the leaking tank — especially the possibly unwetted upper portion.

Good practice now also requires: permanent water spray systems and perhaps lagging on tanks; insulation of tank supports (which collapsed when weakened as a result of engulfment by flames) with concrete; a far more generous layout of the storage area. Water curtains may be installed to prevent ignition. Better emergency planning and liaison with and technical briefing of the public fire brigade are needed.

Management should have been more aware of the risk of such an event. The prospects of fighting the fire successfully should have been estimated promptly and, if it had been concluded that they were poor, the site should have been evacuated immediately and events allowed to take their course.

Further reading
Marshall[4] and IChemE[37].

5.13 Flixborough (UK)

See Sections 2.5.4 (page 42), 2.10.9 (page 109), 2.12.3 (page 116), 6.1.2 (page 248) and 6.2.4 (page 263).

The Nypro factory, near Scunthorpe (South Humberside, England) was making caprolactam as a starting point for the manufacture of nylon 6. One stage involved the oxidation of cyclohexane to cyclohexanone. The equation of the reaction is:

$$(CH_2)_6 + O_2 \rightarrow (CH_2)_5 C = O + H_2O$$

On 1 June 1974, at about 4.52 pm, an escape occurred of boiling liquid reaction mixture consisting largely of cyclohexane at 9 bar and 150°C (the normal boiling point is about 80°C). The reactor train initially contained about 140 t of the mixture. Flashing vapour produced a large vapour cloud (mass estimated at 45 t). The cloud was ignited and the resulting explosion (VCE) (about 12.5% of the cloud mass exploded) generated a destructive blast wave and initiated a massive conflagration.

Human casualties amounted to 28 killed, 36 injured on-site and 53 injured off-site. Most of the buildings and plant on the site were destroyed or severely damaged, while off-site 1821 houses, 167 shops and so on were damaged (some beyond repair) at distances of up to 2.5 km away. The event occurred on a Saturday afternoon, when only a skeleton operating crew were working — otherwise there would have been far more casualties.

Owing to its size and unfamiliar nature, the incident caused a great public shock, and gave rise to a major public inquiry. The inquiry[36] was mainly concerned with finding the immediate technical cause of the failure (by studying the damage), but it also drew attention to a number of important issues of a more general kind.

It is important to read the accounts of this disaster and the lessons stemming from it, in the literature. Detailed discussion appears in Marshall[4,37], but other authors should also be consulted, as there is still some controversy. Here, the most important issues are listed:

- The escape took place from a series of large reaction vessels forming a 'staircase' for gravity flow of reaction mixture. The immediate cause was a failure of bellows in a temporary unsupported *dog-leg* pipe connecting reactors 4 and 6 while reactor 5 was out of service for repair, with significant implications for the design and approval of plant modifications.
- The VCE was not then a recognized major hazard — the disaster prompted research into the circumstances likely to bring about such an event.

- The plant contained a very large inventory of a hazardous material in an especially hazardous state. This has implications for process selection and process and plant design.
- Almost the whole plant was destroyed, with implications for the layout of plants to minimize 'domino effects' such as conflagration.
- The caprolactam plant control building was the official emergency refuge but 18 of the 28 men killed were inside it and one was on the doorstep, heavy equipment fell upon it and it was totally destroyed. This has implications for the location, design and construction of control rooms and for the provision of emergency refuges.
- The office block was 50 m from the point of escape of the vapour, and was totally destroyed. On a normal weekday, 100 people would have worked in it. This has major implications for the location of such buildings.
- There was neither a competent safety officer nor a qualified mechanical engineer on the site, suggesting a negligent attitude to the safety of the workforce and the public.
- The Health and Safety at Work Act had only recently been published, so the public were somewhat 'sensitized'. Concern over the Flixborough disaster led to the setting up of an Advisory Committee on Major Hazards (ACMH) under the Health and Safety Commission. This produced three Reports which gave rise to various Codes of Practice and Regulations.

Further reading
Lees[1], King and Hirst[5], Parker[38], Marshall[39] (a popular account) and Marshall[4] (technical accounts of various aspects).

5.14 Guadalajara (Mexico)

See Section 2.12.3 (page 116).
On 22 April 1992 a series of explosions occurred in the sewers of the city of Guadalajara in Mexico, killing 252 people and injuring over 1400. It was estimated that damage costing $65 million was caused, including the destruction of 1124 houses, 450 businesses and 600 vehicles.

The explosions were mainly fuelled by a large quantity of petrol which had leaked into the soil surrounding one of the sewers over a number of years as the result of corrosion of a steel pipeline leading from an oil refinery by a holed water pipe that had been laid tightly across it. It appears, however, that this was augmented by a leak of liquid hexane from a nearby cooking oil factory and by an accumulation of rotting sewage which had backed up as the result of a somewhat careless diversion of a sewer during the construction of a pit for a new light rail transit system. Ignition could have come from any of a variety of sources, including a cigarette end.

Responsibility for the event was disputed between the various concerns involved (the state oil company, PEMEX, the water company, SIAPA and the factory, La Central). In particular, there were criticisms that reports of smells from members of the public had not been properly investigated, and that evacuation had been unduly delayed, with tragic consequences.

The propagation of the explosion through a substantial part of the sewerage system appears to have been brought about by a series of explosive deflagrations.

Further reading
Anon[40] and Anon[41].

5.15 Houston (USA)

See Section 2.6.6 (page 66).

On 11 May 1976, a road-tank trailer carrying anhydrous ammonia under pressure crashed through an exit ramp's guard rails on a freeway and fell on to the road, 10 (or, according to one account, 65) metres below. 19 tonnes of ammonia were released instantaneously. There were six deaths, five from asphyxiation and the sixth was presumably the driver who would have been killed by the impact; more than 100 people were injured, at distances of up to 300 m[43].

A photograph taken one minute after the crash showed a white ammonia cloud spreading from the site. The appearance of a substantial area of brown scorched grass suggests that the cloud was initially less buoyant than air. Marshall has estimated[43], by comparison of photographs and maps, that this area was about 1 km^2.

Samples of the air in the vicinity taken by technicians of the City Health Department (but not until 2.5 hours after the incident) showed concentrations of the order of micrograms per cubic metre and were indistinguishable from local analyses taken some days prior to the incident.

Further reading
Marshall[4], Lewis[42] and McMullen[43].

5.16 Ludwigshafen (Germany)

See Section 2.12.3 (page 116).

Two major disasters occurred at the Ludwigshafen works of BASF, one on 29 July 1943 and one almost exactly five years later on 28 July 1948, both involving what have subsequently been identified as vapour cloud explosions (VCE).

Marshall[44] describes both incidents. The first is described briefly because, as he points out, it took place during the Second World War when attention was elsewhere and consequently not very much is known about it. The earlier incident resulted from the failure of a tank car containing 16.5 tonnes of a mixture of 80% butadiene and 20% butylene. The ensuing VCE caused 57 deaths and devastated a block of an area estimated at $35,000\,m^2$.

The later disaster, one of the largest in the history of the chemical industry, killed 207 people and injured 3818, 500 of them seriously. The area of building destroyed was $40,000\,m^2$, only slightly exceeding that of the earlier, smaller, explosion, though the area of 'total destruction plus severe damage' was as much as $300,000\,m^2$. The TNT equivalent has been estimated as 20 to 60 tonnes.

It is clear that the explosion originated in the catastrophic failure of a railtank car containing 30.4 tonnes of dimethyl ether, giving rise to a huge VCE which devastated a large area of the works, though there is no indication that anyone outside the perimeter was killed. Investigators at the time concluded that the failure was due to hydraulic pressure resulting from thermal expansion of the contents (due to ambient and solar heating) exceeding the available ullage. However, Marshall suggests that the evidence for this is lacking and that failure could equally have been attributed to a higher-than-usual vapour pressure acting on a vessel that is known to have been damaged by an accident in the previous year and also probably weakened by exposure to anhydrous ammonia (its plate indicating that this use was envisaged).

Both these incidents drew attention to the importance of ensuring the robustness of vessels to be used for the containment of volatile liquids and of providing sufficient ullage to allow for any conceivable expansion of the contents under external heating (there is no reference in the reports under review to any provision for the relief of excess pressure). Especially remarkable is that it was not until 30 years and many such disasters later that the phenomenon of the vapour cloud explosion was properly identified and investigated (in the light of current knowledge, it may be judged that the crowded site was peculiarly vulnerable to such explosions). In this connection, it should be noted that the large death tolls of these explosions are mainly attributable to the existence of very large population densities in the neighbour-hood of the sources — a circumstance which would not be tolerated today.

Further reading
Marshall[44] and Davenport[45].

5.17 Manchester Ship Canal (UK)

See Section 3.3 (page 153).

On 14 April 1970, the operator of the Cadishead Ferry on the Manchester Ship Canal made some intending passengers wait while he went home to warn the authorities by telephone of an exceptionally unpleasant odour in the air. Eight passengers, growing impatient, leaped into a rowboat to scull themselves across the canal. When they were part-way across, a flammable mixture in the atmosphere ignited. Some passengers with their clothes on fire jumped into the water, but this only served to spread the flames to spilt liquid on the surface. Five died and the remaining three were badly burned. The ferryman, who had taken another boat out in an effort to help them, was also killed.

It subsequently transpired that a small Dutch-owned tank barge called *Tacoma* had been loading gasoline at an adjacent jetty for transportation to an oil refinery not far away. The flammable vapour arose from spillage on to the deck of the barge, which had been allowed to pour on to the canal through scuppers that had been negligently left unplugged. The gasoline floated on the surface of the water, part of it becoming vaporized and forming a flammable mixture with the air which was in due course ignited (the ignition source was not identified, but it might typically have been a cigarette). It was reported that flames rose 15 metres into the air, 'charring the banks and leading to a series of explosions'.

The Canal Company charged the master of the vessel with breaching a section of the Oil in Navigable Waters Act (1955). He pleaded guilty and was fined what was then the maximum penalty of £1000. It became clear at the trial that there had been a gross neglect of supervision of the loading operation, resulting in a large overflow from the tank.

There was no formal investigation, but various informal enquiries eventually led to the promulgation of regulations and codes of practice for the safe conduct of such operations.

Further reading
Anon[46].

5.18 Mexico City (Mexico)

See Sections 2.2.10 (page 34), 2.5.4 (page 52), 2.10.7 (page 106), 2.10.9 (page 109) and 4.11.2 (page 200).

On 19 November 1984, in the Mexico City district of San Juanico, there occurred one of the worst process plant disasters of all time. A series of explosions and fires which lasted most of the day killed at least 500 people and injured over 7000, of whom 144 died in hospital. Some 39,000 people were rendered homeless or evacuated. An extensive account has been published[47]. The present summary is based largely on the description by Marshall[4].

The affected site was a collection and distribution centre for LPG operated by PEMEX, the Mexican state oil company. With a turnover of about 3000 tonnes per day, its capacity was equivalent to about two days' operation and, at the time of the disaster, the total inventory was about 75% of capacity. The installation was originally built about 300 m from the nearest housing, but residential development had encroached to within 100 m of the perimeter by the time of the disaster, much of it very crowded and of flimsy construction.

The initiating event appears to have been a leak in an importing pipeline, which formed a vapour cloud that was ignited by a flare after 5–10 minutes, by which time it had grown to about 150 by 200 m in area and about 2 m in depth. This created a fireball, while the original leak had formed a jet fire, generating another fireball, estimated at 300 m in diameter which soon caused a nearby sphere to BLEVE. There followed a series of violent ruptures of spheres and cylinders, some of them producing large missiles, as well as a large number of small explosions representing the bursting of small LPG bottles.

Notwithstanding some evidence of blast, it appears that there was no vapour cloud explosion. Very few of the cylinders and spheres survived, and some of these had collapsed because their supports buckled. Many vessel fragments were propelled through distances of hundreds of metres and did very extensive damage to houses within a 300 m radius. Some houses also were destroyed by internal explosions.

Studies of this disaster led to a number of lessons:

- the disaster could have been averted if automatic shut-off valves had been provided at the perimeter;
- the residential area had been allowed to approach much too close to the site perimeter — Table 5.1 makes some relevant comparisons with the Feyzin disaster (q.v.);
- the site was much too concentrated, so that 'domino effects' were inevitable once a fire had started (the LPG loading was $450 \, \mathrm{kg \, m^{-2}}$);

Table 5.1 Comparative table

	Feyzin	Mexico City
Quantity of LPG involved (m³)	ca. 6,400	ca. 12,000
Number killed	18	> 500
Number injured	> 80	> 7000
Distance of housing from perimeter (m)	> 500	100

- the fire-fighting system was much too small for an installation of this size and was very close to the centre of the site and therefore vulnerable;
- the lessons of the Feyzin disaster had not been learned, as no measures such as water sprays or insulation of the legs had been provided to protect the spheres from overheating.

Further reading
Marshall[4] and TNO[47].

5.19 Mississauga (Canada)

See Section 2.4.2 (page 37).
On 11 November 1979, 25 or 26 cars of a train of 106 cars were derailed in a manner somewhat similar to what occurred in the Crescent City incident. One of these cars contained chlorine, 11 propane, three toluene and three caustic soda.

The incident is not well reported, but it appears that the escape, flashing and ignition of propane from at least one tank car led to a major conflagration involving a series of BLEVEs (one missile was reportedly projected for 667 metres) and caused the partial failure of the chlorine tank and the escape of about 60 tonnes of vapour from its load of 90 tonnes. The latter tank was eventually patched and towed away. There were no fatalities or injuries, but 220,000 people were evacuated until the situation was brought under control.

Further reading
Marshall[4] and Anon[48].

5.20 Oppau (Germany)

See Sections 2.10.8 (page 107) and 2.13.3 (page 126).
On 29 September 1921, at the Oppau, Germany (near to Ludwigshafen) works of the Badische Anilin und Soda Fabriek (BASF), there occurred a major dense-phase explosion. There were 561 fatalities, including four in Mannheim,

7 km away; 1500 people were injured and 1000 houses destroyed, including 75% of all houses in the town of Oppau.

The source of the explosion was a stockpile consisting of about 4500 tonnes of a 50% by mass mixture of ammonium nitrate co-crystallized with ammonium sulphate (so-called *mischsaltz*).

The cause of the detonation is almost certain to have been the effect of small explosive charges which were used routinely by the company to break up caked masses of the hygroscopic material. At first glance, this would appear to have been a highly irresponsible procedure, but it was based on the results of exhaustive tests indicating that mixtures containing less than 60% by mass of NH_4NO_3 could not be detonated, and on long-established practice without incident. In the course of a detailed discussion Medard[49] indicates that there had been minor changes in the manufacturing process, causing a decrease in the moisture content of the mixture and slightly different physical properties, and that these, together with the possible inhomogeneity of the mixture (so that in some parts the concentration of NH_4NO_3 would be above the threshold), may have been responsible. He concludes that the company should have tested the altered mixture's vulnerability to detonation.

The explosion produced a large crater with a depth, breadth and length of 10, 75 and 115 metres, respectively.

Further reading
Marshall[4] and Medard[49]. The Marshall report includes photographs of the destruction and of the crater. It is at odds, however, with Medard, in respect of the date (citing 21 November) and in implying that the whole of the heap exploded, whereas the latter reports that some unexploded mixture remained.

5.21 Organic peroxides
See Section 2.13.3 (page 123).
Stull[50] cites an incident which must have occurred some time before 1966, in which a truckload of containers of peroxides including benzoyl peroxide, methyl ethyl ketone peroxide, lauroyl peroxide and tertiary butyl hydroperoxide, amounting to 17.5 tonnes in all, exploded during unloading. The initial fire escalated into a detonation, killing four firemen and destroying two buildings as well as seriously damaging several others.

Further reading
Stull[50].

5.22 Port Hudson (USA)

See Sections 2.12.3 (page 116) and 2.13.2 (page 122).

On 9 December 1970, a failure occurred in a pipeline carrying liquefied propane, leading to a very large escape of propane. There followed a major vapour cloud explosion and fire but, because the area was very lightly populated, there were no fatalities and only 10 cases of injury. The incident was investigated by the US National Transportation Safety Board[51] and has subsequently been intensively studied[4,52,53] because of its important implications for the understanding of such occurrences.

It is clear that the initiating cause of the escape was the rupture, due to corrosion, of a weld in the 200 mm diameter pipeline. The amount of propane present in the vapour cloud at the time of the ignition was about 60 tonnes, but it appears that the escape continued for some time after the explosion, so that the eventual total loss was about 400 tonnes. It is accepted that the major VCE was initiated by an internal explosion in a warehouse, probably ignited electrically in a deep-freeze installation, but controversy has arisen over the assertion by the NTSB and by Burgess and Zabetakis that — uniquely for open-air conditions — the explosion was a detonation. Gugan and Marshall both argue, on grounds of witness observation and blast damage patterns, that it was actually an explosive deflagration. Marshall estimates, on the basis of comparison with Flixborough, that the TNT equivalent of the VCE was about 64 tonnes.

Further reading
Marshall[4], NTSB[51], Burgess and Zabetakis[52] and Gugan[53].

5.23 Seveso (Italy)

See Sections 2.7.6 (page 78), 2.8.1 (page 80), 2.8.4 (page 89), 4.12.2 (page 201), 4.12.3 (page 202) and 4.12.4 (page 202).

There have been a number of releases of this kind, but this one was the largest and has become especially symbolic. A batch reactor was making 2,4,5-trichlorophenol (TCP) by the reaction of tetrachlorobenzene with caustic soda in ethylene glycol and xylene.

On 10 July 1976 (over a period of 20 minutes), a bursting disk failed and a plume was emitted, containing several tonnes of a mixture mainly of phenol, sodium trichlorophenate, sodium glycoxides and sodium oxalate, propelled by hydrogen. This mixture would have been harmful enough, but the event was given special significance by the inclusion of about 2 kg of the by-product dioxin (2,3,7,8-tetrachlorodibenzo-p-dioxin) (TCDD), reputed to be 'one of the most toxic compounds known'. The plume contaminated an area of $17 \, \text{km}^2$ with $3.8 \, \text{km}^2$ seriously contaminated.

Harm caused

Human injuries
Of 3500 people in the worst-hit area, 179 contracted chloracne, 447 received 'caustic' (possibly phenolic) burns (34 suffered both). All eventually recovered, although 15 severe cases remained scarred. Dioxin is suspected of having chronic systemic effects on humans (notably accumulation in the liver and genetic problems), but there is no evidence of these at Seveso. No-one on the plant was injured or contracted chloracne.

Animal casualties
More than 80,000 animals died, almost all deliberately slaughtered to stop dioxin entering the human food chain. Many suffered caustic burns and some became ill after eating contaminated fodder, but recovered.

Harm to vegetation
There was some defoliation of nearby plants, probably by caustics. Dioxin is not apparently harmful to plants, but is quickly absorbed, lingers and enters the food chain if the plant is eaten by animals, so badly contaminated land was barred from grazing for some years.

Harm to water supplies
No dioxin was found in the water courses, but some was detected in stream-beds (it is strongly adsorbed by clay, which thus helps to decontaminate the water).

Causes and circumstances
It is generally agreed that the immediate cause of the failure of the bursting disk was a pressure rise resulting from a runaway reaction. The Italian Parliamentary Commission which investigated the incident failed to establish why this occurred; nevertheless it condemned the company for many alleged failures, and closed the plant down.

The reactor was in a 'rest' condition, having been shut down for the weekend after completion of the reaction and partial vacuum distillation to remove glycol and xylene, with heating and agitation discontinued. The heating medium was 12-bar pass-out steam from a turbine, which would have a saturation temperature of about 190°C, so the temperature should not have been high enough for an exotherm to start (various investigators had found that this would not occur

236

below a temperature of 220°C). However, because the plant was shut down the turbine was out of action and consequently the steam was superheated to 300°C. It seems likely that residual heat in the coil warmed up the top layers of the reaction mixture by radiation sufficiently to initiate the runaway.

Conclusions

This was indeed a very serious incident, but its gravity has been greatly exaggerated by ill-informed comment (there were no human deaths, the environmental damage was of short duration and much of the social harm caused was due to unjustified anxiety and trauma). Marshall[4] argues that:

- a common criticism of the company for departing from the recipe of the original patent is not supported by any technical arguments (there is no evidence that the patentees foresaw the mishap which caused the disaster and were concerned to avert it);
- it may be argued that the stopping of the operation for the weekend was carried out without sufficient consideration of possible consequences;
- the specific circumstance which gave rise to the runaway would have been hard to foresee;
- the harm to humans resulting from the incident was due as much to other agents as to the dioxin which has been the object of so much concern, and the significance of the small release of dioxin has been greatly exaggerated;
- the company was justifiably criticized for inadequate emergency arrangements and (together with the local authorities) for the delay in ordering an evacuation, but the report's harsh censure of the operation was incompetent and unfair.

This incident gave its name to the so-called *Seveso Directive*, which has been the mainspring of much European legislation in the field of process safety.

Further reading

Marshall[4], Gough[20], HSE[54], Marshall[55], Marshall[56], Temple[57] and Whiteside[58].

5.24 Spanish campsite disaster

See Sections 2.2.10 (page 34), 2.5.4 (pages 45 and 51), 2.5.7 (page 56), 2.10.7 (page 106) and 4.6.7 (page 185).

A disaster occurred at San Carlos de la Rapita on the Mediterranean coast of Spain on 11 July 1978, when a road tanker loaded with 23.5 tonnes of liquefied propene (propylene) burst as it passed the campsite of Los Alfaques and released a large cloud of flammable vapour. The cloud was ignited, probably by a camping stove, producing a conflagration, and killed 215 people (including the owner-driver), seriously injuring another 67 and destroying buildings, vehicles and tents over an area of 50,000 m^2.

There has been a great deal of controversy among investigators over two issues — the cause of the disaster and its nature. A very detailed discussion, with conclusions, has been published by Marshall[4].

The immediate cause of the tank's failure is generally agreed to have been the expansion of the liquid due to atmospheric heating (this was endorsed by the Spanish court). Argument has centred chiefly on the question as to whether a further hypothesis is needed, given that the ullage provided, though less than is normally prescribed, was, according to some calculations, sufficient for the prevailing circumstances. Thus Marshall[59] argues that, taking all the possibilities into account, failure at a point of relative weakness can be entirely accounted for by the hydraulic pressure hypothesis. Ens[60] is convinced that the failure was initiated by collision of the vehicle with a wall, possibly caused by the loss of a wheel as the result of a tyre fire. The arguments are complicated and do not need to be pursued here.

Concerning the evolution of the disaster, there have been suggestions, based on eye-witness reports and on observations of blast damage, that it included a vapour cloud explosion. Deeper study, however, leads to the conclusion that the limited amount of blast damage can be accounted for by the violent disintegration of the tanker accompanying the rapid flashing of the escaping liquid and by a number of internal explosions in buildings into which the flammable vapour had seeped, and that the injuries to the victims were inflicted by fire rather than by blast. The evidence of there having been a fireball is stronger, though not conclusive. Certainly there was an extremely powerful flash fire. It is also to be supposed that many of the victims were killed instantly by shock, resulting from breathing in the flashing vapour at −47°C and being drenched in the cold liquid, before they were burned.

Several lessons should be learned from this tragedy, in particular:

- the importance of controlling the loading of road or rail tankers to ensure that there is sufficient ullage to accommodate the maximum foreseeable thermal expansion of the liquid;
- the importance of providing a relief valve on such tanks, nothwithstanding that some less serious hazards attend any resulting releases;
- the desirability of routing vehicles with hazardous loads as far as possible away from areas of dense population (it is to be noted that the victims in this case were especially vulnerable because they were very lightly clothed).

Further reading
Marshall[4], Davis[32], Ens[60], Marshall[59] and Spanish Ministry of Justice[61].

5.25 Staten Island (USA)

See Section 2.11.3 (page 111).
On 10 February 1973, a confined gas explosion took place in an empty liquefied natural gas (LNG) storage tank. The explosion blew off the domed steel roof, which then fell back, crushing or trapping 40 men who had been working on the floor. All of them were killed except two men who had been working on a scaffold 20 ft below the roof and managed to escape, having seen warning signs before the explosion. After the explosion a fire started in the insulation and continued for some hours, producing a great deal of black smoke.

The tank was constructed of reinforced concrete with an aluminium-coated *mylar* fabric lining, and was insulated externally with polyurethane foam. It had a capacity of 95,000 m³. It had been out of commission for a year-and-a-half on account of a leak in the lining, and had been purged of flammable vapour before work started.

Investigators had great difficulty in establishing the cause of the explosion, but it seems most likely to have resulted from the release of natural gas which had been occluded in the insulation in the earth embankment and had seeped into the tank. It was noted that there had been a fall in the atmospheric pressure during the preceding days. There were a number of possible ignition sources.

Further reading
Marshall[4], Davis[32] and Zabetakis and Burgess[62].

5.26 Stevenston (UK)

See Section 2.11.4 (page 113).
A fire occurred on 23 May 1973 at the Stevenston works of ICI Nobel Division. There was one fatality, three people were seriously injured and 30 required treatment for burns. Damage amounted to some US$ 600,000 (1974 prices).

The fire was initiated by a drum of nitrocellulose paste, which had been wetted with isopropanol, dropping from a forklift truck. The alcohol vapour was ignited, setting fire to the spilled nitrocellulose. The fire spread rapidly and was very intense, apparently generating a fireball 30 m high.

The open-air storage was 4000 m² in area and contained 4000 227-litre drums of nitrocellulose on pallets, some of them wetted with isopropanol and some with water. About 3000 of these drums were destroyed. 31 buildings were damaged, at distances of up to 140 m from the storage area. One of these, which was eventually destroyed, was the works fire station, so that only one of the four appliances was able to be used and three firemen and a clerk were burned — one of the firemen later died in hospital.

Marshall[4] remarks that contemporary accounts did not refer to the specifically hazardous properties of nitrocelluloses as redox compounds which, having a 'built-in' oxygen supply, burn very rapidly once they are ignited. The incident also draws attention to the risks associated with in-works transportation of hazardous materials.

Further reading
Marshall[4] and MHIDAS Report 1938 B[6].

5.27 Texas City (USA)

See Sections 2.10.8 (page 107) and 2.13.3 (page 126).
On 16 April 1947, a series of fires and explosions on ships in the harbour of Texas City caused at least 552 deaths, 3000 injuries and damage to a value of about US$ 50 to 75 million (1947 prices).

On the previous day the freighter *Grandcamp* had loaded, in addition to other miscellaneous cargo, 2300 tonnes of a fertilizer consisting of ammonium nitrate with an admixture of paraffin, resin and vaseline, contained in paper sacks. In the morning a fire was detected among the sacks. The crew started to try to fight the fire with water hoses. The captain, however, fearing damage to the cargo and apparently unaware of the hazard of anaerobic combustion, ordered them instead to batten down the hatches and cover them with tarpaulins, and to use steam to extinguish the fire.

Far from going out, the fire grew, and after about an hour there was a violent explosion which projected large fragments of the hull and of the screw over 1000s of metres and caused great damage in the port and town, as well as a tidal wave. Burning bales of sisal, which were also projected, fell down and ignited fuel stores.

The fire was probably started by a discarded cigarette end. It could well have been extinguished by cooling with water, but the use of steam aggravated it by raising the temperature. The presumed purpose of excluding atmospheric oxygen was entirely misconceived, since that element is present in excess within the ammonium nitrate molecule itself and the fire proceeded anaerobically. The subsequent detonation would probably not have occurred had ventilation not been stopped by the closing of the hatches. The most tragic consequence of the failure to understand the nature of the substance and to foresee its behaviour were the deaths in the explosion of hundreds of members of the public who had gathered at the dockside to watch the fire.

Flaming materials probably borne on the wind from the land fires then ignited a fire on another freighter, the *High Flyer*, whose cargo contained 1000 tonnes of the same fertilizer, as well as 2000 tonnes of sulphur. Attempts were made to tow this ship out to sea, but it eventually exploded the following day. This explosion caused only two or three deaths because the waterfront had been cleared earlier, but a great deal more damage was caused by blast and by innumerable secondary fires.

The combustion and explosive properties of ammonium nitrate and its mixtures with other substances have been discussed at some length by Medard[49]. A relatively recent article[63] discusses the wider background and lessons, such as the failure to foresee this type of disaster and the consequent lack of emergency provision, especially in the context of the sea-land interface.

Further reading
Marshall[4], Medard[49] and Stephens[63].

References in Chapter 5

1. Lees, F.P., 1996, *Loss Prevention in the Process Industries: Hazard Identification, Assessment and Control*, 2nd edn, 3 vols (Butterworth-Heinemann, UK).
2. Kletz, T.A., 1998, *What Went Wrong?*, 4th edn (Gulf Publishing, USA).
3. *IChemE Accident Database* (IChemE, UK) (available on CD-rom by annual subscription).
4. Marshall, V.C., 1987, *Major Chemical Hazards* (Ellis Horwood, UK).
5. King, R. and Hirst, R., 1998, *King's Safety in the Process Industries*, 2nd edn (Arnold, UK).
6. *MHIDAS [Major Hazard Incident Data Service]*, periodically updated. (UK Atomic Energy Authority) [accessible on OSH-ROM, Silver Platter International].
7. Kletz, T.A., 1993, *Lessons from Disaster: How Organizations Have No Memory and Accidents Recur* (IChemE, UK).
8. Health and Safety Executive, 1985, *The Abbeystead Explosion* (HMSO, UK).
9. Barton, J.A., and Seaton, H.D., 1986, Preventing dust explosions — a case history, *Chem Br*, 22(7) (July): 647–650.
10. Eckhoff, R.K., 1997, *Dust Explosions in the Process Industries*, 2nd edn (Butterworth-Heinemann, UK).

11. Lunn, G.A., 1984, *Aluminium Powder Explosion at ALPOCO, Anglesey, UK, Report No SMR 346/235/0171* (Health and Safety Executive, Explosion and Flame Laboratory).

12. Anon, 1987, The Sandoz warehouse fire, *Loss Prevention Bulletin*, 75 (June): 11–17.

13. Beck, E., 1986, Fire at warehouse 956, *Chem Ind (London)*, 23: 801.

14. Crossman, S., 1987, Disaster on the Rhine — what went wrong?, *Chem Br*, 23(1): 5–6.

15. Layman, P.L., 1987, Rhine spills force rethinking of potential for chemical pollution, *Chem Eng News*, 65(8): 7–11.

16. Williams, D., 1986, Germany copes with Rhine disaster, *Chem Ind (London)*, 23: 803.

17. Ayres, R.U. and Rohatgi, P.K., 1987, *Bhopal: Lessons for Technological Decision-Makers* (Pergamon, UK).

18. Kalelkar, A.S., 1988, Investigation of large-magnitude incidents: Bhopal as a case study, *IChemE Symposium Series No. 110* (IChemE, UK), pp 553–575.

19. Shrivastava, P., 1987, *Bhopal: Anatomy of a Crisis* (Ballinger, USA).

20. Gough, M., 1986, *Dioxin, Agent Orange: the Facts* (Plenum, USA).

21. Hay, A., 1982, *The Chemical Scythe* (Plenum, USA).

22. May, G., 1973, Chloracne from the accidental production of tetrachloro-dibenzo-dioxin, *British Journal of Industrial Medicine*, 30: 347, 349, 355–6, 361, 365.

23. Brown, B.S., 1919, Details of the failure of a 90-ft molasses tank, *Engineering News Record*, 82(20) 15 May: 384.

24. Anon, 1920, Boston molasses tank trial, *Engineering News Record*, 85(15), 7 October.

25. Marshall, V.C., 1988, *Loss Prevention Bulletin*, 82 (August): 27–32.

26. Marshall, V.C., 1994a, The Allied Colloids fire and its immediate lessons, *Loss Prevention Bulletin*, 116 (April): 1–8.

27. Marshall, V.C., 1994b, Safety management of multi-product batch plants — wider lessons from the Allied Colloids fire, *Loss Prevention Bulletin*, 118 (August): 3–7.

28. Fowler, A.H.K., Tyldesley, A. and Owens, K., 1998, Chemical warehousing — results of a HSE survey, *Loss Prevention Bulletin*, 141 (June): 8–10.

29. Gladwell, P., 1998, Some incidents involving AZDN, *Loss Prevention Bulletin*, 139 (February): 3–7.

30. Health and Safety Executive, 1994, *A report of HSE's investigation into the fire at Allied Colloids Ltd, Low Moor, Bradford on 21 July 1992* (HSE Books, UK).

31. Keller A.Z. and Wilson, H.C., 1992, *Hazards to Drinking Water Supplies* (Springer, UK).

32. Health and Safety Executive, 1994, *The Fire at Hickson and Welch Ltd* (HSE Books, UK).

33. Kletz, T.A., 1994, The fire at Hickson and Welch, *Loss Prevention Bulletin*, 119 (October): 3–4.

34. Davis, L.N., 1979, *Frozen Fire* (Friends of the Earth, USA).

35. Elliot, M.A., Subel, C.W., Brown, F.N., Artz, R.T. and Berger, L.B., 1946, *Report on the investigation of the fire ... at Cleveland, Ohio ...* US Bureau of Mines, RI 3867.

36. Lewis, D.J, 1991, Crescent City, Illinois, 21 June 1970, *Loss Prevention Bulletin* 101 (October): 22–32 (a very detailed account).

37. IChemE, 1987, The Feyzin disaster, *Loss Prevention Bulletin*, 77 (October): 1–9.

38. Parker, R.J., 1975, *The Flixborough Disaster: Report of the Court of Inquiry* (issued by the Department of Employment) (HMSO, UK).

39. Marshall, V.C., 1979, *Disaster at Flixborough* (Wheaton (Pergamon), UK).

40. Anon, 1992, Sewer 'blockage' triggered Mexican petrol blasts, *New Civil Engineer*, 30 April 1992.

41. Anon, 1992, News report under heading 'overseas fires', *Fire Prevention*, 254, November: 44.

42. Lewis, D.J., 1985, Dramatic exit in Houston, *Hazardous Cargo Bulletin*, November, 6(10): 52–54.

43. McMullen, G., 1976, *A Review of the May 11th Ammonia Truck Accident* (City of Houston Health Department, USA).

44. Marshall, V.C., 1986, Ludwigshafen — two case histories, *Loss Prevention Bulletin*, 67 (February): 21–33 (largely reproduced in Marshall[4]).

45. Davenport, J., 1984, A study of vapour cloud incidents — an update, *IChemE Symposium Series No. 80* (IChemE, UK).

46. Anon ('HJK'), 1981, The day the canal burned, *Hazardous Cargo Bulletin* (May): 19.

47. TNO, 1985, *LPG — A Study* (TNO Department of Industrial Safety, The Netherlands).

48. Anon, 1979, The week they closed Missisauga, *Sunday Star*, special edn, 18 November.

49. Medard, L.A., 1989, *Accidental Explosions*, 2 vols (Ellis Horwood, UK).

50. Stull, D.R., 1977, *Fundamentals of Fire and Explosion*, AIChE Monograph Series no. 10, vol 73.

51. NTSB, 1972, *Pipeline accident report*, Phillips Pipe Line Company, propane gas explosion (US National Transportation Safety Board (Report no NTSB-PAR-72-1), USA).

52. Burgess, D.S. and Zabetakis, M.G., 1973, *US Bureau of Mines Report of Investigations RI 7752*.

53. Gugan, K., 1979, *Unconfined Vapour Cloud Explosions* (IChemE, UK).

54. Health and Safety Executive, 1980, *Seveso: the escape of toxic substances at the ICMESA establishment on 10th July 1976 and the consequent potential dangers to health and the environment due to industrial activity* (Health and Safety Executive, UK). A translation by the HSE of the official report of the Parliamentary Commission of Enquiry, by permission of the Parliament of the Republic of Italy.

55. Marshall, V.C., 1991, Seveso and Manfredonia, their Fifteenth Anniversaries, *Environmental Protection Bulletin* 013 (July): 21–24.

56. Marshall, V.C., 1992, The Seveso disaster — an appraisal of its causes and consequences, *Loss Prevention Bulletin* 104 (April): 10–26.
57. Temple, C.J., 1976, *Seveso: the Issues and the Lessons* (Foresight, UK).
58. Whiteside, T., 1979, *The Pendulum and the Toxic Cloud: the Course of Dioxin Contamination* (Yale University Press, USA).
59. Marshall, V.C., 1986, The Spanish camp disaster — a third view, *Loss Prevention Bulletin* 72 (December): 9–18.
60. Ens, H., 1986, Comments on Marshall, 1986, *Loss Prevention Bulletin* 72 (December): 18–20.
61. Spanish Ministry of Justice, 1982, *Judgement No. OC.8177711, Tarragona 27/01/82*, HSE translation No. 2G (May).
62. Zabetakis, M.G and. Burgess, D.S., 1973, *US Bureau of Mines Report of Investigations* RI 7752.
63. Stephens, H.W., 1993, The Texas City disaster: a re-examination, *Industrial and Environmental Crisis Quarterly*, 7(3): 189–204.

Control of process hazards

6

6.1 Introduction

As stated in the Foreword, the ultimate aim of this book is to help reduce the toll of injury and damage that partially offsets the benefits of the process industries. Chapter 1 is devoted to the discussion of general principles, and Chapters 2 to 5 to the detailed description of hazards and their realizations. This chapter considers how the process industries pursue the above aim.

One of our objectives has been to introduce some structure into a subject which has hitherto been taught in a somewhat piecemeal fashion. Partly to serve this objective, but mainly because of its practical importance, we advocate the adoption of a *strategic* approach to process safety. Section 6.1.1 (page 246) explains this concept which informs the remainder of the chapter and Section 6.1.2 (page 248) defines various criteria for characterizing the hazardousness of a process installation, giving a brief introduction to the principles and techniques of hazard identification and evaluation.

Section 6.2 (page 254) describes the strategic approach to process safety. The overall task is specified in terms of a programme of progressive hazard reduction, employing one of the previously discussed measures of hazardousness — *societal risk*. The programme is then outlined, considering ways of attenuating, first the *magnitudes* of the hazards ('limitation'), then the *risks* of realization of the hazards ('prevention'), and finally the *consequences* of their realization ('mitigation'), with reference to the component parts (sources, receptors, transmission paths and barriers) of the analytical model of a hazard system elaborated in Chapter 1.

Section 6.3 (page 270) discusses the difficult issues of decision-making and achieving *social acceptability* for the process plant.

As this book is directed primarily towards students of chemical engineering and chemistry, we have concentrated hitherto on the technological aspects of the safety problem. It cannot be emphasised too strongly, however, that safety depends ultimately on human actions, both individual and collective.

Such human actions must be guided by scientific knowledge, but are also very much conditioned by psychological and organizational factors, and are notoriously subject to error at all levels of responsibility. It is therefore essential that they are properly regulated by appropriate safety policies and systems designed to prevent errors of all kinds and to facilitate the prompt identification and correction of any that do occur. These matters are considered in Section 6.4 on safety and management (page 272).

6.1.1 Tactics and strategy in hazard control

In an early paper[2], Marshall proposed that, because of the growing size and complexity of process plants, it was necessary to adopt a 'strategic' approach to the control of major process hazards, as opposed to what was characterized as the 'tactical' approach which had largely prevailed until then.

The categories 'strategy' and 'tactics' originate in military science, where 'strategy' relates to an overall plan for the conduct of a war or campaign (this is the business of generals) while 'tactics' refers to the organization of detailed operations within it (the task of junior officers or even of non-commissioned officers). Their use has, however, been extended to other walks of life, notably to the fields of politics and business.

What are the main characteristics of these two kinds of approach in the context of process safety?

A tactical approach may consider a single element of a hazard system in isolation. It tends to take the design of a process plant as 'given' and to depend for assurance of safety on remedying perceived problems retrospectively by superimposing 'bolt-on' devices, such as trips for equipment and protective clothing for operators, and on imposing a very rigorous discipline on the workforce.

A strategic approach, on the other hand, takes into account all the elements of a hazard system described in Chapter 1 — the sources (both primary and secondary), the transmission paths and the receptors — in their inter-relationships. It seeks to 'build in' safety considerations from the inception of a project and employs an iterative procedure of review and amendment at every stage of its elaboration down to its periodic (or even final) shut-down. The latter proceeding is illustrated symbolically in Figure 6.1.

Marshall[2] envisaged nine such stages in the realization of a process plant:

(a) identifying a commercially desirable product;
(b) devising a process for making it;
(c) creating a flowsheet;

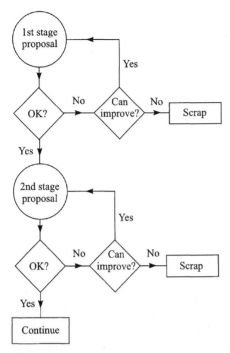

Figure 6.1 Safety reviews at successive stages of a project

(d) specifying and designing the equipment and the control system;

(e) choosing a location;

(f) devising a site;

(g) designing interconnecting piping and layout of instrumention connections;

(h) procuring, erecting and installing the plant and equipment;

(i) commissioning and routine operation of the plant.

Other authors[3-5] follow similar approaches, while adopting somewhat different schemes.

An extremely important requirement of the strategic approach to hazard control is a substantial upgrading of the responsibility for safety in the management structure as compared with the past practice of appointing as 'safety officers' relatively junior staff who had insufficient knowledge and authority to be able to exert significant influence. This subject of safety management is returned to in Section 6.4 (page 272).

A classical demonstration of the consequences of failing to employ an appropriate strategy is that of the Flixborough disaster, which forms the subject of one of the case histories in Chapter 5 of this book (page 227). While the company was correctly criticized for failing to foresee and avoid the incident which initiated the disaster, the outcome was also far worse than it might otherwise have been because of the many fundamental defects in the design, construction, layout and management of the complex.

It may be said that sound tactics are essential for the successful prosecution of strategy, but cannot solve problems resulting from its inadequacy. Conversely, safety strategy aims to maintain a safe environment, so that the need for tactical measures may be minimized and their effectiveness maximized.

In the consideration of hazard and risk reduction, priority will therefore given to strategic measures. Accordingly, the order of treatment in Sections 6.2 and 6.3 of this chapter is approximately chronological, attention being given to issues as they would normally arise during the evolution of a project.

6.1.2 Assessment of hazards

In order to implement the iterative procedure described above for minimizing the hazardousness of a process plant, the various types of hazard need to be recognized and evaluated at each stage as they arise. *Process safety analysis*, as this activity has come to be called, has evolved very rapidly over recent years in response to technological progress and the demands of society for 'safety with economy'. It employs a number of complex techniques, the detailed description of which is inappropriate to an elementary text: therefore only brief introductory accounts are provided and readers who wish to pursue this study are directed to relevant sources. Readers may wish to refer to Jones[6] for authoritative guidance on terminology.

Classification and comparison: hazard indices

There are a number of semi-quantitative methods of rating plant designs (and existing plants) for 'hazardousness', which are generally called *hazard indices*. The *Dow Fire and Explosion Index*[7] divides the plant into processing units characterized by process conditions. Each unit is ranked according to several factors:

$$F\&EI = MF \times GPH \times SPH, \text{ where}$$

- MF is a 'material factor', based on the 'energy potential' of the most hazardous material present in quantity (depending on enthalpy of formation or reaction, reactivity, flammability);
- GPH is a factor for 'general process hazards', accounting for the type of process (batch or continuous), the nature of the reaction, the properties of the materials such as spontaneous heating;

- SPH is a factor for 'special process hazards' such as temperature (relative to flash and boiling points), pressure, quantity, operation within explosive limits.

The *Mond Fire, Explosion and Toxicity Index*[8] is an extension of the Dow Index which seeks also to account for toxic hazards. It includes additional offsetting factors for preventative and protective measures and for the 'quality of safety management'. It can generate separate indices for specific hazards.

These *indices* do not claim to quantify hazards or risks absolutely. They can be used to *compare* processes for selection purposes, and to *identify* hazards which will require attention later on. Edwards[9] introduces a more comprehensive index which seeks to quantify the 'inherent safety' of a proposed process. [The concept of 'inherent safety' — particularly associated with Kletz — identifies processes which depend for their safety on their intrinsic characteristics and not on superimposed devices. This concept is referenced further in Section 6.2.]. The index is intended to take account of 16 parameters, but has as yet only been tested against seven — inventory, flammability, explosiveness, toxicity, temperature, pressure and reaction yield (the quantification of some of these is itself problematic). The results are claimed to be reasonably self-consistent, but the method needs to be validated against other measures and requires more development. At the time of writing, there is no record of its adoption for industrial use.

Identification: hazard and operability studies

The strategy for hazard reduction outlined in the following sections relies for the identification of hazards on the fundamental understanding outlined in Chapters 2, 3 and 4, as well as on the type of accumulated experience represented by case histories such as those included in Chapter 5. The importance of rigorous scrutiny of all technological proposals at every stage cannot be emphasized too strongly. Given the complexity of modern plant, however, it is impossible to be certain that such studies will uncover all the possible ways in which failure could occur. There is therefore an important role for an objective 'catch-all' procedure for scrutinizing the final outcome. This function is almost universally performed by the methodology of hazard and operability studies (HAZOP). This is described extensively by EPSC[10], Kletz[11] and in CCPS[12]. A useful introduction for students is provided by Skelton[13].

HAZOP is a procedure for identifying the potential deviations of a projected or actual plant from its intended operation. It consists of a very thorough and systematic examination by a multi-skilled team of the process and instrumentation diagram (P&ID), employing a series of standardized 'guide words' to stimulate consideration of various kinds of deviation. Other procedures are then used to evaluate these deviations for their likelihood and possible consequences and, on this basis, modifications may be prescribed.

HAZOP is the most widely known and practised 'safety assurance' technique in the field — indeed, so universal has it become that its name is in some quarters a byword for process safety. However, it must be stressed that, by the time it is normally applied — that is, when the P&ID is available — all the major decisions about the process and equipment will have been taken. [This statement refers to the technique in its original form — attempts have been made to extend its scope to earlier phases]. Thus it is essentially a 'method of last resort'. It cannot — and does not purport to — challenge the basic technology or process design, but focuses on details of hardware and operating procedures, and will usually lead only to minor changes such as 'bolt-on' protective devices or amendments to operating instructions.

Criteria of hazardousness

The review process illustrated in Figure 6.1 requires a decision at each stage as to whether the proposal is satisfactory from a safety point of view. This decision will be more or less difficult according to the nature of the perceived hazard(s), as illustrated (somewhat simplistically) in Table 6.1.

The question marks in the table indicate that a thorough evaluation of the hazard is needed before a decision can be made. In order to address this rationally, measures are needed of how 'safe' (or, more usually, 'unsafe') the envisaged process is. This requires one or more criteria of safety (or 'unsafety') which are reasonably consistent as between one installation and another, and whose values can be estimated. This issue is referred to in Chapter 1, Section 1.4.3 (page 21), where 'individual risk' and 'societal risk' are defined, pointing out that these were measures of a binary quantity having the attributes of magnitude and frequency (risk).

The estimation of these and related measures — so-called 'quantitative risk assessment' (or QRA) — is the work of specialists and a detailed treatment of the topic would go far beyond the scope of this book. Only a brief introduction

Table 6.1 Decision concerning a perceived hazard

Consequences	Risk	Proceed/amend
Large	High	Amend
Large	Low	??
Small	High	??
Small	Low	Proceed

to its fundamental aspects will therefore be given here. There is abundant literature on the subject, in particular the following publications: Skelton[13] (specially written for students), CCPS[14], Kletz[11], Wells[4] and Pitblado and Turney[15].

Estimation of individual risk

On any process site, a given receptor may be exposed to emissions from several sources. In the first instance, however, suppose the hazard system considered has only one source. Realizations generally fall upon a spectrum ranging from a minor event to some maximum event. A method for establishing individual risk, therefore, is to divide up this spectrum into segments and to estimate, for any segment, a mean level L of emission. It is then necessary to calculate the consequent dose incident to a receptor i in a specified location, using an equation such as equations (4.2) and (4.3) (page 167). [Special forms of these equations for different types of emission are suggested in Marshall and Ruhemann[16]].

This is followed by estimating the fraction Q_{iL} corresponding to the incident dose by means of the $T_{L \to H}$ transform. Where a probit relationship exists, this should be used. Otherwise, an estimate needs to be obtained of the fractional mortality from a table of correspondences. It will be obvious that this is a difficult undertaking and can lead only to very approximate estimates.

The next step is to establish the frequency f_L with which such emissions may occur within any such segment. This involves the methodology of *fault-tree analysis* (see below). For each segment in the spectrum of levels of emission, the corresponding individual risk is obtained as the product of the quantal fraction and the frequency. The total individual risk is then estimated by summing the products of quantal fraction and frequency for all segments.

Equation for individual risk R_i: $\quad R_i = \sum_{L_{min}}^{L_{max}} [Q_{iL} \times f_L]$ \hfill (6.1)

As indicated, a receptor may form part of several overlapping hazard systems, including those from secondary sources which may be realized from a primary source. The total individual risk associated with a process is obtained by summing the individual risks from all the process sources.

Spatial variation of individual risk: average individual risk

The above calculation, though it allows statistically for variation in the vulnerability of individual receptors, relates to a specific location. Consequently, the values will vary with location and hence, for people — since they move about in the course of their daily activities — with time. Various procedures are available for dealing with this problem, depending upon the purpose under consideration.

If risks associated with particular locations are of concern, *individual risk contours* may be plotted on a plan of the site and/or its surroundings[17].

If the concern is with the risks to a particular person or occupational function, their typical movements may be plotted during the working day or week and the calculated individual risk values integrated for specific locations with time.

If the risks to a population are studied (either the workforce or the residents of the neighbourhood), an *average* value of individual risk may be calculated. This is a convenient statistic but possibly misleading, since it would suggest that individual risk for an installation is inversely proportional to the number of persons exposed.

A sort of average individual risk which is much used in industry is called the *fatal accident rate* (FAR). This is defined as 'the number of deaths occurring among 1000 employees over a period of 10^8 hours'. The basis of this statistic is that $10^8/1000, = 10^5$, is approximately equal to the number of hours for which a single employee is exposed to risk in their working life (50 years $\times$ 50 weeks/year $\times$ 40 hours/week): this is probably (1998) somewhat dated. The historical value of FAR for the UK chemical industry is four. About half of this (two) is attributable to general industrial accidents, and the other half to hazards which are specific to the process.

More detailed discussion of these criteria is found, for example, in Marshall[2], Lees[18] and Pitblado and Turney[15].

Estimation of societal risk

The above procedure can be extended to the estimation of societal risk in the neighbourhood of a process hazard[16]. For this, a distribution of receptors and a population density (both on- and off-site) needs to be assumed, taking account of hour-by-hour and day-by-day variations through the working day or week.

In the previous discussion on individual risk it was shown how, for any level of realization, a quantal fraction Q_{iL} could be estimated for a given receptor. This quantity may be viewed alternatively as an equivalent fractional number ($1 \times Q_{iL}$) of casualties in terms of the specified quantal for each receptor. These fractional numbers can then be summed to give a total number of quantal responses, denoted here by N_L, for the whole population P. Such a value will typically not be an integer.

Thus the calculation of societal risk requires, for a given level of realization, the estimation of the fraction Q_{iL} for each receptor, as set out above for individual risk, and the summation of these values over the whole population of receptors to give an N value for this level.

Equation for societal risk: $$N_L = \sum_{i=1}^{P} Q_{iL} \qquad (6.2)$$

where, Q_{iL} = fractional response corresponding to the $T_{L \to H}$ transform for the ith receptor at the given level of emission; N_L = total number of persons suffering harm in terms of the specified quantal by a given level of emission in a population P.

The N_L values so calculated constitute, with the corresponding frequencies f_L, the co-ordinates of what may be termed a 'probabilistic (or predictive) f/N curve'. Such a 'curve', plotted over the spectrum of possible levels of realization, resembles the histograms known as F/N diagrams in which, based upon the historical record, values of quantals, N, expressed as integers, are plotted against frequency. [In order to 'smooth out' the effects of randomness in 'real life', historical data are usually plotted on 'F/N' diagrams, where the upper-case F represents a *cumulative* frequency — that is, of *N or more* fatalities]. Integral values of N correspond with societal risk as defined by Jones[6] (see Section 1.4.2, page 18).

As with individual risk in the vicinity of process installations, societal risk may derive from a number of sources and these are summated to obtain a total value. An example of this has been given in HSE[17]. Figure 6.2 overleaf is an example of such a 'probabilistic' f/N diagram (with arbitrary data).

Estimation of risk

The use of *fault-tree analysis* to estimate the frequency with which specified chance incidents are likely to occur has been mentioned above. This procedure envisages a series of events, starting with one or more possible initiating causes such as equipment or operator failures and culminating in an undesirable *top event* such as an emission of matter or energy. It represents this sequence by means of a logic tree, working backwards from the top event, through its putative immediate causes and any intermediate events to the initiating causes. It assigns frequencies to independent failures (linked by 'or gates') and probabilities to coincident failures (linked by 'and gates') and then cumulates these according to the rules of Boolean algebra to yield an estimate of the frequency of the top event. It is also helpful in identifying those elements of a system where improvement is likely to lead to significant reduction in the risk of the top event. Data are derived from various data banks[19], taking account of operational factors such as the frequency with which protective devices are proof-tested.

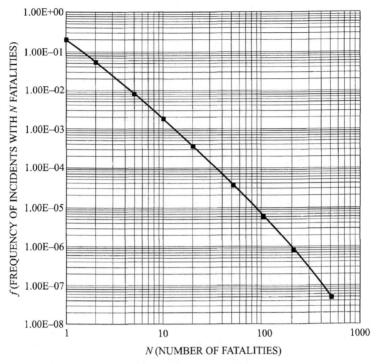

Figure 6.2 Probabilistic f/N diagram (arbitrary data)

Event-tree analysis

This procedure is, in a sense, the converse of the preceding one. It uses a divergent logic diagram to predict the frequencies of various possible consequences from an emission of matter or energy. These two types of diagram and calculation are often linked, as shown in Figure 6.3.

6.2 The strategic approach to hazard reduction

6.2.1 Analysis of the task and definition of the objectives

In the light of the previous discussion, the task of hazard control may be represented as being to minimize the societal risk associated with a process plant (or a multi-plant site) or perhaps (see Section 6.3, page 270) to optimize a number of criteria. This may be addressed by seeking systematically to reduce, on the one hand those of its elements which contribute to hazard magnitude,

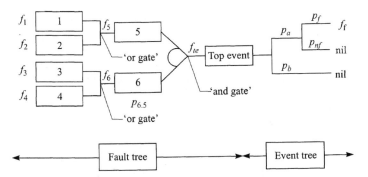

Figure 6.3 Example of a simplified fault-tree/event-tree diagram

- 1, 2, 3, 4 are independent failures of frequencies f_1, f_2, f_3, f_4
- 5 is a failure which occurs if *either* failure 1 *or* failure 2 occurs ($f_5 = f_1 + f_2$)
- 6 is a failure which occurs if *either* failure 3 *or* failure 4 occurs ($f_6 = f_3 + f_4$)
- Probability that failure 6 will coincide with failure 5 is $p_{6.5}$ (this depends on factors not discussed)
- The 'top event' is, for example, a loss of containment of a flammable gas mixture; it will occur if *both* events 5 *and* 6 occur: its frequency, $f_{te}, = p_{6.5} \times f_5$
- If top event occurs, *either* event a (ignition — probability p_a) *or* event b (harmless dispersal — probability $p_b = 1 - p_a$) follows; then frequency of ignition, $f_a, = p_a \times f_{te}$
- If event a occurs, probability of fatality for persons within specified range is p_f
- Probability of non-fatality for persons within specified range is $p_{nf} = 1 - p_f$
- Then predicted fatalities per annum, $f_f, = p_f \times f_a = p_f \times p_a \times f_{te}$

and on the other those which contribute to risk. The various elements may be identified by reference to the conceptual model of Chapter 1.

The progress of this endeavour can be symbolically illustrated by means of a diagram (see Figure 6.4 overleaf) in which a series of probabilistic f-N curves represent successive improvements in the level of safety achieved. This has, graphically, the effect of progressively reducing the area under the curve. This area would represent, if the diagram were plotted on linear scales, the integral of risk with respect to magnitude: it has been suggested as a single-valued measure of societal risk, sometimes called *detriment* (or *expected value*) but it is considered to be of limited utility[21,22]. The ultimate objective is to achieve a level of *societal risk* which satisfies the criteria of *social acceptability* that will have been adopted for the project (this was introduced in Chapter 1: and is discussed further in Section 6.3, page 270).

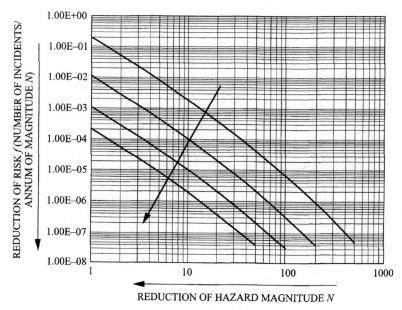

Figure 6.4 Notional reduction of hazard and risk

Public consideration of safety issues tends to confine discussion to the *prevention* of hazard realizations (usually called 'accidents'). This is self-evidently an extremely important objective, but the preceding chapters of this book have demonstrated that equal importance should be attached to the need to *limit* the impact on potential receptors of any realization that may nevertheless occur (using measures of attenuation) and to *mitigate* its effects (by way of remedial action such as medical treatment). These considerations have led to the notion of a tri-partite approach to safety described as 'prevention, limitation and mitigation'[22]. These may be regarded as components of the objective of the *safety strategy* which is set out below.

The accounts of realizations have emphasized that process hazards are typically very complex. Chapter 1 presents a fairly simple conceptual model of a hazard system to facilitate their systematic discussion, and the subsequent chapters have been largely focused on the principal elements of this model. The model will also be used as a framework for presenting and discussing the approach to the control of hazards.

6.2.2 Limitation by reduction of hazard magnitude

The primary sources of process hazards comprise all vessels and equipment containing hazardous materials, whether undergoing processing or in storage or

256

transportation. Virtually all the substances occurring as raw materials, intermediates, products or service media — for example, heat-transfer fluids — in the process industries are hazardous to some degree. Anyone tempted to doubt this statement should consider the incident which occurred in Boston, Massachusetts in 1919, when the failure of a storage vessel containing some 12,500 tonnes of molasses caused the deaths of 21 people by drowning and injury to 40 others, as well as a great deal of damage. See Chapter 5 for a case history (page 217). Nevertheless, some substances obviously pose more serious hazards than others by virtue of their intrinsic physical and/or chemical properties, their thermodynamic states and/or their possible inter-action with other substances which may also be present. The quantity which could be accidentally released is obviously a crucial consideration. The practice of limiting the magnitude of source hazards — in relation to both their intensive and extensive properties — has long been advocated by Kletz[23], who described it as 'inherent safety'.

Chemical properties of process materials

The choice of a process, and related decisions about the substances involved, clearly depend on many physical, chemical and economic factors. It is nevertheless essential, at the inception of a process proposal, to examine the chemical properties of these substances and to consider, if any of them are perceived to be, singly or in juxtaposition, particularly hazardous, whether there may be acceptable alternatives involving less hazardous materials. Information of this kind is available from many sources, but perhaps the most authoritative is Bretherick[24].

Kletz[23] quotes a number of examples of process substitution. One concerns the following structural unit, which is used in a crop-protection chemical:

$$\begin{bmatrix} CH_3 & CH_3 \\ \diagdown & \diagup \\ & N \\ & | \\ R-O-C-O \end{bmatrix}$$

It was to be synthesized from an alcohol ROH and dimethyl carbamoyl chloride (DMCC), but the latter is carcinogenic to animals and volatile, and so is best avoided. A safer route was developed in which a chloroformate reacted with dimethylamine to produce an alternative intermediate:

$$(CH_3)_2NH + COClR \rightarrow (CH_3)_2NCOR$$

This route involved the use of phosgene, itself a highly toxic compound, as an intermediate in the preparation of the chloroformate, but that was considered a lesser hazard than DMCC.

Another example, cited by Marshall[25] and by Kletz[23], is the substitution after the Flixborough disaster (see Chapter 5, page 227) of the alternative process for the production of cyclohexanol, by the hydrogenation of phenol. This is a vapour-phase process and much less hazardous than the liquid-phase oxidation of cyclohexane, but the change only moves the hazard to another site, since the production of phenol (by oxidation of cumene to cumene hydroper-oxide and the 'cleavage' of the latter) is also a very hazardous process.

Minimizing thermodynamic severity

The higher the temperature and pressure of a contained fluid, the greater is the hazard it poses (the propensity for accidental release of matter or energy may be correspondingly greater, and this should be taken into account in consideration of risk reduction measures). This factor must also, therefore, be a consideration in process selection, though it will necessarily be interdependent with the choice of reactants.

The introduction of a catalyst with enhanced activity or selectivity, or of better mixing arrangements, may facilitate the use of a lower reaction temperature or — indirectly — a lower pressure. Similarly, the provision of extended surfaces in heat-transfer equipment may allow lower temperatures to be used, as does *pinch technology*, a systematic application of the Second Law of Thermodynamics to the optimization of heat-exchanger networks.

As indicated in Section 2.5 (page 40), a particularly serious type of hazard is presented by vapours liquefied under pressure, in view of their propensity to 'flash' if the containment pressure is suddenly released. Where there is a choice, this problem may tip the balance in favour of a vapour-phase or 'normal-liquid-phase' process.

Reduction of inventories

In the time-honoured words of Kletz[23]: 'What you don't have, can't leak!', one might think that the desirability of minimizing the inventories of hazardous materials would be entirely self-evident. The fact that this is not so is evidenced by the tragedies, *inter alia*, of Flixborough and Bhopal (see pages 215 and 227).

Historically, the most important way of achieving inventory reduction has been the conversion of processes from batch to continuous operation. Bell[26] describes a classic example of nitroglycerin production, which involves the nitration of glycerol with a mixture of concentrated nitric and sulphuric acids:

$$C_3H_5(OH)_3 + 3HNO_3 \rightarrow C_3H_5(NO_3) + 3H_2O$$

The reaction is very exothermic — if the temperature is not well controlled by cooling and stirring, it leads to a runaway reaction involving an uncontrollable oxidation followed by violent decomposition of the nitroglycerin.

The traditional process (in use up to the 1950s) involved a batch reactor, with an inventory of 1 t. If the reactor blew up, the operators stood no chance, and the plant was totally destroyed. The new process was operated continuously; the glycerol and acids were automatically proportioned by means of an injector, which also ensured good mixing and, consequently, fast reaction at a relatively low temperature, reducing the residence time — and hence the inventory for a given output — by a factor of 60. Similar inventory reductions were effected in the downstream processing. As a result of these changes, the magnitude of the source hazard was reduced to a point where the operators could be protected by a single blast wall, and the risk of explosion was also greatly reduced.

The scope for changes of this sort is limited, since continuous operation may not be economically viable if either the production rate is below some threshold value or the requisite residence times are too long. More generally, inventory reduction is achieved by limiting stocks and buffer storage, by minimizing 'inactive' space in process units such as heat exchangers, distillation towers and so on and by limiting the sizes of vessel openings and connecting pipes. There is, of course, a balance to be struck with considerations of continuity of supply and of pumping costs, but experience suggests that there is usually considerable scope for reducing hold-up of process materials.

Magnitude of emission

The prevention of releases lies in the province of risk reduction. However, beyond inventory limitation, various techniques are available for minimizing the magnitude of any emission which does occur. These depend on the detection of incipient releases, for example by monitoring the plant atmosphere (such systems will be mentioned below in connection with protective devices for risk reduction) or the pressure or temperature in a process vessel, and on alarms and manual or automatic systems for discontinuing the supply to a leaking vessel of the material being released and/or running it off to another vessel ('dumping'). Leaks resulting from over-pressurization of vessels may be limited by emergency water cooling to reduce the vapour pressures.

6.2.3 Limitation by attenuation of emissions

Emissions may be attenuated by distance or by barriers interposed in their prospective paths to absorb or reflect the matter or energy that may be transmitted to receptors in the event of a realization. The latter are generally arranged, for maximum effect, to surround either the source or the receptor. Some barriers are permanently installed, while others are brought into play more or less automatically in circumstances of emergency — that is, either when a realization is anticipated as a result of a warning signal or after it has started. These issues have a special importance when secondary sources are present.

Segregation of receptors

As said in developing the conceptual model, in the absence of receptors no hazard can be said to exist. In principle, therefore, so far as potential human victims are concerned, process hazards could be eliminated entirely by operating the plant in totally automatic fashion, with no humans on the site.

This is, of course, an ideal situation which is rarely capable of practical achievement. It serves nevertheless to highlight an extremely important principle of process safety — that in the design, layout and operation of plant, every effort should be made, so far as technical and economic considerations allow, to minimize the number of people whose presence on the plant is necessary to its operation, and to ensure that nobody else comes within range of its hazards. By the same token, any structure which is not required to be there for practical operational reasons should not be placed within range of a hazard realization. Thus, for instance, in the past satisfactory surveillance of plant operation required control buildings to be close to the plant. Increasingly, remote control technology is rendering this unnecessary as discussed later.

It is shocking to learn how often this obvious principle is overlooked. To take one example, at Flixborough (see Chapter 5, page 227), the main office block was located only 50 to 80 metres from the epicentre of the explosion, and was completely destroyed. Had the accident occurred during office hours on a normal weekday, the number of fatalities would have been perhaps five times greater than it was[27].

Also of concern in this context are emergency services such as the company fire brigade and medical centre. If these were immobilized or destroyed in the course of a realization, a minor incident might escalate into a major disaster. It is clearly essential that they are protected by segregation and/or robustly constructed buildings if any risk of conflagration or large-scale explosion is apprehended.

Attenuation by distance

In Chapter 3, reference was made to the effects of distance in attenuating emissions of matter and energy from hazard sources, noting that these are essentially three-fold (the three aspects being 'geometrical', reflecting the decrease with radial distance from the source of the intensity of radiation and blast effects; dispersion, reflecting the dilution of material emissions by mixing with the atmosphere or other media; and the absorption of radiated energy by the atmosphere).

It follows that, where receptors cannot be entirely segregated from hazard sources, it should be ensured that the distances between them are such as to minimize the consequences of any realization from those sources. This principle has costs associated with it, but land values are not usually a major consideration and the expense of additional lengths of pipe and cable (as opposed to fittings) is relatively trivial[28]. It is acknowledged, however, that marine installations present more difficult problems, since here space is at a premium.

Safe distances may be estimated from data about the attenuation of thermal radiation and blast waves (see Chapter 3 and Mecklenburgh[29]).

Evacuation

Even if the strategy of segregating personnel from hazard sources is implemented quite thoroughly, it may still be impossible to avoid the presence of some workers in the neighbourhood in the course of normal plant operation. It is then also necessary to take measures to reduce further the numbers who may be harmed in the event of a realization, and the degree of harm that they may sustain. This requires the provision of various types of barrier (see below), but also arrangements for early warning, and for rapid evacuation where this is appropriate.

Barriers: construction of plant and buildings

It is not always possible to avoid erecting associated plant and buildings in the neighbourhood of a perceived hazard source. Where no humans are involved, the question of how robust such structures should be is simply a matter of economic balance, remembering that a failure of the source is likely anyway to lead to loss of production and that this need not be 'double-counted', though the potential of the receptor to become a secondary source must be considered (see later). In the case of control buildings, however, where operating personnel are required to be present (and which may even, as at Flixborough, be designated as a place of refuge in an emergency), blast-proof, fire-proof and perhaps air-tight, independently ventilated construction may be necessary. Marshall[2] deals with the question of explosion-proofing.

Other permanent barriers

Liquid spillages may be constrained by providing secondary containment such as a *bund*. Blast walls or mounding constitute barriers against pressure waves resulting from explosions. Shelter from, for example, thermal radiation, blast

261

and toxic gases is provided by appropriately constructed buildings, and of course by vessel walls, which should be as robust as necessary and may be insulated or water-cooled.

At the 'tactical' level, protective clothing constitutes an important barrier of attenuation though it has sometimes been relied upon excessively and should properly be regarded as the last resort after measures of a more strategic kind have been put in place.

Emergency barriers

If partial or total failure of a critical stop-valve is envisaged, it may be supplemented by a 'spectacle plate'. Water or steam curtains may be provided to enhance the dispersion of vapour clouds[30]. As will be mentioned below, relief valves should be vented to a scrubbing unit or to a flare to remove harmful constituents (the catastrophic outcome of the Bhopal disaster described in Chapter 5, page 215, was largely due to the failure of such devices to function).

Receptors as secondary sources

Since most process vessels will contain materials that are hazardous in some way, any such vessel which is a receptor in a hazard system will also inescapably constitute a secondary hazard source. Furthermore, even an item of plant which contains no such material will represent, as will any other structure, a source of destructive potential energy in the event that it is caused to collapse by a realization of the primary hazard. This phenomenon (often called the 'domino effect') has been amply demonstrated in many disasters (such as Flixborough, Feyzin and Mexico City). Where such hazards exist, the importance of safe distances, barriers and robust construction is obviously enhanced.

Fire-fighting

A chemical works of any substantial size normally has an in-house fire brigade. This will have a small core of full-time staff whose time under non-emergency circumstances is devoted to installing, inspecting and servicing fire alarms, fire-prevention and fire-fighting equipment, with a trained reserve of employees normally engaged on other duties (typically on maintenance work).

Reference has already been made to the need to protect such services from the effects of hazard realizations so as to ensure their availability. In the absence of such a facility, recourse must be made to the public Fire Brigade (for large fires, it will usually be necessary to call it in at some point, preferably early). In either case, close liaison must be maintained with the public service, since the fighting of chemical fires will invariably require special awareness, techniques and materials.

As suggested in the case history of the Feyzin disaster (page 225), it is important to assess the prospects of fighting a fire as early as possible, bearing in mind the danger to the fire-fighters themselves. If the fire is becoming a conflagration, it may be best to evacuate rapidly and let it burn itself out.

6.2.4 Prevention of hazard realizations (risk reduction)

The reduction of risk entails the prevention of failures which may bring about realizations of hazards. To argue that other aspects of safety are also essential is not to diminish the importance of this task. It requires the assurance of the integrity of process equipment, appropriate safeguards against malfunctions and highly systematic and reliable operating procedures.

Design and selection of equipment

It is scarcely necessary to point out that the most fundamental means of minimizing the frequency of accidental losses of containment is to ensure that the hardware employed is of the appropriate design and quality. It is a staple requirement of sound engineering practice to adhere to accepted codes governing the specification, design, manufacture, testing, and installation of equipment. The study of these matters occupies the major part of undergraduate engineering courses and does not therefore require detailed discussion here.

Protection against ignition from electrical equipment

Practically all process plants use electricity for powering machinery, for heating and/or lighting and for instrumentation and control. Many fires and explosions are believed to have been initiated by sparks from electrical equipment. For this reason, measures of risk control for such equipment are among the oldest in the process industries, and are the subject of extensive regulation. The approach, broadly, is to classify zones on process sites according to a perceived likelihood of the presence of a flammable atmosphere and to prescribe a degree of protection for the design and construction of the equipment to be used in each class of area. A detailed account of this approach is given by Lees[18].

Control systems

Over a period of about six decades, there have been enormous advances in the techniques and equipment available for the control of process plant, though the extent to which they are exploited varies greatly from one enterprise to another. The reader is referred to Lees[18] or King[31] for accounts of this subject in the context of process safety. More general textbooks in this area have been published by, for example, Bentley[32] (on measurement systems) and Shinskey[33].

In broad terms, the key advances in the control of process plant have been:

- a great improvement in the scope, accuracy and reliability of measuring instruments;
- the introduction of remote registration and recording of measurements and observations;
- the development of control systems which enable these measurements to be compared with desired ('set-point') values and appropriate adjustments to be made to control elements such as valves and switches ('negative feed-back loops'), with increasingly precise modulation to optimize the response, including direct digital control ('DDC') by means of computers;
- more recently, the progressive introduction of 'real-time' computer-management of control systems, making possible the co-ordinated control of multiple variables, the automatic adjustment of set-points and anticipatory ('feed-forward') control, on levels ranging from individual unit operations to entire processes.

These developments were prompted initially by the need to enhance the economic performance of process plants. They also contribute crucially, however, to the attenuation of risk in at least two ways:

- by speeding up and optimizing the response to any potentially hazardous departure from normal operating conditions;
- by minimizing the number of decisions that have to be made by plant operators in conditions of stress (or of inattention due to boredom), and thus the incidence of human error.

It is also apparent that automation facilitates the spatial segregation of the human operators from the plant, thus minimizing hazard magnitude, as previously mentioned.

The new computer techniques are significant in relation to large-scale single-stream continuous plants, but they are even more important in the presently growing field of batch production of high-added-value chemicals, where human intervention has been necessarily much more prevalent and the progress of automation has been slow. In this field, it is common to use a single battery of equipment in different sequences for several different processes, and the risk of operational error in the conduct of a process is relatively high. This subject is discussed in detail by Sawyer[34].

Thus, automation greatly enhances the potential for reducing process risks, but like all technical advances it also introduces new problems, specifically:

- the transmission of measurement and control signals requires a reliable electric power supply, which must be assured, in some cases by making duplicate provision, and secured against the risk of ignition of any flammable material in the atmosphere;
- automation systems are complex and necessarily incorporate many components of finite reliability;
- adaptive control depends upon the formulation of a mathematical model of the process, which can only be approximate and may not anticipate all deviations;
- the programming of the computers requires extremely complex algorithms which are inevitably subject to error;
- the total dependence of plant operation on a computerised system may in principle lead, in the event of a failure of the system, to inability to run the plant or — in an extreme case — to a disaster of the kind that the system is designed to prevent;
- the risk of interference with electronic systems by external electrical disturbances as, for example, thunderstorms (it has been suggested, for example[35], that an oil refinery fire at Milford Haven, South Wales, may have been initiated in this way).

Some of these issues are discussed in Kletz[36,37]. A review of case histories of control systems failures, with lessons, is given in HSE[38]. In extending automatic control, it is obviously necessary to take measures to minimize these new risks, but it appears that as a rule the balance is very much in favour of automation.

The development of automated process control has helped to bring about a great reduction in the numbers of personnel directly involved in the operation of plants. On the other hand, the design, implementation and maintenance of these advanced systems call for much higher levels of education and training among both managerial and manual staff (further reference will be made to this).

Protective devices

It is generally good practice to install devices designed to minimize the risk of a severe hazard realization in the event of some malfunction of the process itself or of the control system. The provision of such devices does, however, increase the cost of the plant and therefore involves an economic decision. It also increases the complexity of the plant and the number of items subject to failure, so that any risk reduction may be less than appears at first sight. For these reasons, it is always wise, as Kletz[23] has pointed out, to consider such measures of risk reduction in association with the possibilities of reducing hazard *magnitude* — that is, enhancing *intrinsic safety* — in order to secure the optimum combination of both.

Catastrophic failure of pressure vessels is averted by making provision to relieve any overpressure arising from a process deviation, by means of relief valves or bursting disks. The sizing of such vents is a specialized subject with a considerable literature[39]. Such provision must, however, be accompanied by appropriate detection and/or alarm systems and arrangements for safe disposal of any harmful matter released — for example, by condensation, scrubbing or flaring, with provision for intermediate storage where necessary. A detailed discussion of this subject is found in King[31]. Kletz[23] suggests that it may sometimes be more economical to provide a vessel strong enough to withstand any foreseeable overpressure. Buildings in which a risk of explosion is perceived may be fitted with relief panels[40].

Other protective devices include:

- detection systems for monitoring the atmosphere, with audible or visual alarms to give warning of hazardous conditions;
- interlocks to prevent unintended operational sequences (these are especially important in batch processing and also in maintenance operations);
- trips which initiate some corrective action in the event of a developing malfunction (e.g. the provision of emergency cooling to a reactor to suppress an exotherm or, in extreme circumstances, to shut down parts of the plant). Lees[18] discusses these matters in some detail.

Plant erection

It would be going beyond the scope of this book to discuss the general safety problems associated with plant erection. One matter worth stressing, however, is that this is a phase in which staff from outside organizations may be involved, and this requires close attention on the part of the operating company to liaise with all the parties to ensure that 'the left hand knows what the right is doing' and that the safety systems of the site are understood and respected.

Plant testing and commissioning

Assuming that the plant has been satisfactorily designed, purchased, and safely erected, all of its parts and systems must be carefully inspected and, where appropriate, tested, before being commissioned.

A concise and authoritative general guide is available[41]. The subject, as it concerns safety, is discussed at length by Lees[18] and King[31].

In this phase, various special features occur which demand extra precautions, in particular:

(a) the plant is new and unfamiliar (this may also be true of the process itself and the operating crew) — thus an important element of training is involved;

(b) pressure-testing and other tests will be carried out under conditions that may be more severe than those of the process in normal operation, and may well involve the use of temporary connections such as hoses, so that the risk of failure may be somewhat greater than under normal conditions;

(c) the control system, as well as the plant itself, must be tested and commissioned, and this will require the fixing of set-points and the imposition of trial deviations followed by appropriate adjustments so that, in the initial stages, the plant may be essentially under manual control.

Plant operation: general

Discussion has hitherto been concentrated upon the various aspects of the creation of a plant, with the intention of showing how an installation can be made as intrinsically safe as possible within the constraints of chemistry, engineering and economics. It now remains to ensure that the plant is operated as safely as possible, again within the above constraints. This is a big subject and can only be considered here in general terms.

The broad scheme of operation is clearly part of the original project specification, dictated by its commercial or service objectives. The detailed running of the plant to meet these objectives is governed by the plant's technological characteristics, moderated by the nature and cost of the available labour resources and by the requirements of safety.

Plant operation: the operating manual

The primary requirement for minimizing safety risks in the operation of the plant is the adoption of a set of procedures which, while allowing the plant to be operated in the manner intended, also address appropriately all the process and equipment hazards that will have been identified during its conception, design and erection.

The automation of plant operation has already been discussed. The operating procedures envisaged will influence the design and setting up of any control systems, but even the most highly automated plant cannot work without some human activity and this must therefore be regulated.

The operating procedures are usually embodied in an *operating manual*, which must set out instructions for start-up, normal operation (including altering the output rate, and dealing with variations in raw material or product specifications and with changes in external conditions), normal shutdown and

267

response to deviations, equipment failures and emergencies (including shut-down where necessary). The various sets of instructions must be both intrinsically correct and mutually co-ordinated since any conflict or disconti-nuity between them can cause dangerous confusion.

It should be particularly noted that the risk of hazard realizations tends to be greatest at times of change, such as start-ups, shutdowns and shift changeovers. Special care must be exercised at such times, and effective communication between all the persons involved assured.

Plant operation: the log

An important practice is the maintenance of an operating log, in which all relevant process data are recorded. Among these are both routine and excep-tional instrument readings and the taking and analysis of samples; charging and discharging of vessels; and maintenance actions such as taking an item out of service for repair and switching to stand-by equipment. The log should particularly note any unusual occurrences or deviations and any actions taken to correct them. All entries in the log should be dated, timed and signed. The log passes essential information to the new operating team at shift changeover, and may also be a vital source of evidence in the investigation of incidents (like the black box in an aircraft).

This practice must, however, not be allowed to degenerate into a perfunctory routine. It is vital that plant managers study the log regularly to maintain proper supervision of operations and become aware of any developing problems so that remedial action can be taken in good time. Logs have been known, moreover, to be inaccurately completed or even deliberately falsified, and it is therefore essential that they are rigorously monitored.

Plant operation: the working environment

All these provisions relating to the individual plant must of course be supported by the company's general safety policy and site regulations (see Section 6.4, page 272). Safe operation also depends upon the provision of a working environment which is as far as possible inherently safe, so that dependence on training, alertness and special precautions, important as these are, is not excessive. Essential in this context is the proper application of ergonomic principles in the layout of controls and the reduction of the need for protective clothing and other encumbrances which are apt to be irresponsibly discarded because they cause discomfort or inconvenience in the working situation.

268

Plant operation: batch processing

Continuous plants conducting a single process can typically run for long periods with very little human intervention. Plants involved in batch operation, however, commonly carry out different processes at different times and deal with a multitude of raw materials, intermediates and products as well as diverse operating programmes. Thus, they generally require far more human activity in the supply and charging of reactants, the discharging and onward movement of products and the control of operations, as well as the cleaning of equipment between operations. Disciplined procedures are therefore particularly important for such plants.

Marshall[42] has drawn particular attention to the need in such plants to provide appropriate arrangements for the storage and transportation of materials, especially to ensure the segregation of incompatible substances such as reducing and oxidizing agents. The hazards of storage and in-site transportation of chemicals require as much expert attention as those associated with the plant itself but, all too often, they receive much less. An important review of the hazards involved in the warehousing of chemicals and procedures for minimizing the associated risks can be found in IChemE[43], while CCPS[44] provides guidance on this subject. A case history of a warehouse fire which resulted in serious air and water pollution and might well have caused loss of human life is given under 'Bradford' in Chapter 5 (page 218).

Plant maintenance and modifications

It scarcely needs to be said that the safe operation of plant depends importantly on correct and regular maintenance of its equipment and systems. Equally, every plant, however well designed and constructed, will need occasional modification to adapt to changing feedstocks or production requirements, or to overcome problems arising from equipment failures. On the other hand, it is precisely during times when such work is going on, and when conditions are in some degree abnormal, that the risks of accident are highest. It is therefore vital that such activities are supervised by managers who are aware of the plant's normal hazards as well as the special problems associated with the particular operation. Special care must be exercised in this regard when outside contractors are employed on maintenance operations, since these, however skilled, will not be familiar with the specific features of the particular plant. This was one of the problems identified by the Public Enquiry into the Piper Alpha disaster of 1988[45].

Major maintenance and modification activities are normally effected during an annual shutdown, but more minor work is carried out routinely on a daily or

269

weekly basis, often while the plant is running or while only individual units are shut down. Townsend[46] provides comprehensive guidance on this subject.

Maintenance operations typically require people to enter and work in confined spaces where there may be passive hazards such as toxic or flammable materials emanating from ongoing processes or in vessels which have not been adequately purged, or machinery which may be started inadvertently if proper precautions are not taken. This is one of the *passive hazard* scenarios described in Chapter 1 and accounts for many realizations, some fatal.

Of great importance therefore are those procedures which control authorization for undertaking such work and verification when it is completed. These are known as 'permit-to-work' systems. They are often associated with protective measures such as interlocks. Townsend[46] and King[31] give accounts of these procedures. Their rigorous and unambiguous observance is essential. It was concluded[45] that the initiating cause of the Piper Alpha disaster was a failure of the permit-to-work system.

Modifications to an existing plant are a potent source of risk, especially if these are carried out under conditions of stress where a high priority is accorded to continuity of production, (the most notorious example is that of Flixborough[47]). It is essential that such work is subjected to the same rigorous examination, both in design and in execution, as the original plant, so as to ensure that the integrity of a system which may otherwise be satisfactory is not compromised[48].

6.2.5 Measures of mitigation

Mitigation of the harm caused by hazard realizations generally involves measures which are outside the province of engineering. Such measures include, of course, medical treatment of victims, either on site (first aid) or in hospital, trauma counselling, environmental remediation and, generally, financial compensation. These are weighty matters indeed and cannot be usefully discussed in this text.

6.3 The acceptability of risks

6.3.1 Social acceptability

The ways in which a process plant can be made safer have been discussed. But not a great deal has been said about the cost of this enterprise, and to a degree that is right and proper, since nothing can be more important than the protection of human life. Moreover, accidents can be extremely costly affairs in terms, not only of human injury and fatality, but also of destruction of equipment and materials and interruption of output, with ramifications that can include loss of markets (the largest disasters have caused losses in the order of hundreds of millions of dollars[49]), so safety evidently makes economic sense at some level.

However, it is also the case that many of the provisions made in the interest of safety will never be brought into use, and there will always be questions as to whether this or that measure involves a wasteful expenditure, cutting unnecessarily into profits. Ultimately, if every precaution in the book is taken, the project may become economically unviable. There is thus a problem relating to any project involving hazards of the kind described, as to the level of risk that should be tolerated.

On the one hand, it seems unacceptable to place a financial value on human life, though society objectively does this in the context of insurance benefits and compensation awards in the courts. On the other hand, no activity is entirely free of risk, and the price of a total elimination of risks from industry would be the elimination of industry itself. An important recent discussion of these issues is to be found in a Health and Safety Commission report[50].

This is, in fact, a multi-faceted problem which has no simple solution. In considering it, three particular issues have to be taken into account:

- there is a range of possible criteria (see Section 6.1.2, page 248), each of which measures something different;
- the estimation of the criteria (quantitative risk assessment) is at best an extremely approximate undertaking;
- there are usually several parties to such a decision — that is, the proprietors, the employees, the neighbours of the proposed site and perhaps the wider public — and the ultimate decision must reflect their perceptions, which may not all be entirely objective.

There is much debate as to how these risk criteria should be used in assessing whether a project may be accepted[20,21,51,52]. A useful summary is given by Jones[6]. Though the debate is not — and perhaps cannot be — conclusive, it does seem that no single criterion of safety is sufficient and that the analysis should provide estimates of several.

Marshall[22] introduced the concept of *social acceptability* as the fourth of the principal constraints (the other three being customer acceptability, technical feasibility and economy) which determine the viability of a process. He defined social acceptability as 'a condition in which the harms to persons, property and the environment which arise from any given activity are either eliminated, or, where this is not possible, reduced to a level *as low as is reasonably practicable*, or as may be required by legislation'.

271

The idea of limiting risk to a level 'as low as is reasonably practicable' has been generally adopted under the acronym *ALARP*. The decision on whether this is achieved by a specific project must be the outcome of some process of negotiation among the concerned parties, aided by advice from experts such as the UK Health and Safety Executive. It is generally accepted that the test must be more stringent in proportion to the level of the risk.

6.4 Safety and management

6.4.1 Introduction

This book is largely concerned with the scientific aspects of the safety problem. Such knowledge is undoubtedly an indispensable tool in the quest for safety, but it would be foolish to suppose that safety can be ensured by science alone. Like all other aspects of the enterprise, it has to be *managed*. Since the students to whom this text is primarily directed are very likely at some stage of their careers to have managerial duties which will include responsibility for safety, it is appropriate to conclude the treatment with some introductory discussion of this subject.

The safe management of industrial enterprises is a part of the more general subject of management, to which whole books and entire undergraduate and postgraduate courses are devoted. The relationships between safety and management have been explored extensively by Ward[53]. In this text, it is possible only to outline some of the key principles which should inform a responsible and scientific approach to the management of hazardous enterprises. Two excellent and up-to-date books have been used: Health and Safety Executive[54] which is a general handbook relevant to all industrial enterprises, and Wallace[55], written by an international expert and orientated rather more particularly towards the process industries. Both texts are recommended for further reading. A useful booklet[56], directed to prospective line managers in the chemical industry, includes advice on their responsibilities in relation to safety.

A distinction should be drawn at the outset between *safe* management and *safety* management. The former is the responsibility of the *line* management, which controls the company's operations and organizes the labour force, while the latter is essentially a *staff* function with the role of organizing specialized expertise on safety (and often on health and environmental issues too) and providing authoritative advice to line management. Both of these functions are of course subordinate to the *general management* of the organization, which has the ultimate responsibility for the strategic oversight of safety and for compliance with legislative requirements.

6.4.2 Safe management

Our intention throughout has been to convey a sense that the safety of employees and public should be a central preoccupation of management. This is so, in the first instance, for ethical reasons, but also because a legal obligation to this effect is laid upon them in most countries, and because, as we have suggested, it makes good business sense.

How then, is this responsibility exercised? Both of the above-mentioned books stress, in different ways, a number of basic principles. The essential features of a safely managed organization are summarized here.

Safety policy

The company's approach to (health and) safety should be enshrined in a *safety policy*. This document, which should be public and widely circulated, should include:

- a proclamation of the prime importance of the health and safety of the work force to the success of the company's activities;
- an acknowledgement of the management's responsibility (ultimately that of the Chief Executive) for health and safety, in line with both ethical standards and legislative obligations;
- an expression of a determination to seek the active participation in the preservation of safety of all involved in the enterprise, without forgetting that the degree of responsibility must be proportionate to the level of authority, and, usually, of remuneration;
- an undertaking to promote a *culture of safety* throughout the company;
- an undertaking to devote the necessary resources to identifying and assessing the hazards of the company's operations, and the technical and administrative means of minimizing them, and to ensuring that they are understood by all those working in it;
- a statement of its determination to ensure that all unsafe incidents (including 'near-misses') that occur are properly reported, recorded and investigated, and the relevant lessons are drawn from them and, where possible, to study and learn from the experiences of others;
- an account of the company's organization, indicating clearly the lines of responsibility for health and safety matters;
- a broad description of the way in which the company will manage its activities in order to give effect to these declarations.

273

In some countries, the publication of such a policy statement is required by law.

Organization

The practical implementation of such a policy requires appropriate organization. Firstly, the company should have a rational and transparent management structure with unambiguous definitions of authority, responsibility and accountability.

Secondly, it should establish clear lines of communication to convey information quickly and reliably both downwards and upwards through the hierarchy and sideways for liaison.

Thirdly, it is necessary to adopt systems of work at all levels of activity from corporate planning through project approval, plant design, plant and materials purchasing, plant erection, plant testing and commissioning, plant operation, transportation and maintenance which require safety issues to be explicitly addressed and resolved.

At the level of plant operation, these will involve procedures which are designed to ensure that safety is normal and, as far as possible, to avoid safety-critical situations — that is to say, those which demand very specific responses from human beings who may be under stress (see also Section 6.4.3, page 276). These procedures must be clearly set out in operating manuals (see Section 6.2.4, page 263).

Personnel

Safety depends ultimately on people and is compromised by inadequate staffing. There must be sufficient and competent personnel, suitably qualified and trained, to carry out all necessary functions for safe operation.

Supervisors and managers must have enough education, training and experience to be able to:

- understand the hazards of the operations under their control;
- implement predetermined procedures;
- use discretion in varying these procedures in exceptional situations;
- very importantly — be aware of the limitations of their knowledge and consult others where necessary.

They must also have the necessary managerial skills to elicit the willing co-operation of their subordinates.

There is a widespread practice nowadays of 'out-sourcing' various functions (especially maintenance, repairs and minor works) — that is, using contractors to carry out functions formerly performed by permanent employees. It is of course incumbent upon the company to employ firms with the necessary skills, but even so, such firms will not generally be familiar with the specific conditions, hazards and procedures of the site. The company must therefore take steps to ensure that responsibilities for safety are clearly defined and agreed, and that contract workers and their supervisors have the necessary briefing to work safely on the site.

Hazard and risk assessment
This topic has been discussed in previous sections of the book — notably in Chapter 1, Section 1.4 (page 17) and in this chapter, Section 6.1.2 (page 248) — referring chiefly to the elaboration of manufacturing projects. It is now good and sometimes mandatory practice to conduct such assessments in relation to all proposed systems of work, whether for routine or emergency plant operation, repair and maintenance works, or for plant modifications and, where necessary, to revise the systems in order to reduce hazards and risks.

The safety culture
The success of any operation, and especially one concerned with safety, depends upon the willing participation of all those involved in implementing it. This is not easily achieved and requires the establishment of what has come to be called a *culture of safety*. In our view this concept, includes the following features:

- safety is presented, not merely in negative terms, as an absence of danger, but as a positive good to be continually striven for and enhanced;
- management leads by example ('do as I do', rather than 'do as I say'), and demonstrates its commitment through its everyday policies and practices;
- the company's policies of recruitment, reward, promotion and discipline are clearly consistent with safety policy, in terms of both conduct and competence;
- staff at all levels receive appropriate general and job-specific safety training, both initial and recurrent;
- systems and procedures are elaborated in full consultation with the staff who are required to implement them (typically through their trade union safety representatives) and their views are properly considered;
- employees at all levels are expected to be constantly alert to safety issues and positively encouraged to report upwards any situation or practice that seems to them to pose a threat to safety, while supervisors are required to respond properly to such reports (this is crucial: it is not unknown for employees to be reluctant to report such observations for fear of criticism and even punishment);

275

- management actively combats any tendency to complacency, by encouraging the continual monitoring and questioning of working methods and efforts to improve them;
- the work force consequently has confidence in management's commitment to safety.

6.4.3 Human error

To err is human

Much has been written[36,57] on the subject of *human error* and aspects of it have already been referred to. The elements of safe management listed above are relevant to this subject, but its importance is such as to justify a few more specific remarks.

It is emphasized, first, that the problem of human error has been, in recent years, the subject of a great deal of scientific study[58]. Perhaps the most important conclusion to emerge from this study is that, as the saying goes, 'to err is human' and, except for the rare case where deliberate negligence is apparent, it is both unjust and unhelpful to treat it as a fault to which blame is attached. On the contrary, the most productive approach is to understand the circumstances in which errors arise and to contrive working situations which avoid them or which can tolerate them — for example, by providing an automatic warning signal and time to correct the error.

A corollary of the above is that all failures are ultimately a consequence of human error at some level, ranging from the plant operator who opens the wrong valve to the Board of Directors which has sanctioned or tolerated flawed procedures or processes, though the term is usually reserved for the failures of those in the lower ranks.

To put matters into perspective, it is perhaps also worth pointing out that humans are not merely flawed machines, but are actually highly resourceful and, on occasions, extremely courageous, and that, within limits, they may well have the capacity to extricate themselves — and rescue colleagues — from the consequences of their or others' errors.

Many useful concepts about the role of management in avoiding or overcoming human error have arisen from these studies, but only five are mentioned here.

Clarity of communication

Close attention should be paid to ensuring that all working information and instructions, whether oral, written or graphical, are absolutely clear and unambiguous (Mill[58] quotes an example in which a control-room indicator *instructing* operators to close a valve was interpreted as a statement that the valve *was* closed).

Workers are not stupid

Workers at all levels must be treated as intelligent beings. They must be educated and trained in the hazards associated with their jobs, and encouraged to feel responsible for their own and others' safety. They should have specific training in responding to plant emergencies and should never be subjected to the temptation to 'cut corners' where any question of risk is present (on the contrary, concern for safety should be an intrinsic part of all incentive schemes).

Employees' welfare

It is vital to maintain a proper, though not intrusive, concern for the general welfare of the workforce, not only on grounds of common decency but also to ensure that the stresses to which employees are subjected, and their hours of work, will not impair their alertness and ability to respond to operating problems. It is generally accepted that a healthy and well-motivated workforce is a pre-condition of safety. For the same reasons, modern personnel management will accept a measure of responsibility for counselling and helping workers with personal problems which could affect their efficiency.

The need to audit and review safety systems

The importance of contriving working situations which inherently minimize the risks of human error has been mentioned at various points. These are commonly described as 'safety systems', but the concept embraces a very wide range of levels, from the grand corporate system designed to ensure that investment decisions are made with due regard to safety considerations to the everyday permit-to-work system for controlling maintenance activities. A common feature of all these systems is that they tend to degenerate through complacency bred by familiarity and — sometimes — through deliberate negligence due to haste or idleness. Periodic (though not too regular) auditing of systems can keep such tendencies in check and can also provide information for improving and updating the systems.

6.4.4 Safety management

While these matters are arranged differently in different companies, there is an increasing consensus that safe management in the process industries requires, not only that line management accept and carry out responsibility for safe operation (this is universally required by law), but also that there should be a specialized safety management organization which has — with variations — the following functions:

- to act as a repository of safety expertise and to provide safety advice to the Board and to line management at all levels;
- to draft and recommend safety policies and systems, and monitor and advise on their implementation;
- to be aware of all relevant legislation and advise the company on compliance;
- to conduct in-house safety training for staff at all levels and facilitate the participation of staff in appropriate external training events;
- to conduct in-house investigations of incidents;
- to maintain liaison with regulatory agencies;
- to advise top management on the communication of safety information to the public;
- to help to organize and conduct safety reviews and audits.

If this function is to be effective, it must be staffed — at least at the top — by persons who are of senior status and appropriately educated, trained and experienced in the field of process safety. Many safety professionals are now employed both by process companies and by the regulatory authorities (see below) and also as independent consultants. The latter provide these services for enterprises which are too small to support an in-house function, and sometimes where special expertise or independence are of particular importance (for example, for auditing safety systems). In this connection, it is noteworthy that, in the UK, both IChemE and the Royal Chemical Society have for some years now kept Registers of Safety Professionals.

The reader is referred to IChemE[59] and to Wallace[55] for more detailed accounts of safety management systems.

6.5 The role of the law

6.5.1 Introduction

This book has deliberately not entered into detailed discussion of safety legislation and enforcement because it was more appropriate for the intended readership to concentrate on basic principles. Legislation and the organization of enforcement are very complex, vary widely from one country to another and change with time. While it is essential to comply with legislative requirements, we were also anxious to avoid implying that this was the sole or primary rationale of safety strategy.

It is appropriate, however, in conclusion, to offer a few general statements which may help readers to understand what is involved.

6.5.2 The legislative framework

If industrial activities were simpler than they are, it might be possible to control them by means of an itemized series of prohibitions of the form of the *Ten Commandments*. This approach is absolutely excluded by the technological complexity and diversity of production processes and the impossibility of employing, in the enforcement agencies, staff in sufficient numbers and with a sufficiently wide range of expertise and experience to give detailed instruction to producing companies. Moreover, any attempt by government to impose detailed control of industrial developments would introduce intolerable bureaucratic delays and would stifle the initiative of enterprises.

The general practice, therefore, in industrialized countries, is to require companies to engage in *self-regulation*, subject to a generalized legislative obligation to conduct their operations in such ways as to protect the health, safety and welfare of their employees and of third persons (including contractors and visitors to their sites, and the surrounding population). In the UK the main relevant law is the Health and Safety at Work Act, 1974, supported by many subsidiary Regulations.

6.5.3 The regulatory authorities

Governments then establish state regulatory authorities to ensure, so far as possible, that these obligations are fulfilled. [In the UK, the relevant body is the Health and Safety Executive, guided by a consultative body called the Health and Safety Commission]. In this regime, the authorities have, typically, the responsibility to:

- advise government on needs for new legislation and draft specific regulations;
- advise planning authorities on applications for permission to undertake new industrial activities and major extensions to existing ones;
- require enterprises to declare the hazards of their operations and undertake assessments of the risks posed by them;
- require them to explain how they intend to control these hazards, including both routine procedures and plans for dealing with emergencies, and give appropriate information and advice to the local community;
- advise them on good practice (for example by issuing, after consultation, approved *Codes of Practice*);
- monitor their compliance (including inspecting premises);

- if appropriate, issue warnings or prohibition notices in specific cases;
- require enterprises to report significant accidents — especially any causing injury or death;
- investigate and report on serious hazard realizations;
- institute prosecutions where they consider that there has been negligence or malpractice;
- undertake or sponsor research and publish their findings.

In general, under such legislation, the courts will have the power to impose penalties on organizations and/or individuals convicted of breaching regulations.

6.6 Concluding remarks

In this final chapter, the outlines have been conveyed of the scientific, technological and managerial strategies that the process industries employ in their efforts to minimize the incidence and the severity of the harms described in earlier chapters.

There has been much progress in recent years in the understanding of process hazards and the means of controlling them. It must be noted, however, with regret, that the incidence of hazard realizations at all levels is still unacceptably high as is shown, for example, in Marsh and McLennan[60]. [This publication does not report human casualities: the accidents mentioned did, however, cause a large number of these].

It is apparent, therefore, that this is a never-ending struggle, which allows no complacency, and that much of it entails rather tedious and repetitive work with meticulous attention to detail, but also that it benefits from the adoption of a perspective that transcends this detail.

This struggle does, of course, have a strong economic motivation, but it is also a cause which is consistent with the highest humanitarian ideals, to which readers will wish to contribute through their professional careers and even, in some cases, to dedicate themselves as specialists.

References in Chapter 6

1. Marshall, V.C., 1976, The strategic approach to safety, *The Chemical Engineer*, April: 260–262.
2. Marshall, V.C., 1987, *Major Chemical Hazards* (Ellis Horwood, UK).
3. Turney, R.D., 1990, Designing plants for 1990 and beyond, *Trans IChemE, Part B, Proc Safe Env Prot*, 68(B1): 12–16.

4. Wells, G., 1996, *Hazard Identification and Risk Assessment* (IChemE, UK).

5. Wells, G., 1997, *Major Hazards and Their Management* (IChemE, UK).

6. Jones, D.A. (ed), 1992, *Nomenclature for Hazard and Risk Assessment in the Process Industries* (IChemE, UK).

7. AIChE, 1994, Dow's fire and explosion index: hazard classification guide, 7th edn (AIChE, USA).

8. ICI, 1993, The Mond fire, explosion and toxicity index — a development of the Dow index, 2nd edn (Mond Index Services (under licence from Imperial Chemical Industries Ltd)).

9. Edwards, D.W. and Lawrence, D., 1993, Assessing the inherent safety of chemical process routes, *Trans IChemE, Part B, Proc Safe Env Prot*, 71(B4): 252–258.

10. EPSC, 2000, *HAZOP: Guide to Best Practice* (IChemE, UK).

11. Kletz, T.A., 1999, *HAZOP and HAZAN (Identifying and Assessing Process Industry Hazards)*, 4th edn (IChemE, UK).

12. CCPS, 1992, *Guidelines for Hazard Evaluation Procedures*, 2nd edn (AIChE (Centre for Chemical Process Safety), USA).

13. Skelton, B., 1997, *Process Safety Analysis, an Introduction* (IChemE, UK).

14. CCPS, 1989, *Guidelines for Chemical Process Quantitative Risk Analysis* (AIChE (Centre for Chemical Process Safety), USA).

15. Pitblado, R. and Turney, R., 1996 (eds), *Risk Assessment in the Process Industries* (IChemE, UK).

16. Marshall, V.C. and Ruhemann, S., 1997, An anatomy of hazard systems and its application to acute process hazards, *Trans IChemE, Part B, Proc Safe Env Prot*, 75(B2): 65–72.

17. HSE, 1978, *Canvey: an Investigation of Potential Hazards* (HSE, UK).

18. Lees, F.P., 1996, *Loss Prevention in the Process Industries: Hazard Identification, Assessment and Control*, 2nd edn (Butterworth-Heinemann, UK).

19. CCPS, 1987, *Guidelines for Process Equipment Reliability Data* (AIChE (Centre for Chemical Process Safety), USA).

20. HSE, 1992, *The Tolerability of Risk from Nuclear Power Stations*, 2nd edn (HMSO, UK).

21. The Royal Society, 1992, *Risk: Analysis, Perception and Management — Report of a Study Group* (The Royal Society, UK).

22. Marshall, V.C., 1990, The social acceptability of the chemical and process industries — a proposal for an integrated approach, *Trans IChemE, Part B, Proc Safe Env Prot*, 68(B2): 83–93.

23. Kletz, T.A., 1991, *Plant Design for Safety — a User-Friendly Approach* (Hemisphere, USA).

24. Bretherick, L., 1995, *Handbook of Reactive Chemicals Hazards* (P.G. Urban (ed)) 5th edn, 2 vols (Butterworth-Heinemann, UK).

25. Marshall, V.C., 1979, *Disaster at Flixborough* (Wheaton (Pergamon), UK).

26. Bell, N.A.R., 1971, Loss prevention in the manufacture of nitroglycerine, *IChemE Symposium Series No. 34* (IChemE, UK).

27. Marshall, V.C., 1994, Flixborough — the beginning of a cultural revolution, *Loss Prevention Bulletin*, 117: 1–6.
28. Sachs, G., 1970, Economic and technical factors in plant layout, *The Chemical Engineer*, October, pp. CE304-CE311.
29. Mecklenburgh, J.C., 1985, *Process Plant Layout*, 2nd edn (Godwin (in association with IChemE, UK)).
30. Pugh, R.W. and Johnson R.W., 1988, *Guidelines for Vapor Release Mitigation* (Center for Chemical Process Safety of the AIChE, USA).
31. King, R. and Hirst, R., 1998, *King's Safety in the Process Industries*, 2nd edn (Arnold, UK).
32. Bentley, J.P., 1988, *Principles of Measurement Systems*, 2nd edn (Longman, UK).
33. Shinskey, F.G., 1988, *Process Control Systems: Application, Design and Tuning*, 3rd edn (McGraw-Hill, UK).
34. Sawyer, P., 1993, *Computer-Controlled Batch Processing* (IChemE, UK).
35. Cox, J., 1991, *The Chemical Engineer*, (571), 11 August: 10.
36. Kletz, T.A., 1991, *An Engineer's View of Human Error*, 2nd edn (IChemE, UK). 3rd edition due in 2001.
37. Kletz, T.A., Chung, P., Broomfield, E. and Shen-Orr, C., 1995, *Computer Control and Human Error* (IChemE, UK).
38. Health and Safety Executive, 1995, *Out of Control* (HSE Books, UK).
39. Wehmeier, G., Westphal, F. and Friedel, L., 1994, Pressure relief system design for vapour or two-phase flow? *Trans IChemE, Part B, Proc Safe Env Prot*, 72(B3): 142–148.
40. Harris, R.J., 1983, *The Investigation and Control of Gas Explosions in Buildings and Heating Plant* (E&F Spon in association with the British Gas Corporation).
41. Horsley, D.M.C. (ed), 1998, *Process Plant Commissioning*, 2nd edn (IChemE, UK).
42. Marshall, V.C., 1994, Safety management of multi-product batch plants — wider lessons from the Allied Colloids fire, *Loss Prevention Bulletin*, 118: 3–7.
43. IChemE, 1996, *Loss Prevention Bulletin*, 132: 3–33.
44. CCPS, 1997, *Guidelines for Safe Warehousing of Chemicals* (AIChE (Centre for Chemical Process Safety), USA).
45. Cullen, The Hon Lord, 1990, *The Public Enquiry into the Piper Alpha Disaster*, 2 vols. (HMSO, UK).
46. Townsend, A. (ed), 1992, *Maintenance of Process Plant: A Guide to Safe Practice*, 2nd edn (IChemE, UK).
47. Department of Employment, 1975, *The Flixborough disaster: Report of the Court of Enquiry*, (HMSO, UK) pp. 34.
48. Sanders, R.E., 1993, *Management of Change in Chemical Plants* (Butterworth-Heinemann, UK).
49. Marsh and McLennan, 1993, Mahoney, D. (ed) *Large Property Damage Losses in the Hydrocarbon Industries — A Thirty-Year Review* (M&M Protection Consultants, USA).

50. Health and Safety Commission, 1991, *Major Hazard Aspects of the Transport of Dangerous Substances* (HMSO, UK).

51. The Royal Society, 1983, *Risk Assessment — Report of a Study Group* (The Royal Society, UK).

52. Health and Safety Executive, 1989, *Quantified Risk Assessment: Its Input to Decision Making* (HMSO, UK).

53. Ward, R.B., 1994, The relationship between hazards and management practices in the chemical industry, *PhD Thesis* (University of New South Wales, Australia).

54. Health and Safety Executive, 1997, *Successful Health and Safety Management*, 2nd edn (HSE Books, UK).

55. Wallace, I.G., 1995, *Developing Effective Safety Systems* (IChemE, UK).

56. Cloke, M., 1988, *A Guide to Plant Management* (IChemE, UK).

57. Health and Safety Executive, 1989, *Human factors in industrial safety, Health and Safety Series booklet HS(G) 48* (HMSO, UK).

58. Mill, R.A. (ed), 1992, *Human Factors in Process Operations*. A report of the Human Factors Study Group of the Loss Prevention Working Party of the European Federation of Chemical Engineers (IChemE, UK).

59. EPSC, 1994, *Safety Management Systems* (IChemE, UK).

60. Marsh and McLennan, 1996, Large property damage losses in the hydrocarbon chemical industries, *Loss Prevention Bulletin*, 129.

Index